S0-BZQ-821

Books by Kathryn Hulme

ARAB INTERLUDE

DESERT NIGHT

WE LIVED AS CHILDREN

THE WILD PLACE
(*Atlantic Nonfiction Prize Award, 1953*)

THE NUN'S STORY

ANNIE'S CAPTAIN

Annie's Captain

ANNIE'S CAPTAIN

BY

Kathryn Hulme

An Atlantic Monthly Press Book

LITTLE, BROWN AND COMPANY

BOSTON / TORONTO

COPYRIGHT © 1961 BY KATHRYN C. HULME

ALL RIGHTS RESERVED. NO PART OF THIS BOOK MAY BE REPRO-
DUCED IN ANY FORM WITHOUT PERMISSION IN WRITING FROM THE
PUBLISHER, EXCEPT BY A REVIEWER WHO MAY QUOTE BRIEF PAS-
SAGES IN A REVIEW TO BE PRINTED IN A MAGAZINE OR NEWSPAPER.

LIBRARY OF CONGRESS CATALOG CARD NO. 61–5734

FIRST EDITION

ATLANTIC–LITTLE, BROWN BOOKS
ARE PUBLISHED BY
LITTLE, BROWN AND COMPANY
IN ASSOCIATION WITH
THE ATLANTIC MONTHLY PRESS

*Published simultaneously in Canada
by Little, Brown & Company (Canada) Limited*

PRINTED IN THE UNITED STATES OF AMERICA

For my brother

PHILLIP CAVARLY HULME

with love and gratitude for his

gift of the family papers

Acknowledgments

I T WOULD REQUIRE A FULL CHAPTER to say my thanks to the many people who gave me a helping hand with the material in this book. Yet a few must be named, for without their expert knowledge of the bygone days of clipper ships, of the long-defunct Pacific Mail Steamship Company and of San Francisco in its maritime heyday, I would have gone far off course. Gratefully I acknowledge my debt to Professor John Haskell Kemble of Pomona College who gave me both encouragement and his invaluable booklets — "A Hundred Years of the Pacific Mail" and "Side Wheelers Across the Pacific" — to start me off; to Mr. Karl Kortum, Director of the San Francisco Maritime Museum and to Dr. John Lyman of Washington, D. C., for their authoritative advice on clipper ships; to my recently deceased aunt, Elizabeth Cavarly Henzel, the last of "the Cavarly girls" who relived for me her memories of the home life of Annie and her Captain and of San Francisco in the '70s and '80s.

Librarians everywhere were like guardian angels. In the Huntington Library of San Marino, California, the Bancroft Library of the University of California at Berkeley and the University of Hawaii Library in Honolulu, they gave me access to their Rare Books sections and files of rare letters and documents; the Archivist of Hawaii's Board of Commissioners of Public Archives, Miss Agnes Conrad, opened up that invaluable source for my Hawaiian researches, which were rounded out by

A C K N O W L E D G M E N T S

generous help from the heads of the excellent Mauai County Free Libraries at Lahaina and Wailuku — Mrs. Mary Ellen Lindley, Miss Hatsumi Kadotani and Miss Gail Portwood.

To the two editing experts in whose hands the blue pencil is a double-edged sword — my cherished agent Bernice Cozzens and my revered editor Ted Weeks — I give special thanks for having borne me up and borne with me through the writing of this book.

K. H.

x

Foreword

THE SMALL SQUARE of blue letter paper with its few handwritten lines resembled a social note of sorts. On the first excited examination of my seafaring grandfather's old diaries, logs and scrapbooks, recently come to light in a family attic, I skipped over it, unaware that it was a key to his story.

Here in my hand was the material to flesh out the shadowy figure of that Connecticut Yankee grandfather who had sailed around the Horn to San Francisco in the decade after the Gold Rush, to pioneer the Pacific with the first wooden side-wheelers that churned non-stop from the Golden Gate to Yokohama in twenty-two days. My mother's reminiscences about her salty father had sowed the seed of a deep interest as long ago as my childhood. Then, I used to think of him as a sort of composite Bluebeard and Wizard of Oz.

He died a half-decade before I was born, but I knew how Captain John Mansfield Cavarly looked at almost every stage of his career from clipper ship Mate and Master to Pacific steamship commander. For their scattered relatives those clipper seamen had frequent photographs taken, undoubtedly to amplify their sparsely worded health bulletins sent home from distant ports. They had the habit, too, of jotting down in unexpected places occasional vital statistics about themselves as if, in their ceaseless voyagings around the Horn when self became an extension of the ship, they needed to remind themselves of their own dimensions as individuals. Thus, on the flyleaf of my grandfather's Bible, written in red crayon, was his notation — "My height April 4th, 1859 — 5 feet 9 3/4 inches."

Photographs showed the Captain was a handsome man, wide-shouldered and long-waisted, with a seaman's beard that sprang curly and dark from a chin whose angularities it copied in its neat square trim. His eyes were large and dark, dark as the polished lava that spills into South Pacific seas and glistens blackly when the surf breaks over it. My mother claimed his mariner's eyes could look at the sun without wincing and count ten stars in the Pleiades without aid of binoculars. He was a man's man who apparently attracted the respect and friendship of that dedicated breed of Cape Horners who lived for their ships and seemed to be mystically wedded to them. Until his marriage, women did not exist for him.

He had a young sister, eleven years his junior, and a mother in New London who had fought tooth and nail to keep him from going to sea lest he become quite possibly like his father — a cripple in early life after a fall from a mainmast. On his rare visits to the home port, he talked mainly with the old man who was still a sailor at heart, yearning for the sea tales his son could spin. Sometimes his younger brother Phillip, whose frail health would never allow him to go to sea, was permitted to listen. He had yarned of everything except the girls a sailor was supposed to have in every port; of winds and storms and monsters of the deep encountered in the Antarctic fishing grounds. Though familiar with every bordello from Rio to Singapore, he knew them only as would an efficient first mate who rapped on their shabby doors on sailing day to round up his crew. He had steered his course clear of women in his formative years, but not of love. Always, he had been in love with the sea.

"He went from sail into steam," my mother said often and I would wonder as a child what that really meant.

The innocent-looking note which had catapulted my grandfather out of one age into another was pasted in a scrapbook among yellowed clippings of the '6os, '7os and '8os about wrecks and typhoons, illustrated with occasional engravings of dismasted clippers rolling in heavy seas or side-wheelers aflame in Yokohama harbor or aground on a reef off Panama Bay. Interspersed with the maritime news were recipes (How to Cook a Turkey), jokes about Connecticut nutmegs and love poems clipped, of all things, from the English-language newspapers of Hong Kong.

In my box of memorabilia there were also bundles of letters under rubber bands (with all the old stamps snipped from their envelopes) and shoals of photographs to examine. One was a puzzler — a Chinese mandarin sitting with fan in hand beside a teak table on which stood a vase of chrysanthemums and a tiny cup of tea; on the back of this, written in my grandfather's hand, was the notation "Boston Jack, Hong Kong, August 19th 1869; Steamer *Great Republic.*" Mainly the photographs were of bearded men in frock coats and of bustled women in small tilted hats abloom with feathers, most of the latter of the same woman, my elegant little grandmother, the Captain's adored wife Annie.

Somewhere in that material lay the explanation of Captain Cavarly's abrupt transition to steam after seventeen years of racing in clipper ships over the seven seas, a transition considered in those days as comparable to giving up the sea. There, I knew, was the turning point of his life. There at the switch . . . from the towering creations of wood, hemp and canvas to the coal-burning paddlers that followed gracelessly in the clippers' wakes, looking for all the world like cumbersome Mississippi riverboats accidentally adrift on the open sea.

The Captain and Annie had been married in 1859 aboard the last of his clipper ships, the *Anglo-Saxon,* in the harbor of San Francisco. Tantalizingly brief notices describing their unusual wedding appeared three times in a scrapbook, the same wording in all three, but clipped from the marriage columns of different papers:

> In this city, Nov. 27th on board the clipper *Anglo-Saxon* by Rev. Dr. Anderson, Captain John M. Cavarly to Miss Annie

E. Bolles, daughter of B. F. Bolles, Esq., of Lahaina, Sandwich
Islands; both of New London, Conn.

One of my mother's stories, told to reveal his lightning-like
temper, seemed much more revealing of his deep pride in his
command, in always having as he expressed it "everything working well fore and aft the ship." He was escorting Annie aboard
in San Francisco one afternoon after their marriage. As he
helped her from the gangway down to the main deck, a drunken
sailor, newly recruited from a Bay Shore crimp house, stumbled
across their path, pausing an instant to stare at the Captain's
lady. In that instant, the Captain's fist had shot out and Annie
had seen an inert body slide like a sack of ballast into the scup-
pers. With the deck thus cleared, he calmly led her aft to the
Master's quarters.

Why, I wondered, had he quit these ships of his heart? Long
after he gave them up, he followed their fortunes as a man,
having renounced a great love, secretly spies through the press
on her goings and comings. News stories about sailing ships were
scattered through all the scrapbooks down to the last pages devoted almost entirely to the marvels of the steam age. I read the
fine print of old newspapers, I searched between the lines of his
laconic letters and even on the backs of them for a hint, a clue, a
protest or just one short sentence beginning, *I have decided to go
into steam because* . . .

All the while the answer lay under my nose in the form of
that square of blue writing paper which I had skipped over,
thinking it to be only an invitation, or a regrets, politely penned.
It was, in a sense, both.

It was the note that was handed to my grandfather when his
Anglo-Saxon had been taken prize by the Confederate cruiser
Florida off the coast of France in the middle of the Civil War,
after he with officers and crew had been transferred aboard
the enemy ship to be carried as captives to the neutral harbor of
Brest. It was a bidding to hold his tongue and control his fists
while he stood at the rail of the Rebel cruiser and watched his be-

loved clipper go up in flames, with two broadsides of shot and shell sent smashing into her racy hull to hasten her destruction.

C.S.S. *Florida*
At Sea, August 23rd, '63

Capt. J. M. Cavarly,
Late Commander of the
U.S.S. ANGLO-SAXON.

SIR:

Your Parole binds you to a strict neutrality of conduct toward the Confederate States of America until regularly discharged.

J. N. MAFFITT, C.S.A., *Commanding*

Brief and palely tinted, suggesting a billet-doux . . . I saw him clutching the blue note as he stood at the rail of that Rebel cruiser and watched across a stretch of flame-reddened water his seventeen years under sail ending in holocaust. He was only thirty-one when it happened, but a part of him must surely have died with that beautiful ship.

It had been his first command. He had been her Mate in '58 and her Master since '59. Six times in those five years he had battled around Cape Horn in her. On his last trip westbound he had encountered terrific gales from south to southwest off the Horn and had fought for thirty-nine days to get enough southing to clear the land and save his ship. He had met, courted and eventually married aboard her the elegant little Annie Bolles who was never cut out to be a sea captain's wife but who became one gladly, slightly madly, when he asked her to. All my mother's, aunt's and uncle's stories about their seagoing parents came alive in memory as I held him in imagination at the privateer's rail with that piece of blue paper in his hand and saw what he saw going down.

K. H.

Annie's Captain

Chapter 1

HE HAD NO INTIMATION that Fate had taken a hand in his affairs on that July day in 1859 when the clipper ship *Anglo-Saxon* was at anchor in New York harbor, taking on the last of her cargo for San Francisco and the Sandwich Islands. Actually, a glint of hostility came into his eyes as he watched the dockside farewells of the first passengers his ship had ever carried — the Bolles family, mother and three daughters, from New London bound for the Sandwich Islands, special friends of the ship's owner who had authorized the passage and had informed him about his female passengers the night before, laughing at his look of dismay, telling him it was high time he discovered there were women in this world, not just sailors.

From the safe height of the quarterdeck, he watched his lady passengers come on board. They had to tilt their hoop skirts as they climbed the narrow gangway. It appalled him to see how much space they took up on the main deck, how silly his sailors looked trying to work their way around swirls of crinoline with the preposterous luggage that accompanied them. There was a crate shaped like a piano which three men handled with difficulty. Boxes of household furnishings, rolls of carpet and matting followed, then what seemed an endless procession of Saratoga trunks with those bulging rounded tops that posed such a problem for efficient stowage in the hold.

3

That passengers, and female ones to boot, should have been thrust upon him for his first voyage in full command almost took the edge off his elation for what he considered his extraordinary good luck. On the previous voyage he had been plain Mr. Cavarly, First Mate, serving under a captain who had been sick for many weeks. He had brought his ship home around the Horn, crowding every inch of sail on her to get his skipper as quickly as possible to medical help. When he had reported to the ship's owner, he had been congratulated and told he was to take the *Anglo-Saxon* on her next trip to the Pacific, and was given his Master's rating. From fo'c'sle to full command in less than ten years was a record stride in those days of iron men and wooden ships. He could scarcely believe he had made it, but the indomitable will and character which had brought him to command at the age of twenty-seven showed in his darkly handsome face as he stood by the helm. He supposed that he should step down to the main deck and give his passengers a welcome aboard, but hesitated, wondering just what he might find to say. He waited until he saw the pilot making ready to come aboard, then approached his passengers on his way to greet him. The matriarch of the ladies' group seemed a bit startled that one so young should be introducing himself as the Captain, but recovered herself quickly when she saw how the sailors stepped back and went the other way around him to the open hold. She presented her two youngest daughters, Julia aged fifteen and Mary aged eleven, who curtsied to him, and waited for her eldest to disengage herself from the embrace of a young man with sideburns and silk cravat — her cousin, Mrs. Bolles explained. Presently Miss Annie Bolles turned around and extended her hand to meet the Captain's, meeting at the same time his eyes alight with appreciation for the sight of a pretty girl. Their expression was familiar to her, but not the curious little shock like a physical thrust that coursed from his bare brown palm into hers, gloved in black net.

Clad in a frock coat, as befitted the Master of a clipper ship, with his bowler hat in hand and dark wavy hair blowing in the wind, he might have been any one of the beaux who had come to the wharfside to see her off, except for his probing eyes which seemed to be asking "Will you be a good sailor?" He appeared to be almost a foot taller than she as she looked up at him.

Her ribboned bonnet framed a face as grave and lovely as a cameo, with high forehead and wide-spaced blue eyes. Two blond finger curls brushed to a glossy sheen lay on either side of her slender white throat below a pointed chin that was sculptured to strength like the fragile-seeming bow of a racing clipper. He tore his eyes away from the loveliest sight he had ever seen on any of the seven seas and glanced toward the foremast where seamen were shaking down fore course and fore lower topsail to the chant of "Come Down, You Red Red Roses . . . Come Down."

"Excuse me," he said, "pilot's coming aboard," and he left his passengers abruptly, calling to Crux, his colored steward, to show the ladies aft to their cabins when they were ready. He was glad now that he had moved his First Officer from the saloon cabins the night before. That little Miss Bolles was certainly a fine figger of a woman who might be quite distracting to a middle-aged shellback like Mr. Boxer.

Crux waited until their last farewells were said, then led them through a low door that gave into the between-decks of the half-poop. Neither Annie nor her sisters had ever been on a sailing ship. They thought at first that this low-ceilinged place with transom windows too high to look out from was where they must live for the voyage. But Crux went past the officers' cabins strung along the starboard side to an opposite door. Mrs. Bolles followed serenely after him. She has been twice around the Horn and knew what to expect when you were a friend of the ship owner.

The after door gave directly onto a small landing at the foot of a companionway — a flight of nine steep stairs with brass treads cut out in scrollwork. Annie heard the Captain's voice coming

5

down the companionway and thought how very close everything was on these clippers as she passed from the landing into a handsomely paneled saloon shaped to the curve of the *Anglo-Saxon*'s stern. Here at last was something familiar — a spacious room furnished with surprising luxury. There was a built-in highboy at one end and a semicircle of upholstered seats along the opposite wall, covered with red velvet that glowed warmly. A square mahogany table with benches stood in the center beneath a skylight that protruded up from the paneled ceiling to let the deck light fall through its frosted-glass panes etched with elegant patterns of rose baskets.

Crux told them that this was the Captain's "settin' room." He opened doors so cleverly set into the carved walnut paneling that you didn't realize sleeping cabins lined the port and starboard walls, two on each side. He opened them all, invited them to make their choices and left them alone to do it with a deep bow and delighted smile.

"Did we evict *him?*" Annie asked her mother. She had not caught the Captain's name when introduced. Mrs. Bolles smiled and pointed to a door at the foot of the companionway just outside the saloon. Those were the Captain's quarters, she said professionally.

Julia and Mary chattered like magpies as they inspected the plate-racks set into the wall over the highboy, the bronze dolphin rails around its top shelf, the big swinging lamp with brass chain and trim and the carved arm-rests of the dark polished benches around the table. They began to squabble as to who would have the cabin next to Annie, but Mrs. Bolles settled that promptly. She would take Mary on her side and leave Julia opposite with her eldest.

The cabin Annie walked into was impeccable. A plate-glassed porthole gleamed above the built-in berth and a new candle stood in the brass lamp affixed to the wall, beside a mahogany cabinet with mirrored door above a porcelain washbasin. Built into the opposite corner was a bucket-shaped privy with a wooden lid handily knobbed. White paint covered walls and ceiling and the deck beneath was scrubbed to the finish of bleached bones. A hooked rug beside the bed and red velvet curtains at the porthole gave warm bright patches of color. The long narrow stateroom had surprising space, yet everything for decent living was there within arm's reach. Annie gave a little laugh of delight as she looked around.

She removed her bonnet before the mirror, listening to her mother sternly instructing her sisters on the deportment that would be expected of them while at sea. Passengers, Mrs. Bolles warned, were subject to the same discipline as the ship's crew. There were places topside where they must never venture unless invited — that quarterdeck above them, for example, which was the domain of the captain, officers and helmsman. When they were on the main deck, they must act as if sailors did not exist and learn to keep out of the way when there was man's work afoot. Never speak to the Mates while they were on duty, remain as quiet and unobtrusive as possible and always obey the Captain promptly when he ordered them below, as he most certainly would do in rough weather.

Crux's knock interrupted her exhortation. He put his head in the door to announce that the Captain invited the ladies to come up on the poop if they'd care to see the ship cast off. They followed him up the steep companionway, clinging to the handrails on either side. At the top, the chartroom opened directly from the right onto the small landing. Annie shot a quick glance into this tidy little nerve center of the ship, saw cabinets, drawers and tiers of cubbyholes holding signal flags, and the Captain, his back to them, bending over a desk spread with charts at which the pilot pointed. Plate-glass windows, barred protectively on the outside, framed views of the ship forward and to starboard and port, and from a small thick-paned porthole in the aft wall was a view of a bronzed sailor standing beside his huge spoked helm. With only the slightest turn of his head, the Captain could see four ways at once. Annie wondered amused if he had ever heard of Janus.

Crux helped each in turn over the high coaming of the doorframe onto the immaculate splendor of the poop deck through which protruded the rounded top of their saloon skylight looking now like a small domed house brightly varnished. Behind this stood a compass like an enormous brass-sheathed eye with a thick pane of greeny glass through which they peered at a quivering red needle. The compass was upheld on the tails of three bronze dolphins, perfect little creatures exquisitely cast. Back of the compass was the great helm wheel, spoked and knobbed, nearly as tall as the sailor who stood before it staring straight ahead.

Crux shepherded them then to the forward rail of the halfpoop. What breath was left in the girls expired completely. The whole ship lay out before them in scenes of seeming chaos. Their eyes could take in only piecemeal the decks strewn with tackle and lengths of anchor chain, the men swarming in the mazelike rigging and out on perilous yardarms to do God knew what with hundreds of knotted ropes, the sailors beneath tugging up and down at windlasses to which they seemed to be permanently affixed like marionettes. Sounds arose from the *mêlée* like a giant orchestra tuning up, with booms, thumps and clanks; with rattles, creaks and a wooden-throated groaning that seemed to come from deep in the ship's timbers. There were human voices in the cacophony, hoarse and unintelligible.

The First Mate standing on the fo'c'sle head far forward was apparently the conductor of this chaos. Distance drowned out his commands but you could see them relayed aft from man to man as seamen stood by to cast off. Watching his unhurried gestures and calm stance, Annie remembered her mother saying that the Captain had been First Mate on the ship's previous voyages. She thought perhaps that that was why he remained in the chartroom instead of out on the poop where she erroneously imagined he belonged at this moment. Shy of his new authority, no doubt, still too young at commanding to be at ease with passengers, he was certainly a far cry from the worldly old sea captains who had frequented their home in New London and who could take divas and actresses gracefully in their stride when chance put them aboard their commands.

"They've got the towboat's hawser aboard," said Mrs. Bolles with a tremor in her voice. "Listen, now, girls, see if you can hear . . ."

And then it floated down the decks, from the Mate standing arms akimbo on the forepeak to his officer beneath on the main deck and thence to the seamen lining the wharfside rail — a command clipped, sharp and joyful for which the whole ship seemed to be waiting in a momentary hush. *Let go everything!* Then its echo in reverse: *Everything let go, SIR!* And the *Anglo-Saxon* came gently alive beneath their feet.

The first movement was made visible by the upslanting bowsprit that thrust out from the prow some twenty feet. It swung slowly past the shabby fronts of warehouses, past the lifeless ships moored at adjacent docks, past the mansard-roofed and church-steepled skyline of lower Manhattan, slowly like a long wooden finger counting off with a trace of scorn each landbound object left behind as it described its haughty arc toward the gleaming channel that led to the sea.

Annie blinked back her unaccountable tears as the vessel moved, light as a butterfly at the end of her towline, down the bay stream that resembled watered silk, gray-green, shot through with irregular patterns of sunlight. Something mysterious seemed to be taking place between ship and sea; a kind of whispering and chuckling rose from the waterline around the lean black hull. Below, on the main deck, two sailors in striped singlets grinned broadly and spat on their hands as if they interpreted that watery music as the happy beginning of a fight. "If *only* we didn't have that dirty little towboat out front!" Annie exclaimed to Julia.

She was unaware that the Captain stood a few steps behind her. He had come to the quarterdeck to see how his ship rode, if his cargo had been well stowed and equably, giving no list. His long squint had already found satisfaction in the way she was trimmed and he was looking thoughtfully at Annie's erect little back when she spoke. He winced slightly when he heard her say "out front," then cleared his throat.

"We'll drop that dirty little towboat in the lower bay," he said as she swung about startled. He had not seen her without her bonnet until now. He looked at her blond hair as if he'd expected it to be some other color.

"Oh Captain, I only meant . . ." Annie paused, flustered that he had overheard. With the sun at his back he really loomed. "That towboat jars like a wrong note," she said quickly. "Just by herself" — she swept her hand out to include the whole of his wooden world — "*she's* so very beautiful, Captain."

"Aye, aye," he said smiling. "She *is* that. She is indeed!"

He nodded to Mrs. Bolles and went back to his chartroom, looking aloft up the mizzenmast as he rounded the corner of the deck-housing. When she was sure he was out of earshot, Julia giggled and said that he hadn't been talking about the ship at all. "The way he stared at Sis — my *goodness!*" she exclaimed. Mrs. Bolles silenced her with a glance that needed no words to express what she thought of romantic-minded adolescents, then suggested they all go below to unpack.

The Captain came to dinner with them that night. It was probably the only time, he said, when he could avail himself of that pleasure, now while they were lying at anchor in the lee of Staten Island making ready to go to sea. Once under way, he would mess with his First Mate, Mr. Boxer, in the forward cabin as, customarily, he messed with him here in the saloon. He brushed off Mrs. Bolles's suggestion that he re-establish his regular routine, telling her that shellback talk wouldn't be very interesting for ladies. "Mebbe even not edifying for the young ones," he added with a twinkle.

He headed the table with Mrs. Bolles on his right, Annie on his left and the two young sisters at the ends of the benches mute with wonder, Annie noted with relief, for the novelty of their first shipboard meal. Crux served the substantial three-course dinner of split-pea soup, roast beef rare with potatoes and fresh vegetables, and a pink-iced cake for dessert which drew compliments from Mrs. Bolles. George was his Negro cook, the Captain said, a hand he wouldn't trade for any ten able-bodied seamen, but the ladies would have to wait until after they crossed the line to discover his real virtues in the galley. All fresh vegetables perished at the Equator and meats began coming then from the salt barrels, but they would hardly know the difference.

During the meal, Mrs. Bolles did most of the talking, asking the Captain with neighborly interest about his family in New London (spading a bit too obviously about the roots of his family tree, Annie thought) and remarking with some surprise that she had never met his mother and sister socially. The Captain smiled and told her they were country folk not much given to gadding about. He changed the subject by asking the object of their voyage to the Sandwich Islands.

He listened intently while Mrs. Bolles told how her husband had gone out to the Islands seven years before, to make a new home for them, transferring his New London chandlery to that busier crossroads of the Pacific. Though she had gone out once to visit him and he had come once to New London, it had been a lonely time for all concerned, but most of all for him. The Captain recalled the Bolles chandlery back of the sea wall at Lahaina but said he had not met her husband, who was probably away when he had touched there.

Annie studied his profile, noting the firm modeling of forehead and nose and the good flat way his big ears set closely against his head. His thick beard was quite obviously not culti-vated to conceal a weak chin; his jawline was a sweep of strength. Now and again when her name was mentioned, he turned suddenly and caught her eyes. It would have been quite unnerving had he not glanced with equal fervor, and much more often, at the barometer on the highboy opposite him. That and the ship's bells claimed enough of his attention to give her the reassuring impression that only half of this powerful young man was really with them; the remainder of him was up on the quar-terdeck sniffing around for the westerlies he said would be rising before dawn.

"If I figger rightly, we'll be off Sandy Hook by sunrise," he said in reply to Mrs. Bolles's query about the sailing schedule. At some time between 120 and 140 days from that moment, they would arrive in San Francisco harbor; after that, another ten days, say, of sailing to the Islands, and then they'd be safely in their new home with Mr. Bolles. Eighteen to twenty weeks of sailing, seventeen thousand miles of ocean to traverse and every weather and climate known to exist . . . he stroked his beard as he shared with them the statistical wealth of the voyage ahead and told them confidently that they would not find it monoto-nous. "No two days at sea are ever the same," he said. "No two hours, if you come right down to it."

After Crux had carried off the dessert plates, he sat turning his ivory napkin ring around and around in both hands as if he had suddenly run out of conversation. Now the two curled-in fingers on his left hand showed up clearly, a slight crippling of some sort, the only marks his rough early life had left upon him. Annie saw questions popping in Julia's observant eyes and pressed her foot quickly beneath the table.

But Mary's eyes like little gray copycats had followed her sis-ter's startled glance. "Oh sir, how did you get hurt like that?" she asked, her young voice vibrant with sympathy.

"Mary!"

"That's all right, Ma'am," the Captain said quickly to Mrs.

Bolles, "it's a most natural question." He laid his left hand out on the table palm up so the girls could see the slight incurling of the fourth and little fingers and the scar at the base of them. He told them it was really nothing, just a small memento of a fracas with a mutinous crew when he was Mate on the *Golden Eagle*. He glanced at his hand, then looked up with a broad grin. "The sailor who bit through that palm deep enough to sever the tendons lost a tooth, I'm proud to say."

Julia gasped, her black eyes bright with hero worship already. Mary begged details at once, but the Captain shook his head good-naturedly. It was time he got topside to see how the ship was making out. He promised they'd have plenty of time for yarning as he arose from the table. Plenty of time, he repeated smiling down into Annie's upturned face flushed with embarrassment for her outspoken sisters. The glint in her blue eyes suggested plainly the kind of what-ho the young ones were going to get as soon as he was gone.

"See you on deck in the morning," he said. He nodded good night to them all and stepped nimbly over the coaming, pulling the door firmly closed behind him.

He didn't have a glimpse of Annie for the next week. Though Mrs. Bolles and the young sisters appeared on deck without her, after Cape Hatteras was passed, he could control his eagerness to see her again. He knew exactly when that next meeting and all subsequent ones would take place, what approximately the weather would be, what phases the moon would be entering or leaving and which constellations would be the most resplendent in the skies. As he plotted his course on his charts, he made dots in the latitudes where a young lady on her first sea voyage would be able to forget her seasickness and come up on deck to view his watery domain in its fairest and most beguiling form.

From latitude 30 degrees North Atlantic all the way down to 30 degrees South, he strung them out like the imaginary lines of the ocean currents they would be traversing. The beautiful trades blowing from the northeast over the North Equatorial Current would give her a taste of sea life at its best. He planned to tack his way as skillfully as possible through the doldrums, then pick up the Brazil Current for the long easy swing down to Cancer. He made no dots in the Roaring Forties, skipped all the vast spaces of the West Wind Drift and the Cape Horn Current, then resumed his peculiar plotting south of the Tropic of Cancer in the Pacific. Each dot represented a day of potentially fine weather. He did not have to add them up to see how many possible meetings lay ahead of him. He had made this passage around the Horn so often, the timing of the clipper tracks was in his blood. Miss Annie Bolles could profit from her good long fortifying rest. He had a universe to show her when she would come topside, worlds of winds and stars and the endless moving expanses of the clipper tracks that had no mileposts save those existing in the memories of their mariners.

Meanwhile, he made firm allies of Julia and Mary, gave them free run of the quarterdeck and managed with guile to extract from them considerable information about their eldest sister. She was a musician, the girls told him, but not for money, of course. She had recently graduated from a conservatory of music in New York, she was nineteen going on twenty and the only poor sailor in the family. Even on the Fall River Line coming down to New York from Boston, she had been seasick, fancy that. She was their father's favorite, they told him without a trace of jealousy.

Occasionally he sent messages back by them, urging Miss Bolles to come on deck, since that was the only sure way to get one's sea legs. "And tell her," he said once, "how fine the ship looks now, without any dirty little towboat . . . *out front!*" He laughed so hard when he said it, he had to wipe his eyes. Julia reported to Annie that when he laughed all the stern lines in his face broke down and he didn't seem any older then than their cousin who had come to see them off. "But ten times hand-somer, Sis — my *goodness!*" she said, rolling her eyes.

"Go away," Annie moaned. The sight of her sisters' bright

young faces stung pink by salty winds made her sicker, if that were possible.

At the end of the first week out, the Captain sent her a note over his formal signature as Master of the Clipper Ship *Anglo-Saxon* informing her that if she did not come topside for a breath of fresh air that very afternoon, he would order his First Mate below to carry her up forcibly. "He means it, Sis," Julia said breathlessly. "He's got Mr. Boxer in the chartroom right now, standing by."

Annie got up then and began nervously putting on her clothes. The Captain was standing at the head of the companionway when she stepped out of the saloon onto the small landing. The girls hadn't told her he had discarded his frock coat and bowler hat and gone into work clothes tweedy, shabby and substantial. A woolen cap with a broad visor sat aslant on his head, giving him a cocky look. She made a mock bow of obedience to captain's orders and started up the steep companionway clutching both rails with her small gloved hands. He reached down and pulled her up the last step, saying "Well, Miss Annie . . . well" as she stood beside him, breathless with the brightness of topside after her week in the coffinlike confines of the stateroom.

The air blowing through the open hatch door went to her head like wine. From the aft window on the top landing she saw the great helm flashing beams of sunlight from its varnished spokes and beyond the circular white rail of the poop deck the sparkling expanse of a blue-green summer sea bisected by the foamy trace of the wake. He steadied her as the ship rose to an easy swell, then led her into the chartroom and sat her down on the upholstered seat built along the port side. When she got her wind back, he would take her out on deck, he told her shyly, then turned away to speak to his Mate in a very different tone of voice.

Annie felt as if she had risen from the dead into a totally new sphere, bright, fresh and salty. Through the windows fronting the wall-to-wall chart desk she stared at bits of blue sky caught between bellying white trapezoids of canvas crisscrossed by dark rigging. A section of the mainmast looked like a tree trunk skinned of its bark and greased. A band of sunlight slanting through the west window made her blink with its purity. Not a mote was visible in it, not a floating fleck of anything that belonged to earth. A low sweet whistling sounded all around the quiet deckhouse — the voice of the trades like a marvelous free fugue pitched to a tonal key new and strange to her ears. Suddenly she wanted to be out in it, to hear more, see more.

"I think I'm all right now, Captain," she said. He turned quickly and offered his arm as she stood up, his eyes beneath the frayed wool cap-visor glowing with pride to see how easily she adapted to the ship's motion. "Best have something to hang onto for your first turn about the deck," he said matter-of-factly. She slipped her hand in the crook of his arm then and walked beside him out into the thundering wonder of a clipper ship under full sail.

Thus began his courtship, with only seven days wasted of the seventy he had calculated it would take him to reach the Straits of LeMaire off Cape Horn. He knew now, after a week of doing without her, that the incredible had happened to him — he had fallen in love. He hardly dared glance at her gloved hand resting lightly on his sleeve, lest he snatch it up in both of his and tell her then and there that he could never do without her again.

"We've got a fair wind on our quarter," he said, giving her in a husky voice the first of the nautical lessons that would prepare her to be a sea captain's wife. He allowed her to remain on the windy quarterdeck only a few minutes that first time, then led her down to the more sheltered main deck where her mother and sisters were comfortably installed on canvas chairs set out on the lee side of the midship house.

"I'm glad to see there's *some* authority aboard this ship that could get you to your feet, Annie dear," Mrs. Bolles remarked, flashing an amused smile at the Captain, who with one peremptory order had achieved what she had been trying in vain to do for a worrisome week. She gazed with relief at her restored daughter and patted the empty chair beside her saying briskly, "You look well enough to take over your sisters' history lesson, thank heavens. They've progressed to the French Revolution since your absence from class."

The fair wind stayed with them, bearing the *Anglo-Saxon* southward at a pace that pleased the Captain as much as the sight of Annie on deck each day bright and early, sometimes before the sailors had finished swabbing down. Then he would call to her from the poop, inviting her up to the chartroom to keep her feet dry. Every day he had something new to show her.

When they came to the warm latitudes, there were the shoals of flying fish. He picked one up from the deck and spread its gauzy wings for her to see, telling her how they could fly only as long as those wings were wet, fifteen or twenty seconds in the air, then back again to the sea for a wetting; then another brief flight soaring ahead of the bonito and albacore which preyed upon them. He told her of his days before the mast when he used to join with adventurous shipmates and hang a lantern over the side at night, shielded from the officer on watch, to draw the flying fish on board. Mornings they gathered them up and bribed the cook to fry them for breakfast.

Her interest in all things connected with the sea delighted and emboldened him. Once he told her bluffly that he'd make a shellback out of her yet; but when he grinned at her he seemed to have still other plans in his mind's eye.

He helped her hold the spyglass to sight her first whale. A "humpback," he told her, like those he had chased in the Arctic when he first went to sea as a lad of fourteen. Details he inadvertently let slip about his own life interested Annie as much as the wonders of the deeps he was continually pointing out to her.

One day when they had been at sea a month, Annie saw his cabin quite by accident. Scores of times she had tiptoed past the closed door to his quarters at the foot of the companionway never knowing exactly when he might be sleeping. On this day it stood ajar, shaken open perhaps by some unusual motion of the ship. As she gazed with curiosity into his austere and lonely-looking sanctum an overwhelming compassion assailed her heart.

It was a cabin designed obviously for a skipper with family. A brass double bed occupied one side of the spacious room opposite a low bunk that had been converted with velour pads into a sofa seat. A handsome mahogany chest of drawers built between these looked capacious enough to hold the wardrobe of three persons at least. Some books with nautical titles and a few rolled maps lay on the dresser top within handy reach of the brass bed and on all the walls — above the dresser, between the curtained portholes and over a built-in cabinet back of the door — were pictures of sailing ships, stiff little oil paintings such as tea trade skippers commissioned from Chinese artists, showing every sail, spar and stay in meticulous detail and the sea a plaque of solid green peaked in ruffled series of small identical waves.

She stared at the functional furnishings, polished, orderly and completely barren of the human touch. She tried to tell herself that he must have his photographs, knickknacks and mementos stowed away in seamanly fashion in some one of those many drawers, but she knew intuitively that he had none, that no part of his land life meant enough to him to be brought to sea to remind of friends or family or places where happy hours had been lived. She felt as if she were spying and she pulled the door quickly to, thrusting the outside hook firmly down into its brass eye with purposeful protective fingers that trembled slightly.

After that moving revelation which Annie told to no one, Julia began reporting to her mother with greater frequency that Sis was with the Captain again. Mrs. Bolles saw that for herself when they walked the quarterdeck together, their two disparate figures limned against the sky and both their faces turned up to the sails whose names the Captain was apparently teaching to her daughter. Annie had always had a consuming interest in new things. Her part of the diary letter the girls were writing to their father was liberally sprinkled with sea terms, she reflected calmly, seeing no cause for concern.

The Captain began his real courting in the doldrums when there was little for him to do about the ship. Daytimes when the sun flashed down from the zenith giving no sail shadow, he ordered an awning stretched for the ladies and he spent hours beneath it listening to Annie read her mother to sleep with one of Scott's Waverley novels. The warm evenings kept everyone on deck until late. One especially glorious night he suggested to Annie that she get a breath of air from the bowsprit.

He led her forward to the gangway ladder that mounted to the fo'c'sle head. The sharp upslanted triangle of deck gave her the sensation of flying forward into the starlit sea and sky that were all of a piece undivided by any visible line of horizon. The even needling of the bright points through air and water was broken only by an occasional riffle of phosphorescence where some creature surfaced and swam.

"It's like the beginning of creation," Annie whispered, "before God divided the waters from the firmament. Oh, I've never seen anything more beautiful."

The faint rippling of calm waters beneath the bow seemed part of the silence. The Captain looked at her luminous face staring forward like a figurehead's. She felt, without turning, the magnetlike pull of his eyes as he said, "*I have, Miss Annie!*" with startling suddenness in a voice deepened with emotion. Her hand flew out involuntarily to hold him back but she was too late. She was in his arms, crushed against his heart, hearing its cavernlike booming and feeling the hasty beating of her own answering back. His incoherent words about their having been made for each other were quite redundant.

Later, when she had managed to back away from his overpowering embrace and stood safely apart looking up at his wildly happy face, she said softly but with no dismay, "I should have known better . . ." The ship's bells clanged into the incomparable night.

"Five bells!" The Captain looked up wonderingly. You'd have thought he had never before heard the hour of ten-thirty struck aboard his ship.

He began his pursuit of Mrs. Bolles in the Brazil Current, telling her on each encounter that he intended marrying Annie at voyage end and she'd best give her consent now to spare herself a lot of useless palaver. At first she refused to listen to him. Her daughter Annie, she said, was simply not made for the sea or the loneliness of a sea captain's wife. She had been educated for music and the graceful activities of an ordered society such as awaited her in the Islands. Her father, moreover, would never give his consent, even if she herself weakened which she had positively no intention of doing.

The Captain's perseverance increased as they bore south through the 30s toward the Horn. He wanted everything settled before tackling *that* ordeal which provided enough harassment for any man's soul, he told Mrs. Bolles. *She* should know that, having rounded it twice. There was no place she could avoid him since he was all over the decks now, overseeing every preparation to meet the gales of the Roaring Forties. His men jumped to his low-voiced commands as he kept his ship so close-hauled to every wind that her sails looked like white wood carvings incapable of droop or slack. Once he dropped down from the fore topsail yard where he often perched to scan weather ahead, almost startling her out of her wits as she took her morning constitutional around the main deck. He landed like a cat at her side and asked her brusquely why she couldn't recognize an accomplished fact and give her consent to it. He would leave her in peace, then, he said, striding off.

Between his hurried comments which grew more brusque with each encounter and her daughters' ceaseless pleading in the saloon, she really had no peace. Julia was the most vocal in her championship of the Captain's cause. Annie, having once confessed that she not only loved the Captain but intended to marry him even if parental reluctance forced her to wait until she attained her majority, usually sat quietly over her sewing lost in enchanting thoughts. The day after her Captain's abrupt proposal, she had slipped into his cabin and stuck upright in the book nearest his bed the little ornament of artificial moss roses she customarily wore in her hair. It had been marvelous to see how utterly those bits of pink silk demolished the bleakness.

Finally, on a wet squally day off the Argentine coast, which confined them all to the saloon that had shrunk perceptibly as the tensions mounted, Mrs. Bolles capitulated and purchased peace for herself with the announcement that she would give tentative consent to an engagement, pending approval of their father when they would reach Honolulu. She was so positive that her husband would never agree to such a marriage for his favorite that she felt a bit guilty about her calculated concession. "*Tentative,* mind you," she repeated as Annie flung her arms about her neck and Mary and Julia raced up the companionway to tell the Captain.

A few moments later, the Captain appeared in the doorway, clad in a yellow sou'wester, sea boots and scoop-brimmed rubber hat rolled up in front, rakish and wild-looking and dripping all over as if he had leaped out of the sea at Julia's good news. Annie was never to forget her first sight of him in storm togs. Huge, bulky and wetly shining, with raindrops glistening in his dark beard and eyes snapping with exultation, he looked like a god of some sort.

"I had to come below for just a moment," he said, tearing his eyes from Annie to look at Mrs. Bolles. "To tell you, Ma'am, you'll never regret it, never!" Mrs. Bolles started to speak of the tentative nature of her consent, but his deep voice, all business now, drowned her out. They had a bit of weather coming up, he said. Best they all stay below until it blew over. He'd mebbe stop by later, if duty allowed, to have a little glass of Madeira with them. To celebrate, he said with a great grin. Then he was gone.

"Celebrate?" Mrs. Bolles sank back on the upholstered ban- quette. "Celebrate *what?*"

The Captain now had Cape Horn to tackle. He ordered his passengers below when they neared the Falkland Current slashed with rain and snow squalls and told them to remain there until further notice. On her last brief visit with him in the chartroom, he told Annie that he'd not see her again for perhaps a fortnight until the Horn would be rounded and the Pacific smooth beneath their bow. "Mind you keep those sea legs," he said gruffly, but she felt them failing her even as she nodded. He gave her a fare- well embrace that tasted of salt and she shut her eyes as he held her, so as not to see out the windows the awful seas breaking over the bow and slamming aft over the stripped decks. She hur- ried back down the companionway and went straight to her bed.

She was continuously seasick for the entire rounding of the Horn which endured not one fortnight, as the Captain had hoped, but more than two. She longed only for death and once or twice she believed she had died when she stared in anguish at her wave-washed porthole and saw the Captain's face take form in the foam and look in sadly at her for having failed him. Roll- ing in her berth that felt like the ship itself plunging to her doom, she sometimes thought she heard his voice outroaring the gales and she wondered sickly why any man having made this passage once would ever wish to try it again. She never saw the black headlands of Tierra del Fuego as the ship clawed its way through Le Maire Straits, nor the mountains of subantarctic wa- ter crashing over the ice-encrusted bow. But she always thought she had, so vivid was the Captain's tale of that passage, after- wards.

Abreast of Valparaiso, with the freezing latitudes of the Horn behind them and the great Pacific rollers running with them on fair winds. Annie staggered to her feet on Captain's orders, looking like a wraith. He helped her over the coamings from the saloon into his adjacent quarters where he had a tumbler of Medford rum set up for her, plus a dish of plum duff made to his own specifications with plenty of sugar and raisins sprinkled over with nutmeg. This, he told her, would set her on her feet. To her eternal wonder, it did.

Next day she was able to go on the maindeck supported by Julia and her mother. Mrs. Bolles pursed her lips when the Captain stopped by on his rounds to congratulate his fiancée, but the glint in her eyes spoke her thoughts. Remember this wreck your high seas have made of her, it *might* help you to understand when her father turns you down. . . . But, before the end of that afternoon, she herself could hardly recall the pallid invalid she had escorted out to the deck chairs earlier, so swift was Annie's recovery.

The southeast trades gave them golden days. The ship ran itself, leaving the Captain with nothing to do for hours at a stretch. These were the latitudes, he told Annie, where skippers fished, or read or took to drink. His Mates kept the crew busy watch after watch, working them until they were ready to drop, repairing chafing gear aloft, holystoning decks, weaving sennit mats or plaiting new handles for the buckets at the ship's rails. No seaman ever sat down to his work or talked with another. Annie had been aware of this before but now it struck her with pity and she said so. The Captain explained that this was the discipline you had to maintain, especially after the challenging activities of the Cape, to keep the men from growing sullen or dilatory.

Often in the evenings after he had made final inspections, he came to the saloon to visit with his fiancée under Mrs. Bolles's watchful eyes. He always brought his pipe with him and sat until just one bowl was smoked. Now that he considered himself engaged, he observed all the rules of Victorian circumspection. He sat apart from Annie, usually on the rear banquette, seemingly content to watch her bright head bent over her embroidery frame on which was stretched a piece of petit point destined to become a cushion to brighten his quarters. He was so quiet in their presence that Mrs. Bolles almost forgot at times the emotional upheavals of two months before on another ocean.

One night however the pacific picture changed and with it her secret hope that this shipboard romance would somehow blow over. She had been talking of the last voice concert she and Annie had heard in New York. Musingly, she wondered aloud what her daughter would make of Hawaiian singing. "It's quite beautiful and haunting," she said to Annie, "totally different from anything you've ever heard, as I'm sure the Captain will agree."

She gave him the opening he had been waiting for. He nodded agreement with Mrs. Bolles, then said, "And that reminds me that I've never heard Annie sing. Julia here claims she has a right pretty voice."

Annie looked up from her stitching. Her sister was famous for exaggerations, she said, but she would be glad to comply. What song would he like? Had he any special favorites? He shook his head, said he'd like anything she would be pleased to sing. He settled back on the upholstered seat as she took her place before the highboy. After a moment's thought, she smiled at her audience, gave a little bow and said, "Annie Laurie."

She folded her hands together like a diva and began to sing. Her high pure voice soared straight up to the paneled ceiling, dropped back lightly like the early dew she sang of, then rose again with piercing sweetness as she gave a promise true. *Gave me her promise true, Which ne'er forgot shall be* . . . The Captain sat like one mesmerized, his eyes on her face, his pipe forgotten in his motionless hand. Her mother and sisters stared also, but with different expressions. They had never heard her sing like this, never heard those undertones of vibrant tenderness which seemed to transform the familiar old song into something new. Mrs. Bolles realized then that Annie was singing for the Captain alone.

Her eyes were fixed upon him and her slight body swayed to the ship's motion as she sent her voice straight to him. And, from the look on his face, she might have been singing his thoughts about her, had anything in his past life given him knowledge of such phrasings:

> *Her brow is like the snowdrift,*
> *Her throat is like the swan,*
> *Her face it is the fair-est,*
> *That e'er the sun shone on . . .*

Tears were rolling down the Captain's cheeks when at last she came to the end of her song, but not a sound issued from his bearded lips. He simply sat with dead pipe clenched in dead hand, his face wet with crying. Mary did what Annie wanted to do. She ran to him and wrapped her arms about him, murmuring, "Please don't cry, Captain . . . *please!* It's not a *sad* song, really!"

He never knew as he sat there, seeming still to hear her high lyrical voice . . . *Like the winds in summer sigh-ing* . . . that those sweet echoes were to inhabit the quiet saloon for the duration of his next voyage when he was to sail alone, nor that he would bring them to life deliberately, by lighting the lamp and watching its beam swing toward the polished highboy where she had stood, with her eyes dark blue like Annie Laurie's, singing for him alone.

Chapter 2

BY THE TIME THEY STOOD off the Farallones outside the Golden Gate, Annie was completely at home on the sea and had made the chartroom her special preserve. Earlier, she had quieted her mother's scruples with the laughing remark that she was better chaperoned up there than any place else on the ship. With uncurtained windows all around, the Mates walking in and out and the helmsman ever visible through the aft porthole, it was indeed a public place. She refrained judiciously from telling her mother what the Captain had said about the chartroom — that it was the traditional place for the skipper's lady and that he knew more than one clipper master who would refuse the command of a ship if it had no chartroom for his wife to sit in.

The chartroom had served alternately as sewing room and study for Annie. Had she been a young apprentice confided to his care for personal instruction en route, the Captain could not have taught her more. She had learned to read the charts under his guidance, how to look for a landfall when one was due, the uses of sextant and quadrant and even the names of the seabirds that flew with the ship's sails and their identifying cries. She had studied his *Marryat's Code of Signals for Vessels in the Merchant Service* and could put her hand quickly onto the proper signal flag (each one rolled neatly and thrust into separate cubbyholes at either end of the wide chart desk) which might be required to ask or answer the fascinating queries that passing ships put to each other on the high seas.

Now off the Farallones, waiting for the pilot to come out, Annie was as eagerly curious as the Captain about their next port of call after San Francisco and Honolulu. He hoped it would be Australia, with cargoes for discharge en route in Tahiti, Samoa or the Fijis. He showed her their pinpoint dots on the chart, then swung his compass over the Coral Sea southwest to Sydney, telling her how the South Pacific reefs were discernible at first only as color barriers dividing ocean blue from green shallows, resolving themselves into scallops of foam as you drove toward them under reefed sails while watching sharp ahead for the break in the surfline that indicated the channel. And, as she listened to him, glancing from his face alight with communication to the chart over which he twirled his compass, she realized with a start that the Pacific was like a lake to him.

She watched him complete his log. He set down the date — November 12th 1859 — and computed the days out from New York, 139 exactly. It was no record run, he told her. In '55 when he was First Officer on the *Golden Eagle,* they had made it in 108 days with the canvas piled on to the skysails and overhauling no less than a half dozen ships that had cleared New York weeks earlier. But *that,* he said with a grin, was a passage he'd not care to repeat with ladies aboard.

"You won't ever race again, promise me?" Annie asked tremulously. "Risking your life for the sake of a record . . ." He gave her his promise, looking with wonder into her eyes clouded with anxiety for him.

When the pilot had the helm, he escorted her to the quarter-deck and dispatched Crux to invite the rest of the Bolles family to join them, to view the Bay of San Francisco as they approached. He stood with the ladies, his feet planted far apart, presenting the Gate and the Bay beyond as if he owned them.

The sun shone brightly that November afternoon. Every cove and headland came forth richer in color than he had ever seen them before, though he didn't tell this to his breathless audience. Nor did he explain that he had timed his entry so they would come in ahead of the fogs which, in a few hours, would start unrolling like a dingy blanket aft, to be borne in and spread grayly by the same winds which carried them forward now into the splendor of blue waters circled by red cliffs and green hills.

He named the coves and headlands as they glided past and introduced the lights that guarded the Gate. Off to port was the Point Bonita light set up on the highest promontory of the Contra Costa hills. Opposite, to starboard, was Mile Rock. Ahead, directly mid-channel, was the oldest lighthouse on the northern coast, constructed just five years before on the rocky island named Alcatraz. He drew Annie closer as they passed Fort Point. Once beyond that headland with the old Spanish fort they would see the most beautiful harbor in the whole world and the city overlooking it which he hoped that Annie would love. San Francisco, he said fervently, was the place every sailorman dreamed of making his home.

Mrs. Bolles gave him a startled glance. His certainty that marriage was to be the culmination of his shipboard romance would have been frightening without her reliance on her husband taking command of the situation, once they arrived in Honolulu. Ever since the Captain had bullied her into giving conditional consent to the preposterous engagement somewhere back in the South Atlantic, she had regretted her momentary weakness. She prayed that her husband's letters awaiting them in port would be filled with other plans, especially for Annie's coming. She would read these aloud to the Captain on the way down to the Sandwich Islands to prepare him, if possible, for the refusal that would end his wild dreams. Meanwhile, she would charitably allow him to have his moment of triumph. It was a big one for a man of twenty-seven years.

Every sailing ship in the harbor ran up signal flags as the *Anglo-Saxon* rounded Fort Point. The Captain read their messages aloud as his own ship answered back with the numbered pennants that were run up the mainmast. Annie held his salt-stained code book, amazing her sisters with her facility in finding the answering numbers, almost quicker than the Captain.

Soon they were within hallooing distance of the moored ships and the Long Wharf. The Captain pointed out for Annie the ship's agent on the end of the wharf with a megaphone in his hand, calling through it something about sailing orders. That was good news, the Captain whispered to Annie. Now they wouldn't have to wait until Honolulu to learn where they would be spending their honeymoon.

He gave them time to contemplate the immense scene spread out before them, the forests of masts and funnels, the noisome piers crowded with drays and stevedores and the muddy hills behind with scattered houses clinging to their steep slopes like gulls' nests; then he suggested they go below while the *Anglo-Saxon* docked. He would send down all mail the ship's agent would deliver and would order a carriage to take them to a hotel for the few days they'd be in port discharging cargo, with gangs of dock workers swarming the decks. He smiled protectively as he escorted them to the companionway. It was the last happy smile they were to see on his bearded face for many days.

Moments later the agent climbed aboard and handed him a letter from the *Anglo-Saxon*'s owner in New York. It was post-marked six weeks earlier and had come via the Panama route. It informed Captain Cavarly that as soon as expedient after arrival in the port of San Francisco, he was to transfer all Honolulu-bound passengers and freight to the *Frances Palmer,* due to sail for the Islands that same month, and that he was then to proceed to the coast of Mexico to pick up a cargo of dyewood in Mazatlan, thence around the Horn and across the Atlantic to England for discharge of said cargo. It was a stroke of fate he refused to accept.

In later years when her beaux-conscious daughters pressed Annie for details of her marriage aboard their father's ship right there in the Bay, she always showed, said my mother, a peculiar evasiveness not at all in keeping with her forthright nature. Instead of protecting her girls from any possible desires to emulate her own hasty marriage (as they thought Annie sought to do by acting vague and memoryless) she somehow managed to convey the singular impression that there had been something of the nature of a "shotgun wedding" in her hurried nuptials — an impression which only added excitement to their romantic imaginings.

"It was like trying to pin down a hummingbird," my mother said once. "We never really knew all the facts, and of course never dared ask Papa about it . . . he was so terribly private about his feelings." There had been a great hullabaloo with Grandmother Bolles, my mother recalled, possibly because she thought Annie was marrying beneath her. There had been a honeymoon quite brief, probably only a week or so though no one knew for sure, then a long separation when Annie went out to the Islands and her Captain sailed in the opposite direction.

After tracking them down for myself through yellow acres of old newsprint, I learned the dates of the wedding and of the subsequent sailings in opposite directions. The duration of Annie's honeymoon had been exactly two nights, then had begun the year of separation. As I stared at the desolating dates I thought I understood why Annie had preferred not to talk about her brief ceremony. It had a touch of melodrama, something so outside her sheltered experience that she probably could find no words for it. No words, that is, which a well-bred Victorian would ever dream of saying to her daughters. Passion had no euphemisms, even in that age of comely equivocation.

I copied out the dates on a piece of blank paper and looked at them again, all in a row now, clear and easy to read. Arrival of *Anglo-Saxon,* November 12th; wedding on board November

27th: sailed barque *Frances Palmer* November 29th; sailed clipper *Anglo-Saxon* December 5th. The blank space of fifteen days between arrival and marriage gave back echos of the great hullabaloo my mother had remembered. From the echoes the scenes took shape . . .

The Captain thrust his letter in his pocket, curtly told his First Officer to take over and sent Crux on the double to fetch Mrs. Bolles to his quarters. His altered appearance so startled her that she put forth her hand impulsively, thinking him ill. He laid the letter on her outstretched hand without a word.

A small gasp of relief must have escaped her lips as she read it. She looked up with a smile of genuine compassion, prepared to say something about it all being for the best, and found herself staring into his eyes that had become suddenly two black holes. He told her that he would not give up Annie, that he intended to marry her and take her with him to Mazatlan and to wherever else his sailing orders would send him for the remainder of his life. She *was* his life, he said thickly.

Mrs. Bolles gasped *No* and sat down. There began between them a contest of wills which was to last for the next ten days. She started by telling him that her husband would never forgive her if she arrived in Honolulu without Annie; as to a marriage without his consent, it was absolutely out of the question. Benjamin Bolles, she said, was no man to trifle with. He had been living for the day when he would have his family reunited about him. He had built a business, a home and a place in society for them, denying himself the joy of their companionship for much longer than he had originally intended, because he wanted Annie to finish her musical education. Annie herself would refuse to give such heartbreak to her father. The Captain said they would see about that. He strode out of his cabin, rapped on the closed door of the saloon, calling for Annie to come at once and alone.

With burning eyes he watched her read the letter and when

she dropped it and ran to his arms with a cry of dismay, he looked at Mrs. Bolles over the top of her curls, too filled with emotion to speak. But Annie was weeping for two men just then, torn with the knowledge that one of them would have to do without her and she without one of them. She wept, but when she lifted her face from the broad chest that shielded it, she had a determined look. With the quiet reasonableness which neither strong will confronting her could ever command in a crisis, she said, "There *must* be a way out of our dilemma, we have only to think and we shall find it."

The arguments continued in the carriage that conveyed them all to the Occidental Hotel on Montgomery Street which the Captain had selected because it was homelike and accessible to the docks. They continued after dinner in the plush lobby where Mrs. Bolles felt more at ease than when cornered in the Master's cabin aboard the *Anglo-Saxon*. She pointed out a fact, that first night, that the Captain was aware of but refused to admit, even to himself — that Annie was not a good sailor, certainly not of the caliber required of a sea captain's wife; she had never really got her sea legs during their four months of sailing, said Mrs. Bolles, except when they were practically at a standstill in the doldrums. The Captain reminded her in a cracked voice of Annie's singing night; they were in the trades then, coming up from Valparaiso. Did Mrs. Bolles remember how seaworthy her daughter had looked then? He caught her off guard with that one, for she remembered how *he* had looked that night. She swallowed hard and changed her tack.

Annie did not join in the discussions. She sat quietly apart with her large blue eyes seeming to sink deeper into her worried face day after day. Nights she drove to the ship with the Captain, to pace the decks for an hour or two arm in arm with him while he begged, cajoled and pleaded. Then they rode back through the gaslit streets to the hotel where Mrs. Bolles was waiting up for her. The Captain would return to his ship and take a last turn, staring at the *Frances Palmer* moored nearby, aboard

which all the Bolles furniture had already been transferred —
everything except Annie's trunks and her piano.

Annie said afterwards that she knew from personal experience the sensations of being drawn and quartered. Her mother,
with the advantage of land beneath her feet and no longer at the
mercy of a captain aboard his ship, had become completely ob-
durate. Neither threat nor entreaty could wring consent from
her.

Disobedience to her mother's wishes was inconceivable. One
night on their lovers' walk, Annie told the Captain that they
would have to part — at least for the time being. The stars had
failed them, she said. The Captain was silent. He stared over the
rail at the *Frances Palmer* whose skipper had told him that day
that he'd be ready to cast off for the Islands on the 29th, a week
hence. In the carriage driving back to the hotel, he parted the
curtains so Annie could see the skies and asked her to look up.
In a voice that rang with conviction, he told her that his stars
had *never* failed him, nor would they now.

When they were back in the hotel, in the privacy of the Bolles'
suite, he cleared his throat, looked Mrs. Bolles straight in the eyes
and declared that he had decided to give up his command.
Tomorrow he would hand in his resignation to the ship's agent
and transfer his sea chest to the *Frances Palmer*. He would sail
with them, as a passenger, to the Sandwich Islands to ask Mr.
Bolles for his daughter's hand.

Mrs. Bolles was unprepared for this, and visibly flustered. He
was at the beginning of his career, she protested, and it would be
sheer madness on his part to give it up. Captain replied that
Annie was more important to him than any command — he had
known that from the day she had stepped aboard his ship.

Annie sat opposite them, staring from one emotion-racked face
to the other. Her lover looked like a madman talking hoarsely
about adjustment to a landlubber's life, her mother reduced to
tears as she implored him to be reasonable. Had her father
looked in on them just then, Annie knew exactly what he'd have

said. He'd have given her a wink and whispered: "They're having a hallelujah for themselves, those two, now aren't they?" And suddenly she thought of a compromise.

She would marry John, she declared calmly, right here in San Francisco and aboard the *Anglo-Saxon* as he desired. Then she would sail with her family for the Islands and wait there for her husband's return. Certainly, it might mean a year of separation, perhaps longer, but she must get accustomed to that as a sea captain's wife, must she not?

She knew then (but refrained from saying so) that they had only one more week together and would obviously have less than that as man and wife. Her betrothed had taught her well where to look for the maritime news and how to read its nautical shorthand. Not a flicker of this awareness showed in her shining face as she smiled up at her thunderstruck mother and lover.

Annie took charge of everything from the moment she had made up her mind. She was like a little general campaigning against time. She assigned each one's duty and stamped her foot impatiently when they paused, even for the fraction of a moment to gape at her. Julia and Mary she named as bridesmaids and sent them forth to a "horticultural depot" on Sansome and Pine to see what flowers they could find. "Smilax, too, don't forget! We'll need yards of that for decorating the ship's saloon." Her mother was dispatched to the *Anglo-Saxon* to request First Officer Boxer to stand up as best man. "It would be best coming from you as matron of honor, considering . . ." She gave her mother a quick smile of forgiveness for the days lost in deadlocked argument. She sent the Captain to Shreve's to buy two wedding rings — "Of *course*, we'll have a double-ring ceremony!" — and gave him one of her own small rings to match for size, since she had no time to accompany him. She was fiercely on the track of a minister, preferably Unitarian.

She finally located the Rev. Dr. Anderson whose name she

had noted in newspaper marriage columns in connection with nuptials held in the better sections of the city. November 27th was the earliest opening on his calendar and she accepted the late date without a quaver. "At five bells in the morning?" she asked. "Ten-thirty, that is . . . John and I have a certain sentiment about ten-thirty, of the first watch," she added, smiling.

Evenings she set Julia and Mary to penning the few invitations she and her betrothed had decided to send. At first the Captain wanted no one outside her own family, but she knew he had friends aboard some of the ships docked in the harbor and brushed aside what she recognized as his timidity about introducing his old sea dogs to Mrs. Bolles. "Certainly, for one — our ship's agent — we need him to escort our matron of honor," she said. "And what about Captain Paty who'll be skippering the *Frances Palmer* to the Islands? Mama knows his Honolulu family. And then, those Masters of the *Daring* and *Southern Cross* and *War Hawk* now in port? Don't tell me, John, you haven't sailed with some of *them* in your time!" She flashed a smile at her mother and said, "They're all close as kissing cousins, these clipper ship men!"

On the day before the wedding, Mrs. Bolles asked if she might be permitted to supply the catering for the wedding luncheon; she had found a French chef who she was sure would serve them well. Annie shook her head.

"We simply couldn't deprive our faithful George of that privilege," she said firmly. "Or Crux of serving the champagne John has already set in." A twinkle came in her eyes. "That's the *only* thing my groom-to-be was able to think of for himself!"

If just once her daughter had faltered, or betrayed a hint of fear or nervousness or of any emotion save that of calm, almost majestic, certainty, Mrs. Bolles believed she might then have been able to get from her throat the lump which impeded her speech and, sometimes, threatened to cut it off altogether, as when Annie announced she would spend the two honeymoon nights aboard the *Anglo-Saxon*.

"It may help John not to feel too lonely . . . afterwards," she said in a low voice as if speaking to herself.

On the morning of the wedding, Annie was up and dressed before the others. There had been no time for trousseau, but she had put on a royal blue brocaded satin which the Captain had never seen — a Parisian-styled Zouave outfit with elegant frogged jacket and voluminous skirt hooped out wide with crinolines. A pale blue beaver hat, no bigger than a tea saucer, with cockade of lacquered red feathers, was perched on her head, pulled forward fashionably over the left eye. She needed no jewels. The sapphire shine of her eyes proclaimed her a bride — even so early in the morning, even in the drizzle of rain they drove through which Annie told her sisters gaily would positively clear up by noon. It *had* to, she declared, because John was going to take her for a drive out to the Cliff House in the afternoon.

The *Anglo-Saxon* looked unexpectedly festive, dressed in all her flags and pennants and with smilax twined around the rails of the gangplank. Mr. Boxer sprinted down to assist the ladies from the carriage, to pay the driver and hold an umbrella over their heads as he escorted them on board. He told them he had the groom locked up in his quarters, the only way to keep him from seeing his bride till the proper time. Parson was safely on deck, all invited guests, everything was set for the splicing including the music. Crux had borrowed a portable melodeon which he knew how to play, from a dance-hall friend the night before. He hurried them aft to the officers' sitting room which, he said modestly, he had "fixed up" for the bride to wait in. He had turned it into a bower of flowers. On the table under a vase of hothouse roses, stood a beautiful little cut crystal jar of lavender smelling-salts, with A. E. C. engraved on its silver top.

"Officers' weddin' present for you, Ma'am," he said to Annie. "We thought mebbe you could use a little sniff of that before the organ starts up!"

Annie thought for a moment she was going to cry. Already

Mr. Boxer's flowers, his smilax tacked around the table edge, the bridal bouquets of her favorite white violets ready in nests of white satin ribbons on the sideboard had touched her deeply. And now, this moving evidence of the Mates' affection for her . . . her hand shook as she picked up the crystal jar and opened the hinged silver top carved with her married initials. She inhaled deeply, then she could speak.

"I can't . . . find words, Mr. Boxer."

"Don't try, Ma'am." He consulted his watch. "Five minutes to five bells. I best get along to see if the Old Man is still breathing." The ship's agent poked his head in the door. "Just in time, sir," said Mr. Boxer relieved. He handed Julia and Mary their bouquets, told them to follow their mother and her escort, then the bride. "Your posies, Ma'am," He flashed them a smile as he lined them up. "Aft you all go as soon as you hear the music start . . . all doors through to the saloon are hooked back." He settled his silk cravat nervously and strode out to fetch his groom.

As if she had rehearsed all this, not once but many times over, and had accustomed her heart to the first wheezing chords of the wedding march, to the pacing across the lantern-lit 'tweendecks, out for a moment into the brightness at the foot of the companionway and then over the coaming into the festooned dimness of the ship's saloon, Annie walked serenely to her place before the altar, which was the highboy transformed with candles and calla lilies. She gave one quick steadying smile to her blenched and trancelike groom before bowing her head for the benediction.

The words of the beautiful old promises . . . *For better for worse, for richer for poorer, in sickness and in health* . . . resounded in the low-ceilinged room. Occasionally the distant baying of a foghorn intruded, or the rattle of tackle from nearby ships, but the gentle rising and falling of the carpeted floor, rhythmic and nearly imperceptible, told clearest of all that this was a wedding on water. Annie made her fourth finger stand stiff and separate from the rest of her hand so the Captain could slip on easily the small gold band he fumbled twice before sighting its destination.

Presently it was over and she was in his arms. He whispered, "My darling wife . . ." His new salutation was as breathless as his bridegroom's kiss. But he started the ball rolling for the festivities when he looked up with a grin at his seamen friends and ejaculated, "Holy mackerel! *Now* I know why a man marries only once."

Crux brought the champagne and George followed with the wedding cake. It was a creation the like of which had never been seen on the seven seas — a Pisa-like tower of diminishing layers iced pistachio green with a sugary longboat riding on its top with two passengers in it, the man identifiable by a chocolate top hat and the lady by spun sugar skirts. The Captain looked excited enough to cut the longboat in two as he grasped Annie's hand with the knife, but she pulled the blade back until its tip touched only to the next-to-top layer, then let him press down for cutting.

"The top is for Father," she said with a ravishing smile as she deftly cut off the crown and set it aside on a plate not for serving. It was a small cake all by itself, a perfect little peace offering to start the explanations she knew would be expected from her in Lahaina.

The guest skippers lifted their glasses. "To Captain Jack and his lovely lady!" said one. "May their ship wear well and sail fast," said another. "And never foul an anchor!" boomed a third. And the remainder intoned "Aye, *aye* . . . aye, *aye!*" as they all clinked glass rims together beneath the skylight colored now like the champagne with pale glints of the noonday sun.

The Captain consumed her with his eyes as Annie sipped, wrinkling her nose but unwilling to tell him that she did not like champagne. "Just one more . . . Mrs. Cavarly?" He rolled her name on his tongue as if tasting a new delight. "*Mrs.* Cavarly.

. . ." She held out her glass and heard the eight bells of the noon hour clanging sweetly aloft as he poured.

In another thirty minutes, only one bell would strike, starting off a new watch of half-hour chimes up to eight bells again at four P.M. Then . . . two watches more and it would be eight bells midnight, the end of her wedding day. Ship's time, she thought, seemed to go twice as fast as regular time. It gobbled up the half hours and swallowed them with clangs almost before you could realize.

Eight bells . . . noon again, noon of November 29th, her sailing day. She had one last thing to do before leaving the *Anglo-Saxon*. She waited until the Captain debarked to carry her small baggage over to the *Frances Palmer*. He had been putting her aboard it piecemeal — her trunks and piano the day their wedding had been agreed upon, flowers for her cabin and a box of her favorite French candied violets the evening before, and now her last satchels and hatbox. She watched him stride down the long wharf with his funny rolling gait that she loved as dearly as every other aspect of him. She had seldom had opportunity to see it from afar like this — a sort of port to starboard roll as if he set his feet down on separate waves. Fighting back tears, she waited at the rail until he rounded the end of the pier, then hurried to the chartroom to leave the last small sign of herself aboard the *Anglo-Saxon*.

She opened his signal code book to Part V, to the sentences which passing ships communicated to each other by numbered flags. Key words for the subject of communications were set off in columns to the left of the pages, like a dictionary. She ran her fingers quickly down the pages, through the V's — Value . . . Veer . . . Vegetables . . . Violent . . . Visible, until she came to the W's which she sought. Wait . . . Want . . . War . . . Weather . . . Why . . . then there it was, between Why and Wind . . . *Wife*. There were two numeral flags concerning wives, numbers 6173 and 6174. She checked the one that said the most — #6173, *Your wife and family were all well when I left* and wrote her initials beside it. *Your wife, A.E.C.* She had thought of doing that in the night as she lay in his arms in the big brass bed, listening to the ship's bells sounding the half hours until dawn. . . .

In the main saloon of the *Frances Palmer* the passenger manifest was posted. It was a little strange at first to discover herself listed apart from her family, no longer under the B's:

> *Bolles, Mrs. B. F.*   *Age 40*
> San Francisco to Honolulu with
> daughters Julia and Mary
>
> *Cavarly, Mrs. John M.*   *Age 20*
> San Francisco to Honolulu

But, to start her scrapbook, she had three small clippings which made everything come into focus. The first she had cut after their arrival in San Francisco from the Maritime Intelligence columns of the *Alta California* which her Captain had taught her to watch. It was, in a sense, the story of her courtship in nautical abbreviation:

> *Per Anglo-Saxon* — crossed the Equator in the Atlantic lon 32.00 W, 33 days out; was 70 days to the Straits of Le Maire; 26 days off Cape Horn with heavy westerly gales; crossed Equator in the Pacific lon 111 W, 117 days out. Spoke the Brit barque Roderica 49 days from Swansea for Valparaiso in lat 29.38 S, lon 43.20 W; October 18th lat 5.17 S, lon 107.16 W exchanged signals with Amer whaler showing a blue signal with letters N Y in white.

The second was her marriage announcement and the third she had found that same morning in the advance sailing news:

> Dec. 5th for Mazatlan, Mexico, ship *Anglo-Saxon;* now loading at Long Wharf. Destination England.

Chapter 3

THE YEAR IN LAHAINA on the leeward side of Mauai was an interlude of such bittersweet happiness as to seem afterwards like a dream. Annie, telling her daughters about it years later, often faltered over the bright details as if — recounting such gay social whirls on that surf-fringed isle of perpetual sun, song and flowers — she were somehow revealing an infidelity to her sea-captain husband, who was then eating his heart out with longing, first in a pestilential Mexican port, then battling the ice of Cape Horn which he had to round twice before rejoining her.

Lahaina today is not too greatly changed from the Lahaina of a hundred years ago. If you could put the whaling fleet back in its winter quarters on the gleaming roadstead of the channel, imagine King Kamehameha IV and his entourage once again in residence in his summer capital there and restore my great-grandfather's ship chandlery just back of the coral sea wall (where the Pioneer Hotel stands now) you'd have it pretty much as Annie saw it in the '6os, simple and primitive, a picture a child might have painted.

The same canefields lift immediately back of the town to the west Mauai mountains clad in tropical shrubs, capped with clouds whose forms follow their summit contours and ride just above these like hats veiled in rainbows. The earth is still iron-oxide red, the sky tropical blue and every house, whether native-thatched or foreign-planked, sits under coco palms or kokui trees facing the shining channel. Against the pastel backdrop of Lanai Island eight miles across the water to the west, you can see the spouting whales that nowadays use these protected waters as breeding and training grounds for their young before the annual migration to the Arctic.

When I visited Lahaina I lost my heart to the Islands as promptly and as completely as Annie must have done. Paradise is a word that has had all the shine worn off it by the travel agents of our time; nevertheless, Lahaina must surely have seemed like a paradise to Annie after her chilly fortnight in San Francisco and the chillier memories of her New England girlhood. I could understand as I wandered entranced through the drowsy village streets, which all end quickly with views of canefields on the land side and views of tropical water on the sea side, why she always told her San Francisco-born children every time they packed for a trip to the Islands — "We're going home, my darlings. Going *home!"*

From the moment she flew into her father's arms on the docks of Honolulu, Annie was home. First it was simply his great embrace of forgiveness counterbalanced slightly by a quizzical lift of his eyebrows which suggested questions later to amplify her hasty letters. Then home was his voice on the deck of the small schooner that carried them across the Kaiwi and Kalohi Channels to the gleaming roadstead of Lahaina, his voice rising to that tone of loving banter which had always been their special communication. Finally home became the place to which he pointed on the beach south of the landing — a capacious coral-stone bungalow under coco palms with a wide veranda hanging over the sea like a poop deck.

Her father had already been in Lahaina for eight years. Once in that time he had doubled the Horn to visit them in New London, and once his wife had gone out to take the fifteen-year-old son Frank, to complete his schooling in Honolulu and spend his holidays companionably with his father. He was in his prime when the family was at last reunited — just forty-five years old, a handsome square-set man with a cap of thick black hair that was joined, by sideburns, to a black beard clipped so close over his square jaw that it looked like a chin-strap. He always stood for his photographs with his right hand slipped, like Napoleon's, into the opening of his long sack coat, and he always had a small dog with him in the picture — one of those plump "poi dogs" the natives used to fatten and roast as a great food delicacy, which he doubtless rescued from them with all the indignation of the born animal-lover. Or more likely swapped from them in a deal which only a Yankee trader of his vast experience could make show as a profit item on his ledger.

Now, with three attractive daughters added to his home, it promptly became a social center for the small American colony and for the officers of ships that put into Lahaina for repairs, or fresh water and fruits, or to bring the royal parties down from Honolulu town for their annual summer frolics. There were dances in the social hall of the church, moonlight crab-bakes on the coral beaches and, when the King was in residence, wild pig hunts in the purple gorges of the highlands and *luaus* following a successful hunt.

Music was always in the air. In the Seamen's Chapel back of the missionary house, the wonderfully pure voices of the Hawaiian church choir were heard at all hours practicing their psalm singing to the accompaniment of a wheezing melodeon played by a Hawaiian whom the missionaries had appropriately named Halo. Annie played her piano indoors and her guitar on the veranda, and the natives tagged after her when she walked in the town, humming the tunes on which they had eavesdropped beneath the windows of the Bolles home where they crouched each night, as motionless as the little taro gods that guarded the taro patch behind her father's chandlery.

She wrote a letter each week, addressed to John M. Cavarly,

Master of Clipper *Anglo-Saxon,* and saved them until some schooner came to the landing whose skipper her father knew and trusted to route them out of Honolulu into what doubtless seemed to Annie like a gaping blue void. For all her seaman's instruction, she had yet to learn by what sixth sense every deep-water sailor knew approximately where every other sailing ship was at a given time, or where it could be intercepted with mail.

In her first letters, she told her husband much about her father — how he and she had had a long heart-to-heart talk soon after she had got her land legs, the pointed questions her father had put to her about her unknown husband, which had worried her a little until she had thought to mention the *Golden Eagle.* That happy thought had reassured him. "He remembers you, John," she wrote, "from sometime back in the early Fifties when you touched here; he said you were a real bucko Mate in those days but one who obviously knew how to handle men, to pick a crew and to keep it. That means a lot, coming from Father!"

Until a letter came through from her Captain, Annie did not believe that the seemingly hit-or-miss postal system could possibly transmit her messages over the lonely reaches of the Pacific where a sail on the horizon was a rare sight, hardly once monthly when you were off the clipper tracks. But, two months after her arrival in Lahaina, she had her first letter, from Mazatlan, via the *Anglo-Saxon's* agent in San Francisco, thence by regular packet to the Islands. She carried it out to the sea wall beside the landing, to read it alone facing the eastern horizon beyond which, leagues and leagues away, she knew her husband must be sailing at that moment. Her married name in his strong slant handwriting ran from edge to edge of the long envelope, his own bold signature with a flourishy Mrs. before it.

MY DARLING WIFE, he began, and she paused to stare at that salutation as he must have done, for his calligraphy changed right after it. His words raced across the page like waves rolling in with the crosses on their hasty T's flying out behind like mare's-tails. He told her of his love in terms of the speed to which he had driven his crew in the loading of the dyewood, bribing them with a bonus of rum to work after sundown, as long as there was light to see. The 850 tons his ship could carry would be stowed in holds and 'tweendecks long before she read his lines. She must remember that the eastbound passage of the Horn was easier than the westbound and that when he rounded it again it would be summer down there, if all went well. A guano ship coming up from the Chinchas had brought her first letters (probably sent to Valparaiso) which he had read until they were as ragged as flying jibs in a gale. He sent greetings to her parents and brotherly love to the sisters Julia and Mary. Now that he had a wife, he would take the liberty of enclosing for safekeeping two letters which he hoped she would esteem as much as he did. Her father, he wrote, would doubtless know the Samuel A. Fabens who had penned them, who was now by latest report in Hong Kong, having brought safely to that port his completely dismasted clipper, the *Challenge,* after wrestling his way through last September's typhoon.

As she read the enclosed letters, she knew he had wanted her to show them to her father but was too proud to say as much. He wanted her father to have the reassurance of a sea captain whose name was legend in the world of the clippers.

Both letters were dated *Marblehead, 9 December 1857,* the first addressed to John Cavarly, the second to the owner of the *Anglo-Saxon* who was also the owner of her husband's previous ship, the *Golden Eagle.*

Mr. Cavarly

DEAR SIR:

I received your letter *this evening* and can hardly imagine where it has been all this time. Before leaving New York I had spoken to Mr. R. in your behalf but did not like to encourage you too much. You had better seal this note to Mr. Robertson (after reading it and if you think advisable copying it) and then forward *at once.* Your letter came so late that as I have been in Boston all day I hardly have time to answer it properly but before you leave I shall either see you or write a long letter. You must advise me from time to time how you get on and believe me to be sincerely your friend—

S. A. FABENS

E. M. Robertson, Esq; New Bedford

DEAR SIR:

Received a note this evening from Mr. Cavarly, first Officer of the ship *Golden Eagle* in which he informed me that you were somewhat disposed to give him command of the ship providing he can secure satisfactory proof from me of his capacity to take charge of her and also providing I do not wish to go in her myself.

If you remember I spoke to you in a general way of Mr. Cavarly before leaving New York but I am so much interested in him and his progress hereafter I can hardly help assisting him as far as possible in this matter.

He is a young man perfectly competent to command the *Golden Eagle* in all respects and as far as I am personally concerned, or stand, in the least, in his way I beg you to throw me on one side without a moment's hesitation. During my 19 years as a shipmaster, he is the most capable mate I have ever had, deeply interested in all affairs connected with the ship, economical in his habits, perfectly temperate and above all with a natural business capacity. In fact, he belongs to that class of men who will, most assuredly, be at the head of their professions, whether we will it or not, and the best way is to put them there at once.

I usually avoid giving letters of recommendation to anyone and I believe this is my third (including officers, stewards, cooks and seamen) but in this instance it is an actual pleasure to be able to so fully recommend Mr. Cavarly to your notice as the future Captain of the *Golden Eagle*. I remain, respectfully yours —

SAM'L A. FABENS

P.S. If you think it advisable to give Mr. Cavarly charge of the ship and wish for my services in New York whilst fitting out or loading, I will go on with pleasure charging the ship with my actual expenses only.

S.A.F.

Her father pointed out one aspect of the letters which had escaped her. Both were written in the same upright handwriting, strongly accented in the downstroke; both were originals. Her husband must never have presented his letter of recommendation. Before he had had time to, he had been given the command of the *Anglo-Saxon*, doubtless on the merits of his own seamanship bringing her home around the Horn with his sick captain. "Your John," said her father, "must be quite a man."

That night the natives lingering outside the lamplit windows of the Bolles home heard a new music rippling from the piano keys over which Annie's fingers flew. It had none of the beguiling waltz theme that usually enchanted them at the start of Annie's playing. It was a music that swaggered. As Annie called her sisters to the piano to join her in the boisterous ballad they had learned together on the *Anglo-Saxon*, her listeners heard the words of a chantey that used to roll over the waters of Lahaina when the whaling fleets came in, words that used to cause their old chieftains to send all unmarried girls over the mountains to remain there until the fleets departed:

> *Jack was every inch a sailor,*
> *Five and twenty years a whaler,*
> *Jack was every inch a sailor —*
> *He was born upon the bright blue sea!*

No one ever spoke outright of the fact that Annie's days with her reunited family were to come to an end within the year, but her father secretly reckoned them and made every one count. Twice weekly he roused her before sunrise, her cream-colored mare and his own black stallion were saddled, and together they trotted over the red ribbons of road that ran between canefields and surf, with coco palms bending over the surfside and vast

4 7

spreading monkey-pod trees shading the side toward the mountains over which, before they would arrive at the exquisite crescent of Kaanapali Beach, yellow ribs of hot sunlight opened up like a fan. She rode sidesaddle, gracefully and easily, always on her father's right so she could watch his face as he talked.

His bushy black eyebrows lifted into tufted peaks as he gestured with his riding crop. He wanted her to see everything beautiful about the land he had chosen as haven for the family after the rigors of their New England childhoods. He wanted her to understand why he had laid upon her mother such a stint of loneliness while he prepared the way. There to the left, in the roadstead, he had seen during his pioneering years the anchored ships so closely moored you could walk from deck to deck straight across the Channel and get off with dry feet on the opposite island of Lanai. He had made money then, before the whaling fleet started dwindling. The whalers limped in from the Arctic hunting grounds with scarcely a spar intact, their canvas in tatters, their seams needing oakum and pitch, men manning the pumps. Oakum sold for 12½ cents the pound in those days and copper bolts at 40 cents. A ship's chandler who stocked the necessaries was in constant demand and stood to make money.

He introduced her to his friends along the way, Chinese and Hawaiian fishermen whose houses sat on stilts, back porches over the water, truck and flower gardens in front beside the road. Once they stopped for tiffin in the bungalow of a fellow merchant, Mr. Ah Lum, whose hobby was orchid culture. Ah Lum's garden, hidden from the street by a curtain of bougainvillaea, could have been the setting for a mermaid fairy tale. Amid statue-like branchings of snow-white coral huge lilies with bird-shaped blooms thrust their crested heads, tropical fish swam in a tiny pool framed by seashells, and from the overhead lattice swung dozens of coconut half-shells dropping long tendrils of tiny orchids — pale green, flesh pink, brown-spotted yellows — like clouds of butterflies drifting in the dappled shade. Annie clapped her hands to her cheeks as if to keep her head from spinning off as she gazed around the garden and her father winked at his host. "She better have a seat, Ah Lum!"

Dreamily, she sipped golden tea with petals floating in it and nibbled strange smoked delicacies served on boat-shaped Chinese dishes — unaware that she ate squid and dolphin and bits of tasty seaweed toasted brown and dry . . . until her father told her afterwards, laughing until his eyes streamed tears at her look of horrified disbelief.

She always returned from her rides wearing, in her hatband, a flower her father had stopped to pluck for her. Sometimes it was a cup o' gold he had hooked down from a high tree vine. Sometimes it was a stalk of fragrant ginger, or a small brown wood rose from the ground vines that covered Kaanapali's golden sands down to the high tide level. These also were the dividends for the lonely years he was making up for now — his appreciation for flowers the like of which were never seen back in New London, his joy in identifying them for Annie. She pressed the blossoms in her Bible and occasionally sent one to her husband with an exact description of where and how it grew and what had been its color, texture and perfume before fading.

Her father's Island life, so dimly imagined before she had come out, opened up still more for Annie when he asked her if she would care to put his files in order. She discovered that he had saved letters from as far back as the 1840s, from his old New London store where he had sold everything from ladies' parasols to nautical instruments, from bank drafts (for money sent by Connecticut's Irish immigrants to their families in Ireland) to Navigators' Sun Tables. One day she came upon a copy of a letter adorned with official seals which had been dropped at the back of his pack-rat filing drawers. It was from the Bremen Consulate at Honolulu, dated June 10th, 1851:

To His Excellency R. C. Wyllie, Esq.
Minister of Foreign Relations, Honolulu
Sir:
I have the honor to inform you that I have appointed B. F.

Bolles, resident at Lahaina, Vice Consul of Bremen for the
Island of Mauai. I hope this appointment is acceptable to yourself and His Majesty's Government. Please accept my profound
respects for yourself. With duty to His Majesty, I remain, Sir,
your very humble servant,

STEPHEN REYNOLDS

Her father discovered her turning the letter over, examining
the Hawaiian writing on the back of it, and she chided him for
never having told his family of this honor. He made light of his
official post in the Islands, said that the most he had done in
that capacity was to examine leases of foreigners for sugar-cane
lands. But for Annie it was a big jump from his correspondence
of just five years earlier, ordering for his New London shop in
cautious quantity "three old style Marseilles Quilts" or "two
pieces Mourning Prints, Good Style, at say 11 or 11½ cents."
She looked up at him with a flare of pride in voice and eyes as
she told him how wonderful she thought he was.

Though her Captain's letters were few during the year, and in
their descriptive quality as laconic as a ship's log, they conveyed
nevertheless the message of his overwhelming love in ways often
more telling than the simple words he used to express it. Occasionally he drew little pencil sketches of a crag or headland
he had stared at on some forlorn coast while thinking of her,
longing for her. The marginal illustrations had the odd one-
dimensional quality of contour drawings, every peak and preci-
pice sharply outlined (and doubtless perfectly in scale one part
with the other) but with nothing save an even shading between
the ruled lines of sea level and the carefully jagged line of rocky
summit, not a tree, or house, or human figure or any suggestion
of light or shadow in his headland, only just what he saw with
his mariner's eyes. Sometimes he decorated certain sentences
with red or blue underscorings, to call her attention to the real
meaning in some such statement as ship's miles logged, if the run

surpassed the *Anglo-Saxon*'s daily average and thus brought him closer to her. Exceptional runs of over 200 miles he underlined in victorious red; light, baffling winds which resulted in long tacks off course, he accented in mournful blue. He double-underscored in blue the news that an unexpected cargo loading in London for New York would take him first to the East Coast before he could head for the Horn.

In the terse accounts of their voyages given to newspapers upon arrival in Honolulu or San Francisco, strange skippers often reported on his whereabouts: *April 18 lon 40.10 W lat 23.00 S exchanged signals with Bque Anglo-Saxon leaving Rio en route Liverpool.* If any of those reporting skippers were her father's friends who had touched at Lahaina and had been entertained in their home, Annie knew the number of one telegraph flag that would most certainly have been hoisted up the mainmast of the speaking ship: #6173, *Your wife and family were all well when I left.* She imagined her husband with spyglass glued to his eye deciphering a numbered flag that had never before been used for any communication with his command. She gave herself many a private laugh, thinking about the initialed check-mark she had made against that number during her honeymoon. Her serious husband would examine it from all sides, looking for a point, puzzling over every possible implication until at last the right one would occur to him — that she had meant nothing more than to be as near to him as possible in case any ship mentioned her in passing. *Your wife, A. E. C.*

She clipped each nautical report of his whereabouts from the maritime news sections. As her scrapbook thickened, it demonstrated what busy places the seemingly empty sea lanes really were. Passing ships, she told her father, were really like old whitebonneted gossips with sharp binocular eyes that missed nothing of the other's condition, direction and exact location as they bowed, greeted and swept on with scarcely a pause. She had a foretaste in that waiting year of what her life as a sea captain's wife might be when, for one reason or another, she would not be sailing with her husband. She pictured herself awaiting his return, as she did now, in her father's house. Hawaii was the center port touched by every Pacific sailing ship, outbound or homebound, the logical mooring for shore leave, for replenishment of water casks and for the recruiting of additional crew among the sea-skilled natives who made such first-rate sailors. It was the restful coral hub of that vast wheeling ocean which her husband loved and treated with the familiarity that a landlubber might accord to a lake.

As the year wore on, the Captain's letters became shorter as his patience shortened. In August when he had hoped to be well on his way to the Horn, he wrote her that he would go crazy if he had to wait around New York much longer for a cargo. In September he wrote that a shipment of sugar-mill machinery for the Islands had reached the dickering stage between ship owner and charter-party, but he felt no jubilation. He had already lost his chance to spend Christmas with her. In that letter he sent her a photograph he had had taken while visiting his family in New London. From the glossy sepia oval the eyes of an angry young man glared straight at her, ablaze with frustration.

October brought no letters and Annie began to imagine him safely back on the high seas, crowding on canvas, smiling again as he bent over his charts to mark his daily runs down the descending ladder of the southern latitudes. Soon after the turn of the year, she told her family, they could expect to see his ship sailing down the channel from the direction of Oahu. The blue-and-white checked Rendezvous Pendant would be flying and the Captain himself would be aloft on the fore topsail yard where he usually perched when entering an anchorage new to his ship. Her father expressed some doubts. Sailing orders could be as variable as the winds, he said; but Annie saw so clearly the lean black hull of her husband's clipper sweeping in under a cloud of canvas to anchor in the blue waters before their house that she even persuaded her mother this would be so. Mrs. Bolles rearranged the girls' sleeping quarters so that Annie could have a room of her own with a bed in it big enough for two.

That Christmas, the first time since her father had left New London in '49, Annie saw the entire family reunited. Her brother Frank, now a handsome seventeen-year-old, came home from school in Honolulu with his chum, a dark-eyed chieftain's son who was accepted immediately into the family as soon as Mrs. Bolles learned he was a Christian. He was lithe and beautiful with a swimmer's shoulders and he had a low musical voice in which he sang the plaintive Polynesian chants.

Annie, seated at her piano beneath the sperm-oil lamp, conducting her sextet with little nods that told each voice when to come in, could see beyond the lamplight her father sitting on the mohair sofa with her mother, holding her hand in one of his and his pipe in the other, and longing would flow through her for her lonely husband, in this home so close-knit with affection. She would make up to him for that bleak farmhouse in New England from which he had run away at the age of fourteen, clad like a poor parish boy in borrowed seaman's clothes, to make a mark on the sea which he rightly believed would be deeper than any he could make driving a plow over the stony land.

She knew afterwards that she had been living in the last of her girlhood dreams. Her vision of the Captain sailing down the channel to reclaim her as his own was nothing but a wish. The Hawaiian love songs she had learned for him (the words of which were sure to amaze him) were never to be sung on that moonlit veranda, not in a fortnight, not in a month. It was as if, in that year of separation, all memory of his brief and passionate possession of her had faded, leaving her feeling like a young girl again, waiting to be wooed.

Shortly after the New Year of '61, her father brought home from the store the first letter from her Captain since September. It was stamped New York, November 8th. She stared at the postmark rigid with unbelief, then she tore open the envelope and read the letter slowly.

Her Captain was sailing that day on the turning of the tide. His owner hadn't contracted the sugar-mill machinery; his cargo was exclusively for San Francisco. Therefore, she must meet him there and plan to arrive no later than March 10th, by which date if all went well he also should be dropping anchor. She was to notify the new ship's agent in San Francisco of the date of her passage from Honolulu. Mr. Henry Williams was his name. He would meet her at the dock and take her to his home if the *Anglo-Saxon* had not yet made port. She must not feel shy about accepting the Williams' hospitality; it was the custom for ships' agents to gather in the captains' wives whenever they reached port ahead of their husbands.

His father put his arm about her and suggested they walk back to his shop to consult the sea charts pinned to the wall. They could figure, now that they had a starting date, just about where her Captain was at that moment. Thirty days, say, to the Equator in the Atlantic, that would bring them to December 8th last, then thirty-one days beyond that point at, say, 120 miles a day, would tell them where he was probably sailing this very day, January 9th, 1861. All they had to do was remember that one degree of latitude was about 69 statute miles, then start counting.

She arrived in San Francisco on March 10th, five days ahead of her husband who had been held up by the same head winds which had made her seasick all the way up from Honolulu. Mr. Williams gazed past her as she came down the gangplank, seeking in the throng of debarking passengers someone who looked more like the sea captains' wives he usually received — someone middle-aged, bosomy and substantial, with cheeks colored high by the trade winds.

The delicate slip of a girl in a blue velvet suit with white fur edging the collar of her cape and the ends of her matching muff he took to be a planter's daughter for the way she shivered with her tropics-thinned blood in what was no more than an average March wind over San Francisco Bay, brisk with an invigorating bite of fog in it. He told the Captain later that he had scarcely believed his ears when the schooner's skipper had brought her over to him and introduced her as Mrs. John Cavarly.

Chapter 4

BESIDES THE LETTERS, logs and scrapbooks which were such sure guides in piecing together my mother's memories of her parents, there were in my Pandora's box a few small objects also. Wrapped in tissue paper, obviously mementos of Annie's and the Captain's first year together, I found a gold hatpin, a baby shirt of drawn linen, and a small twin picture frame backed with velvet which held their first photographs as man and wife.

The head of the hatpin was a gold button embossed with the seal of the royal house of Hawaii — "a Kamehameha pin," I remembered my mother calling it when she used to describe Annie's wondrous hats ("her only weakness") which were always held in place by that one special hatpin, even when a more ornamental one aglitter with jet or rhinestone might have been appropriate to the occasion. The Hawaiian hatpin was Annie's Excalibur, a souvenir she had no doubt acquired during her days in the Islands, but which she ever after thrust into the velvet crowns of her bonnets like a sword of secret power that would eventually bring her and her husband back to the Islands to live.

The baby shirt had an edging of Valenciennes lace about the tiny neck and a design in its drawnwork that was something like a star cluster, worked delicately as a spider's web through the sheer linen texture. The fragile garment bore no resemblance to the capacious tail of the Captain's discarded dress shirt from which it had been cut, but those worn evening shirts, I remembered, had been Annie's sole source material for the first layette she stitched when she was making her first and only voyage as the Captain's wife, en route to Liverpool just before the start of the Civil War.

The photographs spoke for themselves. The Captain and his bride had posed separately, each standing in turn before the same partially pulled curtain of *moiré* silk, with right hand resting on a small round tabouret draped with a fringed shawl. The Captain, with his serious eyes and grave mouth above a luxuriant beard, appeared older than his twenty-nine years, which had doubtless pleased him mightily. Annie at twenty-one looked like a girl masquerading as a matron in a tight-buttoned bodice of dark taffeta and voluminous floor-length skirt. For all the Victorian solemnity of their poses apart, you knew at a glance that these two were deeply in love. A restrained glimmer of their mutual passion showed in the eyes of the photographs that had been framed to fold together face to face.

It moved me deeply to gaze at the youthful portraits of those ancestors whose lives I already knew to the end. The foreknowledge made me feel a little godlike and a little sad, too, knowing there was nothing I could do to change their course of events and make come true for them their dream of being always together. Again and again as I read up on the maritime side of the Civil War, I came back to study the two photographs so earnest and appealing, so deliberately framed face to face in the certainty that thus they would always be.

The certainty was, if anything, more clearly and calmly stated in Annie's small face, as if she knew even then what lay ahead of her and, having successfully surmounted in her mind the trials that were to come, now faced the living out of them with perfect equanimity. But, whatever she foresaw, I'm sure it was never the war of separation whose anticipatory drum rolls had not yet reached over the Rockies to disturb the exuberance of San Francisco in that early spring of '61.

The city, which Annie had scarcely seen during her tempestuous previous visit, had completed its emergence from the shaggy decade after the Gold Rush. Main thoroughfares were plank-paved. Horsecar services had increased and the first steam-dummies were running on Market Street through narrow cuts in the sand hills all the way out to Seventeenth Street. Men in silk hats and frock coats still sometimes wore guns in their belts (dueling was then quite fashionable) but the main impression was one of civilized cosmopolitanism. Handsome residences surrounded by vast lawns populated with statuary had begun to stud the city's hilltops and down the Peninsula the great rancho properties were beginning to resemble the domains of noblemen with château-like houses, gardens of imported shrubs and ornate racing stables for the blooded horses that had been brought across the plains. French restaurants like the *Maison Dorée* on Kearney Street matched in elegance the stockbrokers' saloons furnished like gentlemen's clubs, and theaters with dramatic talent imported from New York and London were weaning the old-timers away from the bawdy music halls.

San Francisco at the beginning of its spectacular Sixties was, in short, the perfect setting for Annie's initiation into the shore leave rites of the sailor come home to port and to his wife.

The Captain arrived on March 15th, 127 days out from New York anchor to anchor. Annie was on the dock to watch her future home sail majestically through the Golden Gate with the man on her bridge whose tones of voice she had almost forgotten. She recognized him from afar by his stance. Then she saw him lift to his eye the long black spyglass she knew to be powerful enough to count every hair on her head and she quickly forced a smile to her lips. Above the deafening clatter of anchor chains and the clash of tackle lowering the sails, his great bellow of recognition soared with clarity: "*Ahoy there, ANNIE! ANNIE DEAR!*" Moments later she was in his arms.

He had a layover of about three weeks before they would have to up anchor for the trip back around the Horn to New York and London, with the cargo of lumber, hides and copper for which his ship owner had already signed contracts. The advance chartering would leave him almost totally free to make up to her for her lost year. Mr. Boxer would charge the ship, hire the new crew, replenish the stores. He had *asked* for the job, *Holy mackerel!*

He moved her promptly from the Williams' home to the Occidental Hotel, sent a messenger scurrying to make an appointment with a French dressmaking establishment for the next day, so she could be fitted with proper gowns for London, and asked her what was playing in Maguire's Opera House. She had never seen him in such high-spirited mood. He appeared to have forgotten how small she was. In their first hours alone he picked her up a dozen times and carried her about the room, laughing at her lightness. Once, he carried her to the window to show her the glitter of Montgomery Street below and she thought that if it had been open, he might very well have waved her outside like a flag.

In the following days he seemed bent on buying the town for her, beginning with a pair of diamond earrings for her small pierced ears — his wedding present, he chuckled, exactly one year, three months and fifteen days in arrears. Eventually, she curbed his buying spree by asking him just where, aboard the *Anglo-Saxon,* he expected to find storage space for all her new gowns and bonnets.

Though the Captain spent freely, he spoke scathingly of the easy-come easy-go wealth displayed on all sides, as if that were a different currency from the gold pieces clinking in his own pocket. His bluff comments on the Kearney Street fashion parade gave Annie the impression he thought himself in some foreign port, like Rio or Hong Kong, where no one save his companion understood a word of what he said. She laughed and she cried but knew all the time she was having a celebration she would long remember.

She wept in Maguire's Opera House, watching Boucicault's *The Octoroon* but was not alone in her emotion. There was hardly a dry eye in the audience when the beautiful octoroon heroine was brought up on the auction block for sale to the highest bidder. It was a much more timely theme than perhaps anyone in the opera house had been made to realize by the newspapers, still devoting their front space to new silver strikes in the Comstock Lode country.

The Captain credited the sea exclusively for all the bright changes in the city since their last visit. The Pacific was waking up, he told Annie. The previous year's discovery of the great bonanza in Nevada was to him an *inland* event not to be confused with the real cause of the city's growth which was the sea. The arrival of the Pony Express, which had shrunk mail time from Missouri to San Francisco to a mere ten and a half days with some four hundred galloping ponies running it in relays, was another inland event of transient importance only. He put little faith in those fancy stockbrokers in frock coats and beaver hats who talked of a transcontinental railroad.

The sea was the world's thoroughfare to San Francisco — a confluence of blue highways that forked out beyond the Golden Gate to cover the entire circumnavigable globe. *As if . . .* he would exclaim, any wealth coming from the hinterland could ever hold a candle to what would come from *there*.

They sailed through the Golden Gate on April 17th before news of the first shots at Fort Sumter had reached San Francisco. Annie found many familiar faces on board — the Mates Boxer and Lindquist, the old sailmaker and the ship's carpenter, and steward Crux and galley-man George both of whom had signed on with her husband's crews, from ship to ship, ever since his days on the *Shooting Star* in the China tea races. She discovered to her delight that now she was the skipper's wife, they addressed her more freely than before, took her into their shipboard family, so to speak.

The handsome *café au lait* Crux told her he had been born in Jamaica and had been at sea for as long as he could remember. He never cared where the Cap'n pointed his prow, he said with a flashing smile. All ports were the same to him and he had "friends" in all of them. When he bent over her deck chair to tuck a blanket about her ankles, she sometimes caught a whiff of the perfumed oils that made his thick curly hair shine. It was obvious to Annie that he thought the sun rose and set upon her husband, a sentiment with which she found no conflict.

She obeyed the Captain and spent as much time as possible on the sheltered maindeck in the hope that this time she would really get her sea legs before the Horn. Her chair was moved a half-dozen times each afternoon, from light to shade, from windward to leeward, always to the most protected spot which the Captain knew with infallible instinct. If he could not always be with her on deck, his eyes could always seek her out.

George came to her chair each day to discuss the menu for the Captain's table as if he had scores of alluring possibilities instead of the few dozen chickens clucking in their crates in the longboat aft, the one pig and three piglets penned to the port side of his galley and the inevitable salt pork and beef stowed below in teakwood casks. He called her "Missie Cavarly" now, and always put on an apron of snow-white sailcloth when he came for his menu conference. His gentle ageless face wreathed in smiles had several scars, not all of them the result of barroom brawls. The Captain had told her how once, in a hurricane off the Mexican coast when all hands had been ordered below except the First Mate lashed to the helm and himself lashed to the mizzenmast, George had somehow kept a fire going in his galley and had carried hot drinks to them for the thirty-six hours they had stayed on their punishing posts. He had crawled, the Captain said, belly-flat across the rearing wave-washed decks with noggins of rum-spiked coffee upheld in one hand, the other clawing for holds on ropes or rails. On one of those heroic trips, a flying section of taffrail had caught him square on the temple, but George had come on, bleeding and grinning.

George was the first Negro Annie had ever had opportunity to know. She always hoped she might lure him into talking about his past. She had read *Uncle Tom's Cabin* soon after it was published in '52 and her vivid memories of the book made her wonder if George had been a fugitive slave; but he could never be drawn into conversation on any past that antedated his service with the Captain. He appeared to have no more ties with land than the glossy black cormorant he was always trying to capture in the hope that he could leash its neck, as he had seen the Japanese do, and send it diving into the sea to fetch up some specially delectable fish for her.

Before the end of the voyage, however, Annie was to learn a great deal about George.

In the sixth week out from San Francisco, she discovered that she was pregnant. A flurry of fear shook her as she thought of the man's world she inhabited, its only doctor the wooden medicine chest in their cabin stocked mainly with purgatives, quinine, liniments and bandages for splinting. Then she relaxed with the realization that there would be many months and many ports before her time would come. She decided not to tell her husband immediately.

One afternoon in the chartroom she asked him casually about his sailing schedule. He told her that he should round the Horn and reach New York 120 to 130 days out from San Francisco, have a brief layover there, then cross the Atlantic in something less than twenty days if the prevailing westerlies stayed steady. So then . . . they would be in England before the end of August if all went well, a fine season for her first visit to the British Isles, he said with a happy smile. Then he noticed that she was counting off the months on her fingers as he talked.

He guessed why instantly. His pencil dropped with a clatter to the deck. He stared at her, his dark eyes aflame with joy. *When, Annie? . . . When?*

Christmas, she said, sometime thereabouts, and she bent to pick up his pencil. He moved so fast she was in his arms before she heard his warning cry. He carried her out of the chartroom, down the companionway to their quarters and deposited her gently on the big brass bed. He stood over her and told her she must not stoop down that way again. If the ship had rolled at that moment, she might have gone off balance. *And then what?*

So began the first and only supervision of Annie's many pregnancies which the Captain was to command. She stared up from the bed, her blue eyes saucer-wide with wonder as he laid down the law for an expectant mother. No more bending, no more running down companionways, never alone on deck and never on deck when the barometer was falling.

He had a doctor friend in Valparaiso whom they could visit before tackling the Horn and if there were any signs she might require special care, he would ship her direct from that port to her parents in Hawaii. If everything looked normal, she could continue with him to New York where he had another doctor he trusted to tell him if an Atlantic crossing were advisable. If not, he would leave her with Grandmother Bolles in New London to await his return from England. He sat gingerly on the edge of the bed and took her hand in his. "Christmas . . . or sometime thereabouts!" Now then, she must try to remember exactly.

She told him March 17th, stifling her laughter, but he was already computing aloud in terms of lunar months. Ten lunar months of an average 29½ days each, say 295 days from April 17th . . . Ah! his son would be born on January 4th.

She saw then there was no use trying to tell him that girls traditionally prevailed in her family, no use pointing out that a first pregnancy sometimes lasted longer than average. He had said *January 4th* and *my son*. His elation seemed to have lifted him momentarily beyond communication.

A few days later she did manage to convince him that a call at Valparaiso would be a useless waste of good sailing time. Sea air had given her a ravenous appetite; she was already eating for two, which was one of his prenatal rules, was it not? The thought of a Chilean doctor made her shudder. New York was the proper place for a check; they'd know there what the doctor was saying. He might even be able to tell them that he heard the baby's heartbeat, though that usually was not audible until the fifth month.

The Captain heard his son's heartbeat long before New York. Sometimes when he was aloft in the rigging during the rounding of the Horn, clinging to a yardarm and trusting no eyes but his to see the course through rain and hailstorms, he heard it like a muffled metronome beneath the howling winds. It counted off the duration of each squall, of each gray heave of following sea and once, when the Cape pigeons flew with them past the snow-covered land's end, their silent wings on the downbeat clocked the muted pulsing in his ears.

Annie stayed willingly in the cabin until they crossed latitude 40 South Atlantic. Then she was permitted to return to the chartroom. She came with a sewing basket added to the paraphernalia of books and writing materials which always accompanied her. During her cabin confinement she had gone through the Captain's wardrobe, mending items that needed repair, discarding those beyond salvage. She had found a use for his wornout dress shirts and now sat stitching baby garments she had cut from their extraordinarily ample shirttails. They were of handkerchief linen, fine and strongly woven, and she transformed them into beautiful patterns of drawnwork, gossamer replicas of the constellations she had studied through the porthole.

The Captain was beside himself when she showed him the first creation for the baby's layette. The tiny shirt barely covered the palm of his hand. Its neck was no bigger than a cringle, he exclaimed with awe. He measured with squinting eye the iron ring in the corner of the nearest sail, then looked again from her needlework to her.

Off Rio they spoke to several ships, learned from them about the surrender of Fort Sumter a week after they had set sail from San Francisco, and of Lincoln's blockade of the Southern ports. This was as it should be, the Captain explained calmly. The Civil War was a land affair and would be kept so by that blockade.

They picked up more war news from outbound ships as they sailed north, but all of it concerned faraway places like Manassas and Bull Run, nothing to disturb the Captain's certainty that what he called the immunity of the high seas could never be threatened. He had such complete faith in the efficacy of Lincoln's blockade that he set no extra watches when they came off the Southern coastlines. Had he set a sharp lookout on the night of July 3rd, '61, he might have read a prophecy in the western sky in the form of a red glow low upon the horizon. That night the first prize of the first Confederate raider to escape the blockade was burned off the Isle of Pines.

The prize was the barque *Golden Rocket* from Maine en route to Cuba for a cargo of sugar. She had been caught earlier in the day by the C.S.S. *Sumter* but saved until nightfall for her burning when, by hopeful calculation, her immense bonfire, quickened by chopped straw from her fo'c'sle bunks and lard from her stores, would draw into the raider's orbit other Yankee ships coming in for the rescue.

In New York the Captain paid his respects to the ship's owner and, while Mr. Boxer supervised the additional cargo, he accompanied Annie on the visit to the doctor. The doctor confirmed the pregnancy, going into its fifth month he judged, told them that Annie's bones were small but her muscles supple and that he wished he could send every expectant mother off on a cruise across the Atlantic in August. Nothing to worry about since they would be making the return voyage in plenty of time.

Disaster struck before they were halfway to England. A tropical hurricane coiled up from the Equator that summer, moved in toward the Carolina coast, then suddenly veered away from land and traveled to the northern waters, catching the *Anglo-Saxon* between latitudes North 40 and 50 as she winged with the westerlies over the North Atlantic Drift. The Captain saw its advance waves long before the storm's center darkened the southwest horizon. He refused at first to believe the evidence, so rarely did those tropical storms reach into the northern sea lanes. Then he heard the rising winds coming after him and he knew what they were in for.

He hoped he might outrun it and, for the first twenty-four hours when he thought he was winning, he said nothing to Annie. He kept her below in the saloon so she would not see the crew battening down hatches and clearing the decks. But when he told her to be careful, that they were running into a confused sea that might shake up the ship a bit, she read apprehension in his eyes as clearly as if she looked at a rapidly falling barometer.

In the dim saloon where she sat trying to sew, she had a sudden violent spell of the old seasickness she thought she had conquered during her second rounding of the Horn. She listened to the thunderous slamming of waves on the deck above and whispered a prayer for the helmsman crouched behind the skylight housing. Only in the worst of the Cape Horn gales had the *Anglo-Saxon* shipped her green aft of the mizzenmast. The sounds of winds that came to her in the pitching cabin were terrifying. There would be a moaning lull, then a sudden scream of wind as the ship heeled sharply and threw her flat on the wall seat.

The first real storm wave was forty feet high. She was on her feet when it struck, clinging to the riveted table with one hand, trying to gather up the Captain's pipes with the other. It flung her against the edge of the immovable table and held her there.

Moments later the Captain in dripping oilskins slid down the companionway stairs and picked her up. He held her level while the ship tobogganed from crest to trough of the second storm wave. Then he carried her quickly to their brass bed and tied her down with a sheet.

His words were inaudible in the roar as he bent over her making sailor knots swiftly. He put his ear to her moving lips to hear her tell him she was all right, that he must get back on deck. He shouted something about George and she nodded. After he was gone, she discovered that she was bleeding slightly.

George came with hot rum in one of the lulls when the shrieking winds had hushed enough to allow speech. Skillful as a trained nurse, he put a hand at her back and propped her up so she could sip from the glass he held. Cap'n was right, he told her, that debil storm moved about ten miles an hour. Cap'n would never let them be caught in it. Rains would come soon, Missie Cavarly. They'd slap those big waves right back where they belonged. Meanwhile, all she must think about was that baby she carried, not let it get scared. He knew. He'd helped a parcel of his own in the borning, back in Carolina . . .

Her miscarriage started several hours later at the peak of the hurricane's fury. The *Anglo-Saxon* was then riding the eastern edge of the rotating storm — the dangerous semicircle, as mariners called it. Its internal velocity clashed with the prevailing winds and spun the ship like a cork from crest to crest of opposing waves. Now and again, through a blaze of pain, she saw her husband in the doorway holding himself erect with his two dripping hands on the lintel, his horrified face streaming rain and tears. On one of his appearances, George gave him a sign which she did not see, which sent him back to the deck knowing that she at least was spared.

George talked as he worked, pausing for the crashing sounds on deck, then continuing without a break in his thought. He told her the names of the offspring he had "bawned" in his Carolina cabin. To keep track of them, he had named them alphabetically as they had come. Abraham, Benjamin, Caroline, Defoe, Eusophrina, Felicity, Georgina (that one he had hoped would have been a boy so he could have named it after himself and George Washington).

In later years when her own girls were small and begging bedtime stories, she sometimes told them about a wonderful colored man she had known, who had eight children named alphabetically in the order of their appearance, fancy that. She would go down the list, but she could never remember the eighth name that began with H. *Helen? Hannibal?* Yes, perhaps, she would say, George had a sense of history. But she was never quite sure, for when George had come to the H name in the catalogue of his progeny she had come to the end of her ordeal and fainted. She never actually heard it although she always imagined that she had.

Rains pelted down for five days after the storm, then abruptly ended. A dense fog dropped over the heaving sea bringing with it such an unearthly quiet that it seemed to Annie as if everyone aboard must have died — except the faithful George who came several times daily with broths and gruels and always once, formally apron-clad, to discuss the Captain's menu as if nothing had happened; and her husband who came as often as he could during the eight days she remained in bed.

He never spoke of their loss nor would he permit her to. He talked instead of the ship's losses as if these were paramount — the foremast trussle-trees broken, the iron bowsprit wrung off, the port longboat washed away but not, God be thanked, the starboard boat that held the crated chickens. The creatures had been heavily doused but not drowned. He inspected them each morning watching for eggs. Whenever he found one, he beat it up in a tumbler of Madeira wine, sugared and spiced and gave it to her to drink, to bring color to her cheeks.

Once she woke from a nap and saw him kneeling before the medicine cabinet at the foot of the bed. He was running out of liniment, he told her worriedly. He reckoned he'd used a gallon already on the backaches and bruises in the fo'c'sle. Bandages,

too. He had practically exhausted his supply after splinting Boxer's broken arm.

"*Boxer? Broken arm?*" Annie threw off the covers and got to
her feet. "Good heavens, John, why didn't you *tell* me?" she
cried. Her eyes widened with concern as she looked at him accusingly. She even fought him off with a most satisfactory show
of strength when he tried to press her back into bed. She shot
questions at him as she dressed. Besides Boxer, any other
broken bones? Positively not? Any serious cuts, then? Was he
claiming only bruises in the fo'c'sle because he thought she wasn't
up to negotiating the forward ladders yet? "But I'll find out
when I make the rounds," she said firmly.

What she found out was that her husband was a most resource-
ful amateur doctor. Only two lads of the current watch still lay
in their fo'c'sle bunks with mustard plasters in the small of their
backs. They joked about their back wrenches, told her the grog
ration the Old Man had doled out to them had made it all very
worthwhile. In the officers' quarters she discovered Mr. Boxer
expertly trussed up with his right arm immobilized across his
chest. The Old Man had done such a good job setting the frac-
ture he positively didn't believe it would have to be broken
again when they got to Queenstown. He wiggled his exposed
fingers to show her the nerves were unimpaired, but cursed his
luck that it had been his right arm. Had it been the left, he could
at least have earned his keep copying the skipper's reports as
usual. Annie bathed his face and told him not to worry. *She*
would take his place as the Captain's amanuensis, she said,
grateful to see a need, another job ahead of her directly her nursing ended.

The long lists of ship's damages which the Captain had to have
in duplicate before they docked in Queenstown completely ab-
sorbed her. She had never realized how many things a skipper
had to think about simultaneously. It was as if her husband's
notes had opened a door and given her a glimpse of the huge
hidden machinery of observation, plan and forecast which kept

a merchantman afloat and earning her way every ship's mile she traveled.

Annie did not always understand everything she copied. There were cabalistic words and phrases in her husband's pages — *sheer-legs, Handy Billy, Full and by*. These unheard-of objects or states she copied with care as if rescripting a foreign language. Her delicate writing went so straight across the long sheets of legal paper that the Captain declared she must have drawn a woof thread across them and followed its invisible, perfectly horizontal guidance for each sentence.

He showered her with compliments on her finished work. As a reward, he promised her that he would make a break with his custom and permit the Irish peddlers, who would soon be rowing out from Queenstown in their bumboats, to come aboard his ship. Thus, she would lose no time in her selections of linens and embroideries for their future home. Moreover, if by that time she felt in a bargaining mood, he might ask her to select a few good briar pipes for himself as well. Of course, before any of that haggling hurrah could begin, they must hoist the flag that would bring a doctor out to the ship to have a look at Boxer's arm.

His face, drawn with fatigue from constant duty on the bridge during the fogs, had a forced casual expression. She read his thought as he toiled with it, trying to find a way to suggest that as long as they would have a doctor on board, he might as well have a look at her, too. She made it easy for him by telling him that she also wished to see that doctor; she wished to make sure that she could safely carry their next. She looked him steadily in the eyes as she said it, to show him that she could at last speak of their loss without tears. Then, to round out his relief, she asked to have back her sewing basket which he had locked up in his sacred personal cabinet that held the ship's papers.

The Irish doctor found that Annie was fine, and said so, with compliments to the Captain for having had the foresight to have included a midwife among his crew. They had difficulty making him understand there had been no midwife, only the colored man George from the galley.

Headwinds held them anchored in Queenstown harbor for the next week. There in the sheltered waters among green hills Annie completed her recovery and began her collection of household linens from the peddlers' bumboats, turning the main deck into a bazaar every afternoon. She loved the old Irish peasant women who clambered aboard with their baskets of handiwork. She had not talked with women for so long, she forgot to bargain with them and paid them any price they asked so as not to interrupt the lovely flow of their gossip about sons in America, daughters in service in London and themselves sitting home by their peat fires, embroidering, tatting and waiting for letters. Her musical ear picked up their rich brogue quickly. In the evenings, she entertained the Captain with her perfect mimicry of the garrulous old ladies.

Not all the tears he wiped from his eyes were from laughter. The dreaded thought of losing her, which was to haunt him all his life, had taken shape in his mind for the first time like a hidden reef that would never wear away. As she talked to him in a brogue thick as porridge, his memory often superimposed on her lively countenance the deathly white mask of pain he had seen when the sea had struck her down and he would imagine in desolating detail a life without her.

Only the screw steamers could get out of the harbor. With each one bound for New York the Captain sent letters to the ship's agent, reporting on the condition of the wind exactly as it was at the moment of writing. Frequently he would go up on deck and test it before putting down his descriptive words, amazing Annie with his passion for exactitude. For his last letter from Queenstown, he went topside twice, because he felt the wind changing as he wrote:

Queenstown

October 11, 1861

To Messrs. Wm. L. Coleman & Co., New York

Since my last to you Oct 8th, by the screw steamer *Etna* which sailed from here the evening of the tenth, we have been detained in this port by heavy gales of wind from South to S E, blowing directly into the harbor. By the *Etna* I sent you my disbursements. . . . You will see I pay light dues and tonnage dues on the ship's tonnage British measurements which is 760 tons register. I retain the bill for light dues which I wish to show at our port of discharge; the remainder I sent to you keeping duplicate for myself. My bills at this port are as small as I could have them and get what was absolutely necessary for the ship's use; hope you will be satisfied with same. I was in hope to go to Liverpool; we are so near that port now. But have been ordered to London. While writing these lines, the wind has changed from S E to S W and is now blowing furiously. We have two anchors down and many vessels are coming in here for a harbor. The screw steamer *Kangaroo* from New York has just arrived; hope to hear from you by her and have favorable news from the United States. We are all ready to leave this port as soon as weather will permit.

Respectfully yours,

JOHN M. CAVARLY

Master of Ship *Anglo-Saxon*

Two days later the weather changed. With light winds the Captain set sail for London instead of for Liverpool which he wished to visit more than any other port at that time. He was intensely curious about some rumors he had picked up concerning certain shipbuilding activities in the yards of William C. Miller & Sons. A hull of wood was rising there for a 700-ton steamer, bark-rigged, with two smokestacks, three masts and four gun ports. He told Annie that their U. S. Consul in London, Charles Francis Adams, had protested to the Foreign Office that this hull, and others like it in the blueprint stage, were destined for the Confederate Navy, ordered and paid for by the Rebel underground which flourished fashionably abroad. If this were true, it would make a parody of the blockade three thousand miles away and on the wrong shore. For his own part, he assured Annie, he felt no concern. He wanted to go to Liverpool out of plain curiosity. He would like to have a look at the sailing coal-burner which some imbeciles believed could outrun a Yankee clipper with a fair wind on her quarter and her skysails sheeted home!

Annie smiled sweetly and said nothing. It did not seem to be the time to remind him of the screw-propelled ships they had seen steaming out of Queenstown straight into head winds that had stood up every clipper in the harbor. Nor did she inquire how often had his daily log begun with that rarest of all weather observations — *Comes in fair.* Comes in strong gales . . . Comes in baffling winds . . . Comes in heavy headwinds . . . those were the customary phrases with which he opened his daily sailing record. Yet, one day with a fair wind on the *Anglo-Saxon's* quarter was apparently enough to blot from his memory every adverse wind he had ever known.

They had fair winds all the way of the eight days' sailing from Queenstown, across St. George's Channel, around Penzance Point and through the English Channel to the Straits of Dover. Lizard Point, the Eddystone Rocks, Portland Bill and St. Alban's Head slipped by on the port bow, sailor's landmarks so familiar to the Captain that they scarcely warranted scrutiny through the spyglass before their passage past was entered in his log.

Annie did her sightseeing of the Sussex countryside through the glass. Every time she spied some lovely detail and cried, Oh John, come see! . . . he was staring at his sails filled with a fair wind, without strain or slack, motionless cones of canvas against the clear October sky. This was the only beauty to which, apparently, he had never become used.

Chapter 5

THE PORT OF LONDON was a new world for Annie. Its immensity overwhelmed her from the moment they came off the Isle of Sheppey at the mouth of the Thames and started up the crowded waterway. The river *was* the port, the Captain told her, all the way to the Pool that lay just below London Bridge. That's where they would tie up, within sight of the Bridge, in the London Docks which he preferred to the St. Katharine's because they were bigger and had better repair facilities. She felt a positive relief to hear that he knew his way about in the aquatic labyrinth.

Each huge gray complex of warehouses along the banks appeared to be a city in itself, with their great docks behind impounding ships from every nation under the sun, their bare masts sticking up into the smoky atmosphere like forests denuded of leaves. In tow with the pilot aboard, the Captain was free to give her a guided tour from the poop deck as they progressed inland. He named the sections of the river — Gallion's Reach with the Royal Victoria and Albert Docks, over two miles of those; then Blackwall's Reach and the famous old East India Docks; around the bend which formed the Isle of Dogs, over a hundred acres of docks in that great loop, and on into Limehouse Reach with its West India Docks. Then they were in the Pool, as far inland as seagoing vessels could go. They were practically in the heart of London. Ahead, perhaps a mile or two forward of their bow, Annie glimpsed the granite arches of London Bridge, their great spans etherealized by smoke and distance seeming not to touch the water at all but to float above it weightless and dreamlike.

Then the ship turned, the bridge of her childhood song vanished and the home site for her London sojourn lay before her — the great London Docks with four gateways opening on the Thames and space within for three hundred ships to tie up, not counting the lighters that bustled around, shoving and hauling at the dark hulls. "Three hundred and fifty acres of it, mebbe more," the Captain said like a proud householder as the *Anglo-Saxon* warped in slowly to her berth. Annie concentrated her gaze on what he apparently expected her to think of as her front stoop — a landing stage cumbered with huge stacks of hides, bales of cotton and tobacco and endless rows of enormous winecasks lying on their sides. The cobbled thoroughfare swarmed with dock workers of all nationalities of whom only the Malays, Arabs and Chinese were identifiable by their costumes and the Negroes by their complexions. Her neighbor on the port side was a Portuguese vessel, on the starboard a Greek. Only one small detail in the international bedlam assured her that she really was docked near the heart of London town. At the corner of the immense warehouse, a battered old hansom cab was stationed. Its drooping horse had a long sad Cockney face. Quite definitely English, she concluded with a ripple of inner mirth.

The Captain made ready to pay off his crew, all except the carpenter and sailmaker whom he would need for ship repairs, Crux and George who always stayed by the ship (taking turns for excursions ashore) and Mr. Boxer, with rapidly mending arm in a light sling, who would supervise the cargo discharge. From her perch in the chartroom, Annie watched the sign-off down on the main deck where the Captain had set up a table with his money-box of pounds, shillings and pence. The men came forward from

the fo'c'sle with duffle bags or seachests on their shoulders, all
spruced up in shore togs, boots shined, hair and beards trimmed,
faces alight with anticipation for their run ashore. Most of
them would be plucked clean in a matter of days of those shining
silver pieces her husband counted into their outstretched palms.
It gave her a pang to see how casually they dropped into their
pockets the reward for a half year of the hardest kind of work.
Many of the seamen her husband had doctored offered their
handshakes and stumbling words of thanks — acts which obviously pleased and surprised the Captain as much as they touched
her, looking down on their farewells. A few, she knew, would
wait out the *Anglo-Saxon's* London layover and sign on again
when her "Seamen Wanted" notice would be posted. Mr. Boxer
had once told her that the Captain always had several such re-
peaters in his fo'c'sle, which represented, said he, "quite a nosegay
of tribute to the Old Man from a bunch of monkeys like that."

Annie found her dockside life completely enthralling. From
her safe eyrie in the chartroom, she watched the unloading of
the hides, copper and lumber they had taken on in San Francisco,
the beginnings of the repairs on foremast and bowsprit and the
great patchwork jobs the old sailmaker performed sitting tailor-
fashion in the midst of his acres of torn canvas. It was like looking
down on a long pointed stage backdropped by the thrilling panorama of the busiest docks in Christendom. She wrote to her father
that it was as good as being moored in the middle of Piccadilly
Circus.

Plans for her own shore leave, just as soon as the Captain
would be free, grew to mighty proportions as the daily copies of
The Times of London accumulated in the saloon, with their
notices of special attractions underscored by her husband — Edwin Booth playing in *The Merchant of Venice* at the Theatre
Royal, Mlle. Tietjins singing *Il Trovatore* at the Royal Lyceum,
and the Saturday concerts at Crystal Palace, where also must be
seen "The scarlet and other geraniums, calendulas, petunias,

dwarf nasturtiums, in the rosery and in the ornamental beds of the terraces & the marble vases." The advertisement of a silversmith was red-scored as a must: "PLATE — A. B. Savory & Sons, 11 & 12 Cornhill. Manufacturing Silversmiths — the best in wrought-silver spoons and forks, Fiddle Pattern, Queen's Pattern; & every article requisite for table & sideboard." Also red-scored — Madame Tussaud's Waxworks, which had just added to its collection "a portrait model of Count Cavour, Late Prime Minister of Sardinia." Tentatively marked for Annie's consideration was notice of a pair of plays coming soon to the Royal Lyceum — *My Husband's Aunt* and *An Unprotected Female* followed by Miss Lydia Thompson's dance, The Volunteer Quickstep.

The Captain's suggestions struck her as being unfairly weighted in her favor. He had for instance skipped one continuing notice of an attraction she was sure he longed to see — BLONDIN, The High Rope Performer, who was giving his last weeks at the Crystal Palace, on the high rope in the center transept each afternoon and over the fountains each evening, "enveloping himself, his pole and his barrow in a brilliant cloud of colored fires; then, running the high rope blindfolded in a sack." She made her own checkmark firmly against this notice, finding nothing odd about mixing opera with acrobats, Mozart with waxworks. In her eyes it was simply the share-and-share-alike stuff of which happy marriages were made.

On her first spree to the City, the Captain took her in a hansom cab to the pedestrian entrance to London Bridge, to give her, as he expressed it, the crow's-nest view of the whole. He dismissed the cab and walked arm in arm with her to a spot directly over the middle arch, telling her of the Scottish engineer who had designed this 928-foot wonder, of the captured French cannons that had been melted and cast into the handsome bridge lamps and how the great granite span itself divided London into "above" and "below" bridge. Above the bridge penny steamboats chuffed in all directions and long strings of coal barges labored; below, as far as eye could see, were the turgid waters of the Pool with its incredible tangle of masts along both banks, its Chinese puzzle of docks, landing stages and endless warehouses. The Captain pointed to one clutter of high riggings almost lost in the hazy smoke downstream and exclaimed, *"Our* docks, Annie dear . . . can you see them?"* while the wonder of St. Paul's dome, the fluted column of the Monument and the battlemented walls of the Tower, all dear and familiar from pictures, tore at her attention. But he got around to these, after feasting his eyes on the magnificent view of the Pool.

In the ensuing days, she ran down the heels of her shoes trotting beside him over the cobbles of crooked old streets drenched in history, over flagstones and mosaics of museums and churches whose treasures her husband expounded with such interest that he frequently drew paid customers away from the official guides. He had done all these sights many times before. His extraordinarily retentive memory conserved every date, princely name and circumstance of killing or crowning in exact succession and his booming seaman's voice echoed through stony halls with the gusty authority of the quarterdeck.

Their pleasure jaunts always had a business call or two sandwiched in, but these, for Annie, were like continuations of her sight-seeing in parts of the city seldom explored by visitors. The Captain always left her in the hansom cab while he called at shipping offices around the Coal Exchange, the Steel Yard, the Drapers' Hall, in search of a cargo for the *Anglo-Saxon* which his ship's agent seemed unable to secure. She always knew by his face that his cargo quest had been in vain.

He continued to talk hopefully, especially after other Yankee ships appeared in the London Docks and their skippers began visiting back and forth swapping news and cargo clues. The *Flying Fish* came in from Rouen, the clipper *Comet* from Madeira and from San Francisco the *Golden Eagle,* the racing clipper on which the Captain had once been a bucko mate. It was like having a member of the family with them in the docks.

Annie kept open house aboard the *Anglo-Saxon,* unaware that the popularity of their ship's saloon above all others was due to her presence. Most American skippers who customarily sailed with their wives had left them at home since the war began. There was seldom a vacant place at their dining table and never a scrap left of the New England dinners George set upon it, copious and steaming on banquet-sized platters, polished off with Medford rum, neat.

They paid flowery compliments to Annie, said they had heard tell of her in their clipper circles but had not really believed Captain Jack had done so well for himself. The *Comet's* master warned her never to expect fireworks from her spouse. Captain Jack was an old sobersides, unregenerate in his prudence. Hadn't she ever heard the story about the advice he had once given to a charming young thing like herself who was in a dilemma about choosing a husband? *NO? Wa-al now* . . . He winked at his table mates and launched into the hoariest yarn in their mariner's repetory of jokes:

"Once when this husband of yours was sailing the London packets, he had among his passengers a most attractive young lady who speedily reduced five young men to the verge of distraction and naturally they all proposed to her. In her embarrassment of riches she consulted the Captain . . . *Your* man of prudence, Ma'am! . . . and this salty Solomon suggested a way out of the lady's dilemma. On a calm day she would, supposedly by accident, fall overboard, and whichever of her five suitors jumped in to rescue her would obviously be the man who loved her the most. This she did and *four* jumped in to save her! She fled dripping to her cabin and sent for her adviser, asking him, '*Now* what am I to do, Captain?' And you know what our boy here said to that poor distressed young lady?" Annie shook her head. The storytelling skipper paused, glanced at her husband reproachfully, then back at her with dancing eyes. "He says, *Ah, my dear, if you want a sensible husband take the dry one! And that,* by God, *she did!*"

In the gale of laughter that swept the saloon, the Captain tried to tell her that it was an old Dickens yarn, but the guffawing skippers drowned him out. Annie wiped her eyes and poured another round of rum for the crusty old graybeards she had learned to love.

They saved their more serious talk for the after-dinner hours and this, too, fascinated Annie. They were all in rebellion against the London insurance agents who, because of risk from Confederate raiders, had raised rates on Yankee-carried cargoes to prohibitive levels, though each master pretended he was about to secure some freight. Like her husband, not one would admit the possibility of having to return to the States in ballast which represented, Annie gathered, the ultimate in defeat since the ballast was dumped overboard on arrival, a profitless burden carried only to balance the ship's top hamper in the wintry Atlantic crossing that lay ahead of them all. Masks of secrecy seemed to fall over their bluff open faces when they talked about their trips into the City.

She watched her husband's diplomacy which drew from his bearded colleagues hints of cargoes they were working on — coal, steel or machinery — and gave in return a few guarded comments on the textile exporters he had interviewed (but not admitting that every one had turned him down).

They were like old foxes sitting around the demijohn of rum, brushing up their whiskers and talking bravely as they sipped. Every one of them feared he must eventually sail out in ballast for the States but in the presence of rival captains they talked with booming assurance. Only in their letters penned before sailing to their New York owners or agents would they confess their failures to find cargoes. Their letters, like those Annie copied for the Captain, would show a close watchfulness over pounds and pence, but no awareness of the tide of history that was rising beneath their keels:

London, November 10th, 1861

To Messrs. Wm. L. Coleman & Co.

Yours of October 23rd came to hand in due time. You say

you hope I will be able to get some freight to New York, coals, iron or something. I assure you I wish it were in my power to do so. I can do nothing in the way of getting freight to New York. Even the packets here are going out mostly in ballast. The ship "Patrick Henry," one of the London packets, is to leave here for New York in ballast tomorrow. I regret to bring the ship home in ballast but see no other way to get her to New York. We are all discharged and taking on ballast. Will be ready for sea in ten days if nothing happens to prevent us. By going in ballast we have no light dues to pay. I am taking Trinity Ballast; I pay two shillings and one half-penny per ton, on board the ship trimmed. This is very good ballast, and cheap, mostly pebblestones and gravel. . . . My crew all left as soon as the ship was in dock, with the exception of the Mates, Steward and Cook who will remain by the ship. The ship was discharged by the dock company at one shilling per ton on her register tonnage British measurement, which is now 784 tons. Will have to get bread, flour, beef and some small stores to take the ship home. I will do the best I possibly can in all things for the interest of the ship. I am having the ship put in order only as far as is absolutely necessary. Nothing more will be done than what is necessary. Hope you will be satisfied and think I have done well.

> Respectfully yours,
> JOHN M. CAVARLY, *Master*

After she copied this report, the Captain reminded Annie that they were approaching their second wedding anniversary. It was high time they got around to that Cornhill silversmith, he said, adding with an expansive smile that she could choose her present from him regardless of cost. And if there was something she wished to see in the Royal Opera at Covent Garden that evening, she'd better put on one of her fancy "bunnits."

Cornhill had several silversmiths, all, Annie remarked gayly, lying within easy walking distance of the "Old Lady of Threadneedle Street" and the Royal Exchange. Did that proximity suggest that one ought to have entree to those temples of money before venturing over the portals of A. B. Savory & Sons or of Sarl

& Sons Silversmiths a few doors farther down the street? The Captain refused to be intimidated.

He steered her from shop to shop as she made exhaustive inspections and comparisons and finally settled on the tea service of her dreams whose chastely simple design, said the dealer, showed the pure Adam influence. The Captain paid up without a murmur and, when Annie had wandered off to another counter, he told the dealer to wrap up the pair of silver candelabra he had seen his wife hovering over longingly. "Her Christmas present," he whispered hoarsely, then in a loud voice he gave the name of their ship for delivery of the goods, as proudly as if it were an English castle.

Out of the shop Annie said she had been treated royally enough and wished no opera that night. She much preferred to stroll about with him and have a last spree of sight-seeing which she adored. They had hardly scratched the surface of London. On this very street, for instance, there were two treasures her guidebook had mentioned — Thomas Gray's birthplace at number 41 and a small Wren church that was supposed to have in its vestry an organ whose old keyboard had been used by Mendelssohn. After that, maybe a supper at the Cheshire Cheese where they could look at Dr. Johnson's chair?

The Captain grinned and told her to take him in tow, secretly proud of the things she knew that were outside his ken. The only Gray he had ever heard of was Robert, the American sea captain who had served in the Continental Navy during the Revolution and later discovered the Columbia River.

Thus were added to her chain of London memories the last lovely links — a hallowed old organ keyboard which she touched reverently, letting her fingers take in the tactile impressions of its cracked and yellowed keys; a gabled housefront on the site of a poet's birthplace (*"The Curfew tolls the knell of parting day, The lowing herd wind slowly o'er the lea,"* she murmured to her husband, her face a glowing lantern in the fog); a small wooden armchair beneath a Reynolds portrait of the heavy-jowled man who had often sat in it, perhaps in this same dim-timbered tavern named for a cheese but which served, to the Captain's delight, a most hearty steak and kidney pie with a rich brown ale to wash it down.

The only memory she would have cast out, had she been able, was the visit to the London M. D. who had warned her to stay away from the sea until she would have her family. She tried not to think of this just then but the doctor's office on a small fashionable street, his bobbing parlormaid in black uniform and stiff-starched cap and the doctor's wise old horsy face above a gates'-ajar collar intruded momentarily. Strange she could remember every visual detail but not a single word he had said . . . only her own grieving recapitulation of it afterwards, "I'm a sailor in spirit only, John dearest, not made to breed on the high seas like other captains' wives." The Captain had told her gruffly that if she had been in the least like most skippers' wives he knew, he'd not have given her a second look that day she first stepped aboard his command.

She watched him drain his ale, then squint at her through the glass bottom of his pewter mug, using it like a spyglass and muttering *Holy mackerel!* as for some great discovery. Then he set it down with a windy sigh of satisfaction and grinned at her.

"I've *got* London now," she said softly across the table, "for *keeps,* John . . ."

For *keeps,* she thought, so I can follow you in my fashion whenever you return here alone. A queer little hoarder's smile played about her lips. She knew exactly how she would "get back." She would come through the Thames Tunnel, through the enchanting little souvenir viewer her husband had bought for her to make up for not having had time to show her the real tunnel. Her miniature tunnel was a collapsible cardboard affair with two eyeholes cut into the front cover. You held these close to your eyes, then pulled out the accordion-like device and you looked stereoptically down two parallel arched passages filled with sauntering people in brightly colored clothes, ladies on the arms of their silk-hatted escorts, gaily clad children trailing uniformed governesses, Oxford dons in black capes, Arabs in white burnooses and hosts of other Empire visitors in turbans, kilts, sarongs. The people on the cutouts pasted in the foreground of the accordion were a shade bigger than those on the successive cutouts, and they came to life as you stared at them, drew you magically into their glad company so that you were *in* the tunnel after a second's peering, you were in it walking under the River Thames from Wapping to Rotherhithe. THAMES TUNNEL was printed on the cover and its statistics which the Captain knew by heart — "120 feet long, 16 feet below high water mark, was 8 Years Building and cost 446,000 Pounds; Opened the 25th of March 1843."

"And I'll *always* be able to get back!" she added after a slight pause.

They waited on the tide, ready now at any moment to lift anchors. The Captain composed some final letters to clear the deck of the oral reports he would otherwise have to make in New York. Annie copied the pages he completed, smiling at him across the table as he tugged his beard over the minute reporting of pounds and pence of someone else's money, spent by him, or saved:

London, Nov. 17, 1861

To Messrs. Wm. L. Coleman & Co.

Your letter of Oct. 23rd came to hand in due time, nothing from you since. I have taken in 240 tons of ballast at the price named in my last letter to you. Ship drawing 14 feet, 6 inches. Took out the old foremast to have it repaired, as agreed by contract, putting on two pitch pinefishings 25 feet long from cap down, for sum of 25 Pounds, mast taken from alongside and brought back again to the ship free of charge; but in case the mast proved not fit to be repaired, to make a new mast for the sum of 68 Pounds less 6 Pounds for the old mast. Got the old mast up to the mast-house; found to take all the bad wood out of the head it would take the mast-head nearly away. When we came to cut into the mast, we found one side sap-rotten all the way down. Down near the deck it was badly rotten. The mast was much worse than I supposed it was. In fact, it was so bad I did not think it was to the ship's interest to have it repaired. Consequently I had a new mast made which is now in the ship and as fine a spar as ever I saw, *free from sap and knots.* This is the very best I could do out of all my estimates in London.

The rudder port I have had repaired and is now in good order. The copper case was in bad condition, lower part broken away, could put the fingers through into the ship's frame. Had to have a new rudder case. I have had the butts and wood ends caulked on the outside. The ship needs caulking all over but I think we can come home with her as she is. Have got new trussle-trees for the fore topmast, which were broken off, new bowsprit cap ditto, old one wrung off. I have been compelled to have more repairs on that old galley stove. . . .

Off Dover, Nov. 20th, 1861

We left London Docks yesterday. The steam boat towing us thus far is 4 Pounds. Winds strong from West now. I sent my current account, with vouchers, to you yesterday. Left them with MacLean Maris & Co., payable to your order—2,147 Pounds, 19 Shillings, 8 Pence.

I think the freight note was not with the accounts. I wrote to the broker last evening to send you one. You will see that Marietta & Co. have made a discount on the freight money two months from the day the ship was reported. This I could not help. They would not pay the freight without discount of sixty days. *Rule of the port.* My charter-party says freight payable on right delivery of cargo; the charter-party should have said *"in cash without discount."* The charter-party was shown to Phillips Shaw & Brother, the largest brokers in London. They said we would have to submit to the discount. I saw the charter-partys of the ships *Racer, Arey, Reporter* and *Flying Mist,* they were all like mine and, Marietta says, they will all be discounted. I could do no better; have done the best in all things here in London.

The American Consul sent a bill to Patte in Mexico of $34.34.

He paid it without my order. I do not know what the bill was for. The Consul said it was for the discharge of the Third Mate. The Third Mate never saw the Consul at Mazatlan at all. The Consul had nothing to do with him and here he has sent a bill for discharging him. This bill I paid, as I was compelled to, but *I paid it under protest.*

I bought two cases of wine in Mazatlan which Patte paid for—$8.00. The money I have on board the ship. I could not get its value here in London and have it now with me. I write this letter in great haste. *Ship is stiff enough!*

> *Off Bill of Portland, Nov. 24th, 1861*

The Pilot goes on shore this morning. We are out five days. Hope to reach New York soon. I send these letters on shore by the Pilot.

> Respectfully yours,
> JOHN M. CAVARLY, *Master*

Annie had to copy his final postscript on the run, so to speak, with the Captain standing over her shaking the pilot's mail pouch and telling her not to bother with the final folderol, but she wanted it all. She was going to take copies of those letters off ship when they reached New York. She wanted them for her scrapbook, she said, as souvenir of her first close sharing in his nautical life. She wanted every last line of them right down to the final *Ship is stiff enough!* which was like a shout of joy.

Once as she copied hurriedly, she asked him without looking up, if they were passing the Isle of Wight, for no reason at all that he could see. He told her genially that they probably were and wondered what bees were buzzing *now* under the bonnet he stared at, firmly affixed to her coif by that Kamehameha hatpin.

Had she been on deck, she would have trained the spyglass on the Isle of Wight just in case some side-angled view would have given her a glimpse of the channel behind it leading up to the port of Southampton. In the last issue of the London *Times* that Boxer had brought aboard before leaving London Docks, she had discovered a small story hidden in the back pages about a

Confederate steamer named the *Nashville* which was lying at the Southampton docks. "No move has yet been made to supply her with coal or stores," the article read, and there the story had ended, doubtless to be continued in the next issue which she would never see.

Without the pilot after Portland Bill, the *Anglo-Saxon* stood up to the wind like a queen. Annie saw the beauty of her as she bore down channel exactly as if she were one of the figures she picked up on shore with the spyglass, all with faces turned toward the sea. Toward *our* passage, she thought proudly, and she was glad then that she had not shown her husband the disquieting news story of a potential enemy lurking in those bright waters. And, even if she had, he would doubtless have scoffed and told her to take a good look at the coal-burning steamers they overhauled and left astern, as if they were actually anchored midstream.

Off Land's End they caught a northeaster whistling down from the Irish Sea. The great sails gathered in the blow and twisted it their way to keep a safe distance from the coastline of France. Annie felt the hull's shudders pass through her like the muscular contractions preceding seasickness, but she was not in the least seasick.

Only much later would she remember those communicative shudders from the fighting hull and pretend that she had known then that they were sailing over the spot where, on her next voyage homebound from London, the *Anglo-Saxon* was to meet her doom. "Off Brest," she would say . . . "latitude 49 degrees North, longitude 7 degrees East . . . our ship *knew* she was passing over her future grave . . . and so did I, so did I."

And it was very possible that she did, prescience being one of her peculiar endowments.

Chapter 6

LIKE DOZENS OF OTHER indignant Yankee skippers crossing the Atlantic in ballast in that winter of 1861, the Captain was already involved in the Civil War though still unwilling to admit that the tons of gravel in his hold represented a Confederate victory over Union shipping. During their twenty-day passage, he continued to blame the London insurance agents for their profitless situation. He told Annie he positively believed the British had exaggerated the war news so as to swing British exports to their own ships flying the Union Jack which apparently the Confederate raiders never stopped on the high seas. He recalled one London *Times* article they had read together, to the effect that Washington, D. C., was still in a condition of perfect safety.

Still! he snorted. That showed the scare treatment, didn't it? And what about the last paper Boxer had brought aboard, its long editorial about Confederate ships steaming into English harbors? Had she seen *one* Rebel raider in the London Docks? Annie told him then of the C.S.S. *Nashville* tied up in Southampton. Notice of it had been in the same issue, she said quietly. He'd have seen it if the editorial hadn't made him too angry to read on.

Even so, he continued to deride the Confederate raiders. Once his hurricane-damaged ship was put in perfect repair, she could outrun anything the Rebels had. His faith in sailing ships seemed inextinguishable. Nothing in his eyes could ever cause the clippers to vanish from the seas — neither war nor raiders nor the coal-burning packets that were ever on the increase, skippered by men, said he, who had begun their seafaring careers in rowboats and had not made much progress since then.

His brave talk often convinced Annie because she wished, for his sake, to be convinced. But sometimes, when she visited the hold to bring water to her special charges — the pair of wild-eyed cats inhabiting the gloomy cavern to keep down rats — she would listen to the surface ballast pebbles sliding back and forth to the rolling of the ship. The stony cascade of a dead cargo seemed to be saying something less reassuring than her husband's words. She would set down the crock of water and cock her ear thoughtfully while calling the cats with the low whistle to which they responded.

They entered New York harbor on December 10th, took rooms in the Brevoort House for a week's stay before proceeding to Boston to put the *Anglo-Saxon* into the repair dock. As always, upon landing, their first concern was for the accumulated mail and periodicals. Now, said the Captain, they could *really* find out what was going on in the war which the British press had blown up out of all proportion. He noted with satisfaction that the New York *Times* carried all its reports under a single average-sized caption — *News of the Rebellion*. No hysterical headlines, no front-page stories of ship losses . . . hadn't he told her to take everything heard abroad with a grain of salt?

But the inside pages quieted his tone of triumph. There were columns of military want ads which told him clearly just how this inland rebellion might throttle the shipping world. Calls for seamen wanted for the marine artillery, pay same as the Navy with a $100 bounty at the expiration of service: he admitted then to Annie that he might have difficulties finding a crew for his next voyage.

The maritime news sections sobered him still further. Nearly all ships arriving from Europe had come in ballast. Only vessels from South American ports or from California via the Horn or via the Isthmus transfer point at Aspinwall had brought cargoes — coffee from Brazil, mahogany and hides from Vera Cruz, logwood and pimiento from Jamaica, passengers and gold from California. There were brief mentions of ships taken as prizes but no details as to how this was accomplished.

Not until he encountered old friends on the waterfront did the Captain get the full picture of Rebel marauding. Their stories, picked up by signal flags from escaped ships or from American consuls in South American ports, would not appear in newspapers until the captive crews of the prizes, after having been landed in some remote port, would have found their way back to the States as best they could. The Confederate *Sumter,* his cronies said, was the principal raider at the time, though others were surely on the way since the blockade was a sieve through which any smart sailor could pass, as the *Sumter* herself had run it during the previous summer. She was skippered by a fanatic Southerner, Raphael Semmes, who lived off the high seas like a jackal. His hunting ground was the broad belt of the South Atlantic, between Brazil and the bulge of Africa, traversed by all ships bound to and from the Pacific and Indian Oceans around either Cape. Semmes captured coal to fuel his steamer and food to feed his crew and prisoners. The *Sumter* flew whatever flag was convenient — the Stars and Stripes if a Union cruiser was in the offing, the British Union Jack or the French tricolor when approaching a Yankee vessel and signaling a wish to speak her. Only after he had put his first shot across the bow of his prize did Semmes run up the Confederate flag.

The Captain listened to his friends' stories with a feeling of outrage. That no captured crews had been killed, but on the contrary were taken aboard the raider and fed and berthed until a likely port of embarkation was reached, did not in his eyes mitigate the crime of deliberate destruction of a ship. One of his skipper friends had seen one burning. The flames had run up the tarred rigging and ignited all sails simultaneously, so that — for a few minutes before the masts started to topple — you saw the clipper completely outlined in fire.

Some of his graybeard friends advised him to go into steam now while he was young and flexible enough to make the difficult transition. They themselves could not, though convinced that the future of the American carrying trade lay in the sidewheeler and screw steamers. They were old dogs, they said, too fixed in habit to learn the tricks of the new steam engines. He listened respectfully but refused to be convinced. He signed on with the *Anglo-Saxon's* owner to command the next voyage out, and sailed in her with Annie for the Boston shipyard. The repairs his owner had agreed to underwrite reinforced his certainty that his ship would never be taken. Besides a new copper sheathing on her bottom and two complete suits of new sail, the *Anglo-Saxon* was to be fitted with an eight-inch pivot gun aft of her foremast. Mr. Boxer, who had also signed on again, was a prime shot, Navy-trained as a marksman with light cannon.

Annie hid her worries as she prepared to leave the ship that had been her home for almost a year. One of her mother's maxims came helpfully to mind — *You have made your bed and upon it you must lie.* Her mother also had made her bed with a man who had had dreams of wider spaces than New England's to live in. Annie recalled how during the years her father pioneered in the Sandwich Islands, her mother had accepted the separation without a single doubt of its good for all. Without a whimper, Annie told herself resolutely.

They had Christmas in Boston, in the Parker House, where the Captain took rooms for a few weeks to be near the repair yards to watch the start of rejuvenation of his ship. Annie thought he should visit his New London family, but he told her he had no intention of sharing her with anyone on their first holiday together. At the rate the outfitting would go, with so many marine workers off to the war, he'd have ample time to show her off to the home folks.

On Christmas Eve he brought out his surprise package and settled back as at a play, to watch her unwrap the candelabra, exclaiming with joy even before she got all the paper unwound from the fluted silver stems. She stood them on the table, branched and gleaming . . . Like trees, she said, trees that could have sprouted straight out of the Comstock Lode, pretending she had never seen them before so as to give him all credit for his perfect taste. "When we have our home, John dearest . . ." she whispered, and she sat opposite him at the table and gave him a rapt smile through the shining fretwork to show him how it would be.

Later, she brought out her own present for him, also from London — a gold hunting-case watch embossed with a sailing ship, with a gold key to wind it — purchased one day when he had left her in a hansom while making a business call. The fact that they had thought simultaneously of their coming Christmas seemed almost as wonderful to the Captain as the handsome watch with its 18-carat key. Like the kind of divination he'd seen Hindu fakirs practice, he said. He snipped one of her blond locks and placed it between the back covers of his watch, telling her with a chuckle that he must remember never to open that case in a wind, to have a look at the part of her that would henceforth travel over his heart.

They made a round of New Year calls on the Captain's Boston friends, moving always within that small circle of men to whom the buoys and lighthouses of far-flung coasts were as familiar as the bells and beams in their home port, who spoke of the seven seas as a continuous domain without frontiers, theirs by natural heritage. Annie would remember afterwards how comfortingly small the world had seemed when she heard Calcutta, Manila, Java Head, Whampoa, Melbourne and Liverpool mentioned all in the same sentence, or almost. As the skippers swapped news of their voyages, they computed all distances in terms

of sailing days, countable, known entities of time which somehow shrunk space and made it manageable in imagination. And,
when at last her husband would sail, for wherever his cargo
called, she would draw comfort reciting to herself the shrinking
trajectories she had listened to, and hoarded: 87 days Hong Kong
to New York, 98 days Boston to Manila, 88 days New York to
Bombay . . . *aye, aye, give or take a week, depending the season.*

About the Rebel raiders, they admitted the threat but had
plenty of useful advice as to how they could, and had been, out-
witted. One skipper told the Captain that the surest way was
never to show your colors on the high seas. Annie saw her husband's eyes narrow at the suggestion that he sail forth with a
complete set of foreign flags in his signal locker.

He contained his disgust until that visit was over, then he ex-
ploded. He would never, under any circumstances, fly a foreign
flag over an American ship. As long as there was a deck left
for him to stand upon and a mast from which he could order it
to be flown, he would show the Stars and Stripes. Not to do so
would be tantamount to admitting that the Union had forfeited
its rights to the high seas.

Those rights he showed her one day in historical perspective.
He asked her to accompany him to the shipyard in Charlestown
to see the *Anglo-Saxon* nearing completion of her repairs. The
age of steam and iron ships was left behind them as he led her
through the gates. The wooden cradles of the ways, shaped to the
sheer of the clippers they upheld, filled him with joy.

From just such ways as these had come the ships that had made
a maritime nation of the thirteen colonies. Oh, she could not
imagine those first colonial schooners, they were so small — even
a ship of war like John Paul Jones's *Ranger* — barely 200 tons
as a matter of fact. But they had run, he said, nimble as rabbits in
and out of the British convoys during the Revolution. From those
sharp-modeled little ships had evolved the beautifully timbered
frigates of the War of 1812, ships like the *Constitution*. From

them we evolved the racing clippers that had put the United States at the head of the seafaring nations of the entire world. And there, God willing, they would keep her. *This* was how Annie must read her country's history, even now while more of it was in the making. Wars and rebellions had come and gone, but the ships had always sailed on.

For the final month before sailing, they moved from the Boston hotel to her grandmother's home in New London where Annie had elected to wait out the next voyage. She adored her father's mother — a tall, thin and fragile-seeming old lady with a ramrod for a backbone. Through her steel-rimmed spectacles Grandmother Bolles had seen three generations of menfolk go down to the sea — her father, her captain of a whaler husband and all her sons save her youngest who was Annie's father. She lived alone, stoutly refusing to share the roof of any of her married children, teasing when they suggested she must sometimes be lonely. *Lonely?*

Her house stood on a rise of ground far enough back from the port to be called a farm, but near enough to have warranted a "widow's walk" in its architectural scheme. Squared off with white pickets on the truncated peak of its shingled roof, the lookout commanded a view of the Race between Long Island and Block Island Sounds.

As a girl, Annie used to pace that widow's walk with her young sisters. She told the Captain how they would pretend they were whalers' wives waiting out their husbands' return from Pacific whaling grounds. They would shade their eyes and look to sea and try to imagine what their grandmother had felt when she had been waiting through her second or even third year, with so few letters then.

Each evening around sunset she and her Captain climbed the attic stairs that led to the windy lookout, to watch the changing lights over the sea as they talked endlessly about his next voyage. He knew now his destinations — San Francisco with an assorted cargo, thence to Howland's Island on the Equator in the Pacific with stores for that mid-ocean anchorage, where he would take on a cargo of guano for Liverpool, then home. He told her how ghostly their sitting room aboard the *Anglo-Saxon* was going to seem to him. He had grown so accustomed to her presence there, he would probably "see" her quite often, bent over her sewing beneath the swinging lamp. Once he confessed that sometimes his conscience troubled him; she seemed so terribly young to be left alone. With one arm he could still completely encircle her slight girlish figure.

He kept her always to the leeward of himself so his broad back blocked off the breezes blowing in from the Atlantic. Deftly, seemingly unconsciously, he shifted her from one encircling arm to the other each time they came to the end of the walk and faced about. Like a slow dance, Annie thought, stately as a minuet . . . he had never had time in his youth to learn any other.

He postponed showing her off to his family until, through a passage of letters more stormy than diplomatic, he had accustomed his mother to the idea that he was leaving his wife with her own folks. He explained to Annie that he had no intention of marooning her a good two hours' buggy ride out from town and with virtual strangers. Oh, she'd love his father, sister and brother all right, but his mother was just a mite dominant, though a good woman at heart. Annie sensed the antipathy and rightly guessed that her husband and his mother were as alike as two peas in a pod.

Since she had never seen a photograph of her mother-in-law, she was unprepared for the striking resemblance which she had thought to be mainly one of nature and temperament. Mother Cavarly had reproduced in her eldest son her exact replica. She was tall and amazingly handsome, with the same dark eyes and dark wavy hair, the same strong character lines in her face and the same voice, masculine in depth, as she exclaimed, "What a dear little thing, John," and put forth her two hands tapered and shapely like the Captain's. Her firm handclasp was her welcoming embrace.

The remainder of the Captain's family captured Annie's heart at once — the old father with his crippled back, the brother and sister, Phillip and Elizabeth, and the Captain's favorite aunt on his father's side, a gentle ailing widow who looked as if the first wind would blow her away. As she sat in the spotless parlor sipping tea with them, it seemed to Annie that the total strength of her mother-in-law had passed directly to her first-born, leaving only marginal vigors for her remaining children. Phillip at twenty-four already showed in his sensitive face the facile emotions of the tubercular and his sister Elizabeth, three years his junior, was like a frail child who still had years to go before reaching her majority. Both of them gazed at their seafaring brother with unveiled adoration, listening to his tale of the hurricane the *Anglo-Saxon* outrode, with parted lips and little coughs of excitement. From time to time their expressive eyes turned to her, brimming with shy love, and she wanted to snatch them both to her heart. She understood now why the Captain always spoke of them tenderly, as if they were still children, and why he sent money to them to help "piece out" their young lives so visibly restricted by delicate health.

The mother lost no time telling her son what she thought of his resolve to go to sea again, deliberately asking for trouble this time, what with all those raiders about. She had the *Harper's Weekly* for February 1st '62 to back up her arguments. Annie glanced at her husband, hoping he would blow away his mother's anxiety with the same comment he had made to her when she had first seen that magazine in Boston. Its cover showed the raider *Nashville* tied up at Southampton under the watchful guard of the United States naval sloop *Tuscarora*, but the inside pages showed a much more fearful sketch — the raider *Sumter* under full sail and pluming smoke as she bore down upon a brigantine whose jib sails had already been cut loose by a shot across her bow.

When Annie had first stared at that picture of a Yankee prize being taken, the two-masted brigantine had changed into her husband's three-masted clipper and she had not been able to efface from her mind the impression of having witnessed the *Anglo-Saxon's* capture. Even after the Captain had made fun of the drawing by pointing out the anomaly of the brig's sails hanging limp in a calm and those of the nearby *Sumter* bellying out stiff with wind (Wind out of some artist's windy mind! he had snorted) the engraving continued to menace her thoughts. She watched her mother-in-law leaf through the magazine to the *Sumter* picture, then shake it at the Captain accusingly.

"I suppose *this* makes no impression on you, John," she said. He had sworn to Annie driving out that he was not going to let his mother ruffle his temper. Annie saw him count ten before replying.

"Yes it did, when Annie first showed it to me," he said quietly. "But not for the reasons you think. That prize was the *Joseph Parke* of Boston. Her skipper is my friend. Poor man owned that brig, had his total fortune tied up in her and, foolishly, not a red cent of insurance on her. *My* ship is well insured. Even so, they'll never take me" — his voice rose slightly — "and don't you go worrying the young ones with such thoughts, Mother!" He reached for Annie's hand. "You better take a lesson from my little shellback here — *she's* not wringing her hands!"

"John will get through," Annie said, giving his mother her most radiant smile. "He has lucky stars." She nodded reassuringly to Phillip and Elizabeth. They were the ones the mother should be worrying about, she thought. The hint of friction between their adored brother and their mother had made them sad and silent.

In the carriage driving back to town she thought of things she would do for them during the winter. She had seen Elizabeth looking with round eyes at her modish bonnet. She would begin by buying her a hat. And Phillip, the Captain had said, was a real bookworm.

"They're angels, your brother and sister," she said to the Captain. "I'm coming back very often while you're gone." She saw his relieved smile. He snapped the reins over the backs of their rented carriage horses and sent them into a pretty trot.

On his last evening in New London, the Captain told her he had decided to sign her on as a member of his crew, a very special nonsailing member. He was going to appoint her as his lookout for the whole Atlantic seaboard while he would be in the Pacific. Would she do this for him? Would she, for example, come up here on her grandmother's roof now and then and tell him if the fishing fleet was going out regularly? It would be most useful for him to know if those stout trawler skippers remained tied up in the port, afraid to sail the coastal waters.

He estimated he'd be about ten months making it out to San Francisco, thence to Howland's Island, then back around the Horn to Liverpool, two passages through the Rebel-ridden waters of the South Atlantic. What newspapers he would see in that time would be months old when and if he found any in the Pacific ports. She must therefore be his eyes and ears for the war news and always send her letters via the fast Isthmus route to his San Francisco agent. He counted on her to write good seamanly descriptions of any new raiders reported, so he would know what to watch out for on his way back.

She nodded with each new instruction, blinking back her tears. She thought he was making it all up, pretending a need, to give her a sense of sharing in the voyage she could not make with him. Even when he tilted up her chin and looked deep into her eyes saying, These will be my trustiest lookouts all the while . . . she did not believe him. Only after he had sailed was she to discover how accurately he had placed her as his landbound lookout.

From Rio he wrote her with bright underlinings that he had made the Equator in twenty days out from Boston, a near record. No sign of raiders above or below Cape San Roque but, he confessed, plenty of yarning about them in the grogshops of the port. Now as he prepared to hoist skysails for the long easy run down the Brazil Current, he was recalling each day of it when she had been with him. He had his old chart to go by. Dot by dot he would follow their first voyage together.

A pilot-boat letter from the same port asked her to keep her eyes peeled for news of a ship named the *Oreto*. The pilot had warned him about her. She flew the Union Jack and was said to be taking on armament in a hidden cove of the Bahamas, which might indicate a raider in the making.

Not until September of '62 did Annie find the first printed mention of the *Oreto*. The short report was buried in the back of a newspaper devoted almost entirely to the Union defeat at the second battle of Bull Run. Maritime affairs were obviously of less than secondary importance in those anxious days. But, for Annie, they were the whole Civil War. She read the *Oreto* story with mounting anxiety.

She was a raider, as her husband had suspected — a powerful steamer of about 700 tons, bark-rigged with two smokestacks and three masts. On September 3rd in broad daylight she had run the blockade into the Confederate stronghold of Mobile, almost under the prows of two Union cruisers on patrol beyond the bar, whose commanders mistook her at first for a British gunboat. The *Oreto*, recently renamed the C.S.S. *Florida,* was now moored beneath the defenses of Mobile. Why she had come in from the high seas was a matter for conjecture; she may have needed repairs, coal or fresh water. Five Union cruisers had been detailed to keeping the *Florida* penned up in Mobile for the duration.

The Captain received her news in San Francisco as he was completing his loading of stores for the mid-Pacific guano island, his next destination. He wrote back that most people on the West Coast had never heard of the Rebel raiders; they thought he was talking through his hat when he mentioned them. As for that *Florida,* though reluctant to pay a compliment to the enemy, he did not believe she could be bottled up indefinitely in Mobile. Any skipper who could get her over that treacherous bar without benefit of pilot must be a splendid navigator, as capable of getting out as he had been of getting in. He understated the bad weather trip he had had coming around the Horn and reported only that within 700 miles of the Golden Gate he had drifted around for eighteen days in an almost constant succession of light airs and calms, a most frustrating experience.

Shortly after reading the first batch of his San Francisco letters, Annie received one from her father telling a different story. He expressed admiration for her skipper husband who, by report, had stood off Cape Horn for thirty-nine days fighting the worst southwest gales in the memory of mariners. "How he got enough southing to clear the land at all is a truly remarkable feat — but doubtless you've heard all about this, long since, Annie dearest, direct from your John, I suspect." Her heart skipped a beat as she read. Thirty-nine days . . . it was unimaginable. Only the haggardness of her husband's face after having stood the bridge almost continuously through such a dark howling fight, as she was sure he had, was dimly imaginable. She stared miserably at the pile of newspapers from which she must compose her next lookout report for her Captain. Not one cheering word could be found in the columns she had marked.

News of the Confederate destruction of Yankee shipping had moved to the front pages. A hitherto unheard-of cruiser, the Confederate *Alabama,* had appeared off the Azores, powerfully armed, with sails to augment her steaming speed. She had already caught and burned nine whalers and sent their crews, in their own longboats, to land in Fayal.

Through November, December and January the toll of Yankee ship losses doubled, then trebled. Annie envisioned her warning letters piling up in San Francisco as her husband sailed serenely toward the South Pacific. But she continued doggedly to write them into the void of his months-long silence. Soon after the New Year of '63 the *Florida* escaped from the harbor of Mobile on a moonless night. With the two powerful raiders now at large in the Atlantic, together with numerous captured ships which the

Confederate captains turned into raiders by putting their own crews aboard, her husband's chances of getting through seemed to shrink to zero.

The *Florida* and the *Alabama* crisscrossed the sea lanes leading up from the Equator, plucking off their prizes at will, sometimes as many as half a dozen a day. The captured cargoes — flour, lard, candles, whale oil, sardines and wines — mounted to uncounted tons, enough to feed the raiders for a year. Annie gave up listing for her husband the names of the burned ships. She marked crosses on her ocean chart as the capture notices appeared. The blank spaces around the Equator began to look like a graveyard. She ceased her visits to the Captain's family, knowing she could no longer keep up the pretense of courage.

Later, she was to realize that she had been keeping vigil over the death of an era in that crucial year of '63; but at the time she was too overwhelmed with personal anxiety to see this. In February the senseless destruction took on a new and sharper meaning. A name leaped from the small type of the maritime news — *Golden Eagle,* caught and burned at sea by the raider *Alabama.*

It was like reading of the death of a member of the family. She remembered the beautiful clipper sailing into London Docks with her figurehead of an eagle on the wing freshly gilded and the same house flag as the *Anglo-Saxon's* flying from her mainmast. Her husband had come up from fo'c'sle to quarterdeck on that racing clipper. His youth was in the *Golden Eagle;* she had hardened his muscles wrestling her great white shrouds; she had sharpened his mariner's sight and quickened his judgment to compel her speed in flight.

She clipped the notice and tried to think where to send it. She could hear her husband cursing the loss in the low rumbling rounds of seamen's oaths which came to his lips only when he was livid with anger. She reread his last letter telling about his unexpected run to Honolulu, where he had had to take the *Anglo-Saxon* for some vast repairs to her keel, damaged by the idiot Howland's Island pilot who had run her up against a patch of coral on the northwest end of the guano island. "Your good father heard I was here and came up from Lahaina to help me through the long consular inquiry. Afterwards he guided me to the best agents for white lead, tar paper, oakum and bolt copper (not to speak of the 600 feet of oak timber needed) and he used his influence to get us laborers from Oahu Prison for 20 days work each at 50¢ per diem, plus one dollar for their Overseers. . . . I'll sail on Christmas Day back to Howland's for our guano, thanks to him. Shift my departure from Howland's to about February 15th. If I were spooky like you, Annie dearest, I'd say our old *Anglo-Saxon* was pulling every trick to stay out here in safe waters!"

Annie sent the news of the sinking to her father in Hawaii. If a clipper were in San Francisco ready to sail for the Islands, and if it connected with a Panama steamer coming up from the Isthmus with eastern mail, then her father might have the letter within forty days. If . . . if . . . more than two months of waiting hung on that little word. Then her father replied by fastest courier, San Francisco packet and Overland Express, to tell her that he had put her letter on an inter-island schooner which would surely reach Howland's before her husband sailed. The Captain had told him he would finish his loading and be on his way by mid-February which meant he would reach England about June 25th. He chided her gently for worrying. He would lay any odds on the safe bet that her Captain would get through with his guano for Liverpool, no matter how risky the situation looked to her.

Chancellorsville, Vicksburg and Gettysburg were in the battle headlines through the spring and summer of '63 while Annie marked on her chart the ships sunk in the sea lanes she knew her husband traversed. The land battles were too vast to be visualized through the daily communiqués, but each sinking she could imagine vividly. The terse descriptions of the ships' riggings gave her the form their bonfires at sea must have taken. The catalogues of their cargoes gave her the varying smells of their drifting smokes: schooner *Aldebaran* out of New York with flour and clocks, bark *Lapwing* Boston to Batavia with furniture and lumber, brigantine *Clarence* Rio to Baltimore with coffee, clipper *Conrad* homebound from the Argentine with wool . . .

In June a letter from Liverpool ended her long watch. It was the first from the Captain since his anchors aweigh letter from Howland's in mid-February. His strong slant handwriting flew like victory flags across the face of the envelope. But his letter had no sound of victory.

He had got through, he wrote, by breaking for the first time in his life an unwritten rule of the sea. He had not answered a single ship signaling a wish to speak him. He had run away from every sail seen in the South Atlantic as if every other ship but his was plague-ridden. Surely she was enough of a shellback to understand what this had cost him. His whole past had risen up in revolt each time he had tacked away from a waiting ship, which might have had sickness on board, or empty water casks. He still burned with shame for what he had had to do to bring his ship and cargo safely to port. If he had not found a great batch of her letters and clippings in Valparaiso, forwarded there by his agent, he would never had had the courage to act the coward for the sake of prudence. That picture of the *Jacob Bell* she had sent him, for instance . . .

Annie recalled it with a shudder. She had cut it from her March 21st *Harper's Weekly* — a drawing of death, the firing of the great clipper *Jacob Bell*. The artist had chosen the moment for his sketch when fire had reached the topsails of the three masts but not yet the topgallants, royals and skysails which still squared brave and white above the flames. The Confederate raider *Florida*, pluming smoke from her twin stacks, was shown standing to windward under reduced sail, with a group of figures watching the bonfire from her poop. The *Jacob Bell* had been caught in February in the hazardous latitudes of the 20s North Atlantic, off Puerto Rico, as she was homebound from

Foochow with a cargo of tea, cassia and camphor — the most valuable prize until then taken by any raider.

Had Annie known that the skipper's wife had been aboard the *Jacob Bell* when captured? And that she was at that moment approaching her confinement? *Yes, by God,* her husband wrote in angry slashes. Even such a situation had not stopped the pirates. They had taken the poor woman off, along with the captured crew, and had eventually debarked her in the Virgin Islands. He was sure she could understand now why he took no pride in what his London agent had called his achievement of superb evasive sailing.

Annie wept as she read his first letter from England, remembering her happy days there in another port. But she had one big consolation; she knew how carefully he would study that woodcut of the *Florida*. She remembered its descriptive quality, every yardarm and brace clearly sketched, the bark rigging, twin stacks and gun ports depicted as her husband himself might have drawn them with nautical exactitude. The *Florida* was the only big raider he had to watch out for on his final lap across the Atlantic. Her sister ship *Alabama* had vanished from the Atlantic sea lanes, suspected to be heading toward the Cape of Good Hope to prey on Yankee homecomers from the East Indies. The Captain knew the profile of his enemy now, he knew the cut of her jib.

They had time for an exchange of several letters by the fast Cunard steam packets while he took on a cargo of coal in Liverpool ("No ballast *this* time, Annie dearest!") before he set sail for home. *One more run for it,* he wrote. Then he was through with the Atlantic for the duration. He refused to return himself and his ship into skulking jackals of the sea. He had convinced his owner that the Pacific was the place for the *Anglo-Saxon.* Ships were needed there to augment the San Francisco-Panama steamers that were the lifeline now between the two coasts. Sugar from the Islands, salmon from the Alaska fisheries, wheat and bullion from California, all so needed on the beset Eastern shore — he'd never again have to go around begging for cargoes.

In his last letter he sent for her safekeeping a receipt for some insurance he had taken out. He made light of it, writing disparagingly that here was one more example of that prudence his skipper colleagues had joked about when she was with them in the London Docks, the choice of the sensible husband, did she remember? He had heard that the Rebels had an insatiable appetite for nautical instruments. These they confiscated first after boarding a prize. If the inconceivable happened and he was stopped homeward bound, he would at least be reimbursed for the tools of his trade.

"Received from Captain Cavarly of the ship *Anglo-Saxon* the sum of Six Pounds 14 Shillings, upon policy of 200 Pounds effected by me with the Albion Insurance Co., Ltd; upon his personal effects: nautical instruments, charts, watches and sundry. . . ."

The receipt was his roundabout acknowledgment to her that he also had been reading the shipping news: ship *Crown Point* New York to San Francisco with assorted cargo, burned May 13; ship *Southern Cross* West Coast Mexico to New York with logwood, burned June 6th; clipper *Red Gauntlet* Boston to Hong Kong with coal and musical instruments, burned June 14th. His postscript reported that sailor boys were already singing in the rigging "Leave Her, Johnny, Leave Her." She could expect to see him in the last week of August.

She played him home on her piano. Her songs followed the changing chanteys the crew would sing as the *Anglo-Saxon* drove westward. Her repertoire astonished her grandmother who, in her time, had not been permitted to learn the words of some of those sailor ballads.

"Leave Her, Johnny, Leave Her" gave way to "Rolling Home" when Annie guessed her Captain must be mid-ocean. The homebound capstan chantey always put a lump in her throat. "Full ten thousand miles behind us, And a thousand miles before . . ." She tried this time to roll all the way . . . "to our dear Homeland, And the glance of loving eyes," but her voice broke on the last verse. Then she swung into "Oh! You New York Girls, Can't You Dance the Polka?" That one she sang through seven verses, again and again, her head thrown back, her high voice warbling sweetly of sailors on shore leave, drugged liquor and a maid from Bleecker Street named Annie. *My dear Annie . . .* the piano danced to the 2-4 polka measure.

The *Anglo-Saxon* was stopped by the raider *Florida* on August 17th off the Old Head of Kinsale on the southern Irish coast. The Captain had a northeaster whistling through his sails and a drift of fog ahead over the mouth of the English Channel, through which he saw the steamer with sails furled, smoking her way slowly toward the French coast. His spyglass picked up the reassuring red-white-and-blue tricolor flying from her mast. Viewed stern on, with gun ports invisible and her barkentine sails furled, the *Florida* bore little resemblance to the woodcut the Captain had memorized; moreover no pirate had ever yet ventured into these Channel waters after prizes. Nevertheless, he asked Boxer to have a squint through the glass as an extra precaution. The *Florida*'s commander was at that moment having a good spyglass look at the *Anglo-Saxon* — tall, square-rigged, black-hulled, so Yankee in contour that he scarcely needed the added confirmation of the Stars and Stripes flying at her stern. He was on his way into the neutral harbor of Brest for repairs after nearly five months continuously at sea. Since he hardly had to alter his course to take one more prize, he decided to take it.

The Captain had the northeaster behind him like a stone wall when he saw the "French" steamer on his port bow swing about revealing her telltale gun ports. He tried desperately to make a run for it to starboard but the wind drove him back to face his enemy. The first shot across his bow showed, with its jib-cutting marksmanship, what a broadside would do were he foolish enough to ask for it. He gave the order to round to — his last order aboard a sailing ship like a last gasp.

Three weeks later, Annie read a letter from Brest. More frightening than the postmark of France was her husband's handwriting. It had shrunk to a narrow slant prostration, almost horizontal, like the writing you could imagine coming from a dead hand in final quivers after heart and mind had failed. His enclosures told her the story for which he himself had no words. He told her only that the sole possessions he had been permitted to take from his ship were the twin frame holding both their photographs and his small seachest, that he had been aboard the *Florida* for a week, all his crew in irons except himself, his officers and Crux and George, that he had filed his claim with the Geneva Convention for the destruction of his ship, totaling $42,711, for the value of the vessel minus her cargo and that this sum had been recommended for final settlement.

Two squares of paper fell to her lap, one white, one blue. She read the white one first because her husband had written it. It was a copy of his official protest on the burning of the *Anglo-Saxon:*

> On August 17th '63, was stopped by C.S.S. *Florida*, Captain J. N. Maffitt, and declared a prize of war. My cargo was declared contraband and I was informed my ship would be burned. When my ship's company went aboard the *Florida*, all but myself, my officers and my colored steward and cook were put in irons. The raider removed all provisions, nautical instruments and all else they wished from the *Anglo-Saxon*. They set fire to my ship and fired two broadsides of shot and shell at her.

They set fire to my ship . . . his, all his. Not the property of E. M. Robertson, Esq., of New York, her registered owner. *My ship* . . . the vessel I was married on, lost a son on, the command I've had for five years and taken that many times around the Horn without losing man or spar. It was all expressed for Annie in the poignant use of the possessive pronoun. *My cargo, my officers, my ship.* . . .

The other paper was written in a neat steady hand on pale blue stationery delicately watermarked. It was the Confederate commander's parole order to her husband, reminding him of the strict neutrality toward the Confederate States of America which he was bound to respect until regularly exchanged in Brest. Her husband was addressed as CAPTAIN J. M. CAVARLY, Late Commander of the U.S.S. *Anglo-Saxon.*

After the burning, the knife twist, Annie stared through tears at the appellation Late Commander. Out of context, the two words made it sound as if her husband had died. She read his short strained letter once again, crying quietly with relief that this was not so.

Only a part of him was dead: his seventeen years under sail.

Chapter 7

THE SINKING OF HIS SHIP had delayed reactions that shocked the Captain almost as much as had the sight of it going down. Living over and over every flaming memory, a deep humiliation took hold of him. That he had been outmaneuvered and outgunned made no difference. He had lost a ship. The thing which he had said could never happen to him, and had believed with his whole soul never would, had happened. The ignominy of his surrender — not to any fury of storm, not to any dark current heaving him remorselessly upon a grasping reef, but to a man dapper and correct who had spoken with a soft Southern accent and treated him as an equal — smarted and smoldered and made him look about with bloodshot eyes for a way to hit back.

As he paced the deck of the Cunard steamer that carried him home from Liverpool, he pondered his next step, looking for the one that would bring him nearest to the blockade outside Mobile where the Rebel pirates could be stopped at source. He remembered the call for naval enlistees he and Annie had read the year before. Since he was not Annapolis-trained, he'd not be given a commission, but this was irrelevant to the issue as he saw it. Just to be in a place where guns were trained on the clipper killers would be enough. He cast overboard his seventeen years under sail, his seventeen years of merchant marine experience without a backward look as he envisioned himself on a sloop of war going after the pirates . . .

He was aware as he paced that he was no longer canvas-borne. This coal-driven ship bore steadily into headwinds that would have sent his clipper off course again and again. The winds worried futilely at the steamer's furled shrouds, but the power in her screw kept her driving ahead. The engine's steady vibrations drummed their message of energy beneath his feet. When crosscurrents struck the propeller he felt through the soles of his feet the change in vibration. He saw that a real sailor *could* have communication with steam pressure and screw revolutions.

He saw something else when they ran into a southeaster in the Gulf Stream. The skipper appeared on the bridge and sent his crew aloft to set the sails, using the language of old: *Loose the mains'l . . . Belay there! Damn it all what are you standing looking at? Hoist away.*

God's wind and man's steam gave the spurt of speed he felt beneath him. He gazed up at the English skipper who called for steam in the new idiom of engineers and for sail in the time-honored language of shellbacks. Windy *Aye, Aye sir's!* floated down from the main yardarms. The ship, like the man who commanded her, was a creature of transition — white wings of sail forward, black tail of smoke aft. You had to ride one of these coal-burners, he thought grudgingly, to realize that they too belonged in the family of ships.

Annie awaited him on the pier in New York. His eyes found her when he was halfway down the gangplank. He stopped to wave, careless of the people held up behind him, until she waved back. He looked strange to her as a passenger, with no sailor boy at his heels carrying his seachest.

He sounded stranger as they drove to the Brevoort where she had taken the same rooms they had had the last time, when he had come into port with a badly damaged ship and an uncertain future. She had been expecting the return of a man embittered, lost and silent, and had thought that the familiar rooms might remind him of how once before they had laughed and loved and made plans against a future that looked doomsday dark. But he told her in the carriage, almost without preamble, that his plans were made. He would chuck everything and enlist for the duration. He didn't give a hoot if he'd have to start again in the fo'c'sle, as was probable. Boxer had already gone into the marine artillery, with a commission of course, being Academy-trained. His bosun and ship's carpenter had also joined up. They'd got off from Brest on the first ship sailing after they had been formally exchanged. *They* hadn't had to waste a lot of good fighting time around London signing papers, affidavits, insurance receipts. He was unaware, as he ranted on, how he was hurting her with his brusque announcement of a future decided without first talking it over with her, as they had always done.

"There'll not be a hull left in the entire American merchant marine if those damned pirates aren't stopped," he cried.

"There *certainly* won't be one left if all the masters like you jump onto warships," Annie said in her small voice of reason and calm. He appeared not to have heard her. He read a recruitment poster as they rode along.

Then he said with sudden bitterness, "A skipper who's lost his command isn't likely to have shipping agents running after him!"

Annie flashed him a look of complete amazement. He stared straight ahead, stiff-jawed after his self-incrimination. She put her hand over his clenched fist lying on the buggy robe and compelled him to look at her, compelled him with her indignant eyes to listen to her stern words:

"I *never* want to hear such nonsense from you again, Jack! *You* didn't lose a ship. You had it *taken* from you by a superior force in an act of war. That it upset your pride, I can understand, but to let it upset your reasoning — ah *no!*" His hand closed about hers. "You promise me . . . never again?"

"Aye, aye." He swallowed and said it again more clearly. "Aye,

aye . . . Annie dear," looking with wonder into her commanding eyes.

"One thing more" . . . an ironical smile touched her lips.
"You *already* have an offer of a command awaiting you in the
hotel."

Actually, she had it in her little silver mesh bag. She had hurried to the pier with the letter, filled with thanksgiving for the
helping hand, so perfectly timed, so unexpectedly extended from
the other side of the world, to a sailor without a ship. She pretended not to see the glint in his eyes. "Of course," she said airily,
"you'll hardly be interested in a merchant marine offer, now that
you've decided to join up." She put her muff to her face to hide
her smile. Her flabbergasted husband looked almost normal.
Now, all she needed to do was to get him to talk out his pain
for the loss of his ship.

The familiar hotel room unexpectedly helped her. He stared
around it from the high ceiling to the white marble fireplace, to
the French windows opening out upon the avenue, and then at
each piece of furniture — the canopied bed, the little love seat
before the fire, the French dressing table with her hairbrushes
and perfumes already set out neatly upon it — and his brooding
eyes suddenly filled with misery. "The last time, Annie," he said
huskily, "we had the *Anglo-Saxon* with us." She ran to him then
and drew herself up for their first real embrace since they had
had the Anglo-Saxon with them. . . . With them, you'd have
thought, tied right up there in the bedroom, bowsprit sticking
out the window, skysails scraping the ceiling, and it really had
been like that, Annie remembered, almost like a third person
with them all the time. They had talked endlessly about her in
this room, her new suits of sail, her new copper sheathing.

"Oh God, Annie, to have seen her go down!" The Captain
sucked in his breath. "You just couldn't imagine . . ." His voice
shook as he tried to describe it. She wouldn't catch at first, that
was the awful thing. Adrift and abandoned, she seemed to be
fighting her own flames, beating them into smoke with her fog-

damp sails. Only the decks burned where the whale oil had been poured over piles of gutted mattresses and straw sacks. The wind had flattened out the flames like a red rug bow to stern. The Rebels got restless, she was going so slowly. They argued loudly on the *Florida's* bridge, then decided to fire their broadsides. It took two rounds to start her down. She went bow first, keeping her stern colors dry until the very last. The whole of his crew stood at salute as the flag went down, even the fo'c'sle lads who were in chains.

He sank wearily to the sofa and dropped his face into his hands. "It wasn't anything like those pictures you sent," he said in a muffled voice. After a long while, he looked up to see what she was doing so silently. His eyes followed her as she unpacked his brand-new English portmanteau and shook out his brand-new suits.

"At least I had the sense to take out insurance," he said wryly. "Ye'll grant me *that* much, I hope. Annie dear?"

She took time to smooth out a black quilted-silk vest, to examine its Savile Row label and nod with approval. Then she said softly, not looking at him, "I'll grant you *anything* you ask . . . *Captain!*"

Later, the Captain led Annie down to the French restaurant for which their hotel was famous. He had wanted the reunion dinner served in their rooms, but she had put her foot down on that idea. She had an escort for a change, and she had a new gown. There would be plenty of time, she said, to have nunlike dinners in private when he'd be off to the war. Pirate-chasing, she called it.

She had hoped that her father's letter, telling of a Pacific command, would have swayed her husband to the merchant service in which she believed he could serve best. She had read it to him earlier in the serene voice her father might have used had he been telling, instead of writing, of the offer:

Honolulu, Oct. 9th 1863

My dear Captain Cavarly,
New London:

Annie wrote of your arrival in London and trust you will in due time reach home. I don't know that I can write you anything new or interesting. I have taken a store and try to do a little in the way of selling goods and also keep up the old chandlery business I had when you were here. . . . How would you like the command of the San Francisco and Honolulu packets? I was talking yesterday to Captain Smith about it. He says you are just the man he wants. He says he has talked to Mr. John Merrill about the same thing and Merrill would like it. I suggested that on his arrival on the Coast, he telegraph to New York and, if you have arrived, to put the question if you would like the place. It would be very pleasant to have you and Annie here with us. Take all in all, *we* would like the arrangement first rate. But you probably know what is best without my offering advice. My best love to Annie and tell her the folks at the house are all writing to her and can tell her more gossip than I could think of in a month. Don't fail to write us when you find time, as we are always happy to hear from you. And believe me truly yours,

B. F. Bolles

The Captain had been touched by his father-in-law's solicitude but unmoved in his resolve to enter the naval service. Mebbe afterwards, he said, when I'll have to go into steam . . . She hadn't let a flicker of disappointment show, but had given him instead her most disarming smile. She had one more ace up her frilly little sleeve.

Below in the foyer, Captain F. S. Farnsworth was waiting — a skipper her husband had known since his youth and upon whom he had set his sights as a splendid example to emulate. A Vermonter by birth, Captain Farnsworth had always followed the sea and had made his mark in the Atlantic packet services. Stories abounded about his famous runs to London. Often, with a good westerly at his back, he had overhauled a wallowing side-wheel steamer bound the same way, a triumph of sail over steam which he turned into a grandstand play. He would pass the steamer to windward, as close as possible, so her passengers could hear his sailors' joyous shouts and the name they gave to the cumbersome craft as they flew past it — *old tea kettle!* Annie had encountered the Farnsworths the day before when she had checked into the hotel. The friendly old skipper had given her a few fatherly words on how to welcome home a shipwrecked sailor and Mrs. Farnsworth had put her arms about her and whispered, "We *all* have to face it once, Annie dear . . ." Impulsively Annie had invited them to dinner. Her husband would probably be glad to have a man to talk with on his first night, she said. Captain Farnsworth had accepted, with a twinkle in his eyes as he looked into her anxious face.

Annie revealed her surprise party to the Captain as they descended the stairs. His sharp eyes had already spotted his friend in the lobby and, by his happy grin, she knew she had planned well.

It was an evening full of unexpected turns. The finger of fate was in it, Annie said afterwards. She had not known why the Farnsworths had come down from Boston, had had no time to exchange more than the briefest of home news with them. Her lips parted soundlessly when Captain Farnsworth lifted his wineglass and proposed a toast to the tea kettles. "My new service, Jack — and ye better drink hearty to it, though I know it galls ye! But it's all we've got left to sail with, eh?" Mrs. Farnsworth lightly touched glasses with her husband and said in her deep melodious voice, "To the *Orizaba.*"

The *tea kettles?* The *Orizaba?* The Captain looked from face to face as if he had not heard rightly.

Sure, she was an old paddler, Captain Farnsworth explained, no longer considered stylish enough for Commodore Vanderbilt's fleet from which the Pacific Mail had recently bought her. He'd probably have a real tussle getting her through the Straits of Magellan, but she'd be worth her weight in gold on the Pacific

Coast, by God. And she'd carry her weight in gold once she was safely there. "And what are *you* thinking of doing that's better, Jack? Come lad, that look in your eye — I've seen it before!"

"Well, sir . . ." the Captain cleared his throat and looked at Annie, as if for support. "Well, sir . . . I was thinking about a turn in the Navy."

"Eye for eye, tooth for tooth. So *that's* it!" Captain Farnsworth tugged his whiskers and gazed benevolently at the tablecloth. Presently he started talking about the *Shooting Star*. "I remember you when you sailed out in her in '54, Jack. New York to Hong Kong, Captain Kingman — your first crack at the bridge as a First Officer." He looked at Annie and his wife. "Next to you two beautiful ladies, that clipper ship was the loveliest thing afloat. She had a female for figurehead, a female clothed in white garments with a girdle of stars around her waist, blowing hair banded by a gilded zone with the word LIBERTY lettered on it — right foot forward on a gilded globe, right hand extended, pointing onward, onward . . . Ah!" He sighed reminiscently, then resumed: "You took stores out to Commodore Perry's East India Squadron that trip, Jack, remember? You helped to feed the fleet Perry had standing off Japan, waiting to go in and open up a few of those ports to Western trade, to get decent treatment for our shipwrecked sailors marooned in Japan and the right to buy coal out there. You took out food for the fleet, fodder for its cannon and mebbe even some of those folderols of pomp and ceremony with which the Commodore impressed the shoguns. *Yessir!*"

He glanced at Annie's spellbound husband, then winked at her. He spoke quietly now, his clipped New England accent nearly lost in his slow drawl: "Would you say, Jack, that you'd have done *more* for progress then, if you'd been a tar on one of Perry's cruisers? Think it over! Think it over well, Jack. The Pacific offers a similar choice right now — California wheat, California bullion, Hawaiian sugar, all pouring down to the

Isthmus for transshipment to this sad shore. *Somebody's* got to keep it moving, wouldn't you say?"

The Captain nodded. "You made a point there, sir," he said respectfully. "A very good point, if I may say so. Hawaiian sugar . . ." He stroked his beard and glanced at Annie over the dessert of flaming crepes suzette. The brandy flames put dancing lights in his reflective eyes. "Hawaiian sugar, you *heard,* Annie? I reckon we've got to go over that offer again," he said coaxingly, as if *she* were the one who had proved recalcitrant, who now had to be convinced!

With his mind made up, the Captain wasted no time. He had another talk with Captain Farnsworth and then booked passage on the *Orizaba.* He sent a telegraph message to the Honolulu packet agent in San Francisco telling of his interest in the prospect of a command on the sugar ships.

By sailing out on a Pacific Mail steamer to investigate the Honolulu packets of another company, he would really be killing two birds with one stone, he told Annie. Farnsworth had prophesied that the day would surely come when the Pacific Mail would start looking toward the Orient. He'd see their fleet in operation from Panama up to San Francisco and be in a better position to weigh the possibilities of the sugar ships. He would send for her just as soon as employment was certain and arrange for her to come via the Isthmus. No more Cape Horn for her, least of all in a side-wheeler, he exclaimed. Paddle wheels beating into ice floes! He simply couldn't imagine it even in a pipe dream.

Annie wondered that he made no mention of seeing his family. The *Orizaba* would not sail for a week, time enough to get up to New London and back. He bridled when she suggested it, begging her to be his emissary. It would be better that way — no sparks flying.

Reluctantly he showed her the letter his mother had sent to

him in care of his London agent. Annie let out a little gasp as she read it. His mother had started right out with the hope that at last he had learned his lesson. *"I never want you to set foot again on anything that floats"* (she had underlined that sentence with sharp black penstroke) "I want you to *give up* that place you are pleased to call *your ocean home.*" Only his sister's postscript, crowded into the narrow margin, telling her brother she loved him dearly and prayed every day for his safe return, relieved the I-told-you-so tone of the letter. Annie suppressed her indignation as she handed it back to him.

"I'll go of course," she said. "I'll make them understand you simply had no time . . . Elizabeth and Phillip especially." She knew they would be heartbroken and so did the Captain. "I just don't want another set-to at this time," he said miserably. He tore Elizabeth's postscript off the letter and dropped the remainder into the wastebasket.

Three weeks out of New York, the Captain changed status as a passenger aboard the S.S. *Orizaba,* and became the steamship's First Officer, replacing, at Captain Farnsworth's request, his second in command who had fallen ill. Farnsworth called it his good luck to have had him aboard to fill the gap and lost no time initiating him into his job. First Officer Cavarly caught on quickly. He discovered what a deep-water sailor could contribute to these expensive coal-burners — a knowledge of the winds and a sureness about the right moment to loose sail and pick up some free propulsion, thus economizing on the costly coal. Captain Farnsworth made no attempt to conceal his pride in his protégé. "Downeasters like us," he told his engineer, "make the proper complement for fellows like you. You know your engines, we know our winds — young Cavarly there can actually smell 'em coming up!"

The Captain filled his post so ably that when he arrived in San Francisco the Pacific Mail agent offered to make his temporary berth as a First Officer permanent, with a broad hint that a command for him might develop in time. He wrote excitedly to Annie that he had decided to accept. The pay was good, the service much busier than that of the Honolulu packets and the ships a lot larger. He was assigned as a deck officer on the Pacific Mail's *Constitution,* a side-wheeler of over 3000 tons, almost four times the size of their old *Anglo-Saxon,* if she could imagine that. He was about to sail for Panama. Once there he would learn the best connections for her own journey westward and would send for her. Though his company maintained regular service to Panama at ten-day intervals, he wanted *his* ship to be waiting for her when she stepped off the Isthmus train.

Annie saw her bright hopes for a home in Hawaii fade as she read his letter; but she saw also, with a compensating happiness, the possessive pronoun underscored — *my* ship — which proclaimed his proud identification with the new service. Moreover, from his description of the voyage out with Farnsworth, she saw that his precious inheritance from the tough sailing years, his keen sensing of the winds — as mysterious to her as her musical knowledge was to him — would not wither and die in the new life.

She studied the schedule the Captain had sent. Each Mexican and Central American port of call down the coast to Panama was listed with arrival day and date, even the hour specified as forenoon or afternoon. She could scarcely believe that she need never again wonder where he was in watery space. Mazatlan, San Blas, Manzanillo, Acapulco, San José de Guatemala — she hummed the names of his new ports as if reading music.

His good news momentarily swept away her worry about his family. Both his brother and sister had failed visibly during the winter and his father had had a touch of pneumonia that had nearly carried him off. Each week, bundled in fur lap robes, she had driven out through the snow to the sad farmhouse where coughing seemed to be continuous. She had taken baskets of delicacies to tempt the invalids' appetites and wine to warm their blood, but her most restorative gifts had been the Captain's letters. Even his mother listened to her reading of them with a glow of pride in her somber black eyes.

In mid-February Annie drove out to the farm for her farewell visit before sailing to join her husband. She had the best letter of all to share with his family — the news of promotion to captain. He had sent her a copy of his Pacific Mail appointment so both their families might know she was a captain's wife again. She made a little theatrical of its reading, putting on the sonorous voice of officialdom and pausing to lift her eyebrows now and again at Phillip who had once told her laughingly that his brother never took orders from anyone except, possibly, God:

> *Agency, Pacific Mail SS Co.*
> *Panama, Jan. 30th 1864*

Capt. J. M. Cavarly
Chief Officer, Ex-O.
P.M.S.S. Co., Panama

DEAR SIR:

On the recommendation of Capt. F. S. Farnsworth of Steamship "Orizaba," I have determined to place you in command of the Company's Steamer "California" on her present up trip, and as Commander of that Steamer, you will be governed by the following instructions —

You will follow as far as circumstances will allow the general sailing instructions given you by Capt. Farnsworth.

You will take the *inshore course* in crossing the Gulf of Tehuantepec and keep well in sight of land all the way up to Acapulco. On arrival at that port, you will report to D. B. Carr Brently, the Co.'s Agent at Acapulco, who will furnish you the necessary supplies of coal, water and fresh provisions to take you to San Francisco. On reaching that port you will report to A. B. Failus, Esq., Agent, who will give you all the necessary instructions as to delivery of cargo, etc. You will give your particular attention to the *cow* & protection of your large cargo of merchandise. I look to you for special attention to this matter.

I send up with you in charge of the Engine Department my

Supervising Engineer, Mr. Coler, who is a very old employee and who is thoroughly posted in all matters connected with the Company's wishes, both here and along the Coast. He has my entire confidence and I desire you to consult him freely on the voyage to San Francisco. I give you good officers and a good crew & trust all things may go well & smoothly. Mr. Munro, a Clerk at this Agency, goes with you as Acting Purser and Store-keeper. He has checked all the freight into the ship & can give you all information you may require on this point. He will attend to the Store Department and make out such Custom House papers as are necessary to enter the ship at San Francisco.

You will take no passengers either here or at Acapulco. In the matter of speed, you will be governed by the safety of your command, making this paramount to all other considerations. I presume you can reach San Francisco in 18 to 20 days. On this subject you will consult with Mr. Coler especially. He knows exactly what the "California" can do in speed and safety to the cargo.

Your pay will be at the rate of $250 per month from this date, till your turning the ship over to the San Francisco Agent, without primage on your freight. Mr. Munro will pay bills of the ship at Acapulco only on your approval. I hand you herewith $300 for disbursements.

Trusting you may have a successful voyage & with my good wishes, I am,

Very respectfully,
D. M. Corwine, *Agent*

"He's unbeatable!" Phillip exclaimed when she had finished reading: "Just think — barely four months after losing his clipper, he's on a bridge again!" The flush in his cheeks looked like pride. Little Elizabeth couldn't get over the cow. Brother wouldn't know . . . well, which end was which! she said with her tinkling laugh. Annie recorded for her Captain the memory of their happy faces, their joy and wonder in his achievement.

Phillip got out his atlas to study the dimensions of his brother's new ocean home. The old father smiled reminiscently; he had once been in Acapulco, he told Annie. He had run his whaler into the beautiful harbor to find shelter from a Papagayo, one of the great winds that blew up suddenly along that Mexican coast. Remind John of that, he said wistfully. *I will, I will* . . . She never dreamed as she drove away that she had seen the brother and sister for the last time, that the memories she had stored up as the Captain's emissary were to be his saving graces from bitter remorse for not having gone himself. In that same year of new life, new hope, new conquests for him, the two persons nearest to his heart after Annie were to be taken from him.

The Captain's first steam command and his first ship in the Pacific Mail was their famous pioneer ship, the *California*, the first of their side-wheelers to have come around the Horn in '48, the venerable dowager of their fleet now in '64. With a cow to be given special care en route, a valuable cargo and a crew of wise old deck officers to watch over him on his maiden command in steam, he churned slowly up the coast down which he had sailed as a First Officer.

He promptly opened up a new "Compass Book," his peculiar form of diary, and began to make the data entries that he would ceaselessly correct or expand on each successive voyage:

> Distance from Panama to Acapulco direct, 1417 miles. Via the Gulf of Tehuantepec 1462 or, say, 45 miles more via the Gulf than direct.
>
> Course from Cape Corrientes to Creston N by W $\frac{1}{2}$ W should pass Cape Corrientes at a distance from 5 to 6 miles, and at night *look sharp* for Corvetena Rock.
>
> Course steered from Mazatlan for Cape San Lucas was S W by $\frac{3}{4}$ W. It was a good course as we made the Frailes about ahead, perhaps a trifle on the port bow.

By the time he sailed down to fetch Annie in Panama, he was beginning to know the name and look of every cape, headland and offshore island of the 3248 miles of coast between San Francisco and the Isthmus, and had filled his pocket Compass Book with descriptions of their peculiarities. He had accomplished his aim to be master of the coast as well as of his ship before Annie would arrive. He was transferred from the *California* back to the *Constitution* in time to pick her up with the largest side-wheeler then on the Panama run.

Annie reached Panama City in April of '64, just six months and twenty-one days by the Captain's reckoning from the time they had parted in New York. During her five hours' crossing of the Isthmus in a small crowded train, she had sat on her suitcase in the car's corridor, with her flouncy skirts drawn up tightly about her because of the bedbugs visibly infesting the red plush. Flies she had swatted away with a palm-leaf fan, evil odors she had counteracted with her vial of lavender smelling salts. She wept with relief when the journey was over. The Captain seemed like a clean wind snatching her with gale force from the high steps of the train before it came to a full halt.

His tropical jacket smelled of sun-dried starch and salt spray as he embraced her. Then he stood her off at long arms' length and looked her over with his farsighted mariner's squint searching jealously for signs of change in her and, finding none, was able to speak. *Well, Annie . . . well!*

But *he* had changed, at least in outward appearance. Her eyes widened for his new uniform which he had not thought to mention in his letters. Its trim naval lines enhanced his good looks and added (needlessly, Annie thought amused) to his natural air of authority. She withheld comment on his new splendor, remembering that he had once called company uniforms "the monkey jackets of the passenger trade." He moved about her in bright flashes — tunic buttons, cap insignia and sleeve stripes glinting gold as he pointed out her trunks to the porter.

She sensed other changes in him during the short walk to the docks, all immensely pleasing. The rough edges of his nature had been smoothed away by contact with the passengers he now carried. He no longer spoke disparagingly of a human cargo, but rather with pride as he told her of the opera singers who had sailed with him and actresses, like that wonderful Adah Isaacs Menken who, in *Mazeppa,* was the current sensation in San Francisco. Even his rope-toughened fingers had lost their calluses. When he pulled off one of her gloves and held her bare hand between his palms, she felt their new firm smoothness.

The bluff clipper captain with whom she had fallen in love five years before had not, however, completely vanished in the metamorphosis. He wore his commander's cap with a slight tilt to starboard and every time she met his gaze, the unfamiliar feeling of coming alive after a long separation sent flurries of excitement through her blood.

At the head of the docks, he presented his side-wheeler to her, peering into her face to see if she approved. The wooden vessel, anchored a mile offshore, looked like a floating hotel with its portholes on many levels shining in the sun. The walking-beam that drove the huge paddle wheels traced its design of power against the sky. A plume of smoke issuing from the tall stack gave the big steamer a domestic air. It struck Annie with sudden emotion that it was almost as if the Captain had *settled down!*

"She's beautiful, Jack," she said at last. "And bigger, *much* bigger than anything I'd imagined."

He helped her into the Captain's gig that was to take them over the reefs to his ship and sat to windward of her to protect her from flying spray as his sailor boys rowed them out. At the foot of the ship's gangway, he remarked with a chuckle that all his officers had managed to find duties on deck at that moment. Annie's heart went straight out to these grizzled veterans of the service who helped her up to the deck and who had watched approvingly her husband in his new command. Bearded all, slow and thoughtful of speech, but very sharp of eye, they welcomed her with courtly compliments into their exclusive circle which they called "the Pacific Mail family."

The real head of this curious nautical family was David Corwine, the company's Panama agent who was also on deck to greet her. He was a lean Kentuckian, then in his middle forties, who had already been thirteen years in Panama, had buried his wife and child in its Foreign Cemetery and from his own private purse had given substantial support to the Foreign Hospital, the Protestant Church and other such institutions so desperately needed when hundreds of gold-seeking immigrants had poured daily into the ruined old Spanish city, exhausted after their sixty-hour crossing of the Isthmus by foot, native dugout and muleback. They had poured in bedraggled with mud, shivering in torn clothes, wracked with yellow fever, and had then had to face weeks of waiting to get space on a steamer upbound to San Francisco and the gold fields. From '51, when he arrived in Panama, until '55 when the Isthmus railway had been opened, David Corwine had battled for law, order and sanitation and, most importantly, for liaison between the New York and San Francisco offices of his company to have a ship in Panama timed to take over the loads of human beings deposited at the Colón end of the Isthmus. Annie's swift journey — debarking from the New York steamer in Colón in the morning, and sailing out Panama Bay that same evening — was the result of David Corwine's patient labor at the most crucial point of the Pacific Mail's far-flung service.

Annie was of course unaware of this when the Captain presented her to the tall man in floppy straw hat, mussed cotton suit and string tie who looked more like a genial colonial than a mover of ships. Corwine captivated her at once with his slow drawl and lively gray eyes which seemed, in their first quick scrutiny, to be taking the measure of her fitness to be a Pacific Mail captain's wife as, months earlier, they had sized up her husband's potentialities to command. His satisfied smile told her she had passed muster. He promptly claimed the honor of showing her the ship and led her forward over the promenade deck to give her peeps into first-class cabins not yet occupied, at a mirror-hung Ladies' Boudoir which gentlemen could not enter, at a leather-upholstered Smoking Room forbidden to ladies and, finally, over the balustrade of a lightwell surrounded with potted palms, a glimpse down into the elegant dining saloon with its suspended racks of cut-glass wine decanters and goblets sparkling over damask-covered tables.

"It's a far cry from our old *Anglo-Saxon*," she said breathlessly.

"It's a far cry from our old *California,* our maiden ship on this coast!" He pointed down to the Captain's place at the head of the center table and told her, drawlingly, how the ship's purser had to argue his head off to get her husband to accept a lady passenger there on his right instead of one of the Wall Street financiers, or a roving Congressman, whom *he* always bid for as dinner partner. "But I understand now — now that I've met our Captain's lady," he said with a gallant bow. As he escorted her back to the main lounge, he promised her he would keep a weather eye on "Captain Jack."

She stood at the rail with the Captain to watch David Corwine being rowed ashore. Gratitude welled up in her heart for the stanch friend her husband had in this port of his southern terminus. Like an anchor to windward, she thought as she shook her handkerchief toward the longboat rapidly receding over the sparkling swells toward the old Spanish city above which flocks of white pelicans circled.

"I hope he gives you another cow to care for now and again," Annie said as she touched the braid on her husband's sleeve. "To keep your pride in line," she added twinkling.

The Captain's quarters were as masculine-looking as the ship's Smoking Room, furnished with every creature comfort except facilities for skippers' wives. The Captain got around his company's policy of discouraging wives from traveling with their skipper husbands by installing for himself a trundle bed beside the single capacious berth he usually occupied which looked, Annie said, like a mahogany catafalque. But she accepted it in preference to the nearest first-class cabin which would entail too much nocturnal perambulation. "And all *one* way, me to you," she said with unblushing practicality, "since you have to remain within reach of those dreadful speaking tubes!"

They were like rubber ears set into the satinwood paneling at the head of the master's berth. At irregular intervals in the night, a great whooshing sound came from one of them and a sepulchral voice from the engine room said, "Eighteen pounds pressure, sir, wheel revolutions fifty-four per mile." Only the first night was Annie frightened almost out of her wits; the Captain had forgotten to tell her of the precautionary communication direct from boiler room to skipper when the bridge officer did not respond. After that, she risked suffocation, stifling her laughter with a pillow until the mouthpiece at the other end of the tube snapped shut.

Two weeks out from Panama, they sailed into San Francisco Bay. It felt like a homecoming to Annie after all the alien ports she had seen en route — Acapulco at the head of its beautiful mountain-ringed bay, the roadstead of San Blas with its Presidio on a high precipitous rock jutting forth from forest and jungle, Mazatlan white-walled against its background of indigo mountains that dropped to the sea in scarred crags — beautiful, strange and wild places which had once been only names in her husband's letters. Now, perched on a high stool in the *Constitution's* pilot house, she looked eagerly toward the city where she had been married, her eyes aglow with anticipation for familiar sights. The Captain had not told her of the enormous changes the Civil War had wrought, of the factories that had sprung up behind the waterfront to manufacture goods that no longer came around the Horn from back East, of the mansions of Comstock millionaires that had begun to crown the city's hilltops or of the maze of new wharves reaching out into the Bay like extensions of the teeming streets they footed, each long wharf a battleground of charging drays, shouting stevedores and donkey-engines pounding away like small cannon. She couldn't even recognize the Meiggs Wharf mooring where twice the *Anglo-Saxon* had tied up.

The Captain gestured toward the bedlam and said, "Our home, my darling, can you believe it at last?" And, for a few moments, Annie couldn't. As she stared at the tumultuous city spilling down from its hills to the booming wharves, she wondered if there was any place in it for a woman whom the sea would widow five weeks out of every six, a place where she wouldn't be trampled to death by its sheer vitality if she ventured to walk out alone.

Chapter 8

THE CAPTAIN HAD CHOSEN the recently built Lick House for their first abode. During his bachelor months he had sampled the other city hotels to see which was most suitable for his wife; he had observed the ladies of light virtue (genially categorized as *nymphes du pavé* by the press) who frequented them, and the Lick House, he told Annie soberly, had the lowest count on "pavement nymphs," probably because its dignified and gentlemanly owner, James Lick, lived beneath its roof and thus established its tone. The hotel was on Montgomery Street, a section which she knew from their honeymoon days in the nearby Occidental.

He made a triumphal procession of the ride from the docks to the Lick House. A company dray trundled behind their carriage loaded with their travel-worn trunks and crates filled with objects destined for the eventual home — her London silver and Irish linens and his own peculiar souvenirs collected in his sailoring years. Even her crated piano, which Annie had expected would be left in the company warehouse along with the Captain's curios, was in the dray. Obviously her husband anticipated a long siege in a hotel before a proper house would be found. They looked, Annie thought, a little like gypsies as their caravan wound through the clamorous streets.

The Lick House was a Gibraltar of Victorian elegance four stories high and covering the block from Post to Sutter on fashionable Montgomery Street. From the moment she entered its imposing portal, Annie felt at home, connected with a civilized past, secure in an atmosphere she understood. The whole edifice might have been transported bodily from New York's Washington Square, complete with marble floors, rich rugs and bronze statues.

As she stared from the reception desk down the vista of mirrored salons and remembered that just four years ago, when she had returned from the Islands to rejoin her husband, this site had been a waste of sand with a circus tent pitched upon it, a little laugh of delight escaped her lips.

The suite the Captain had selected was in a quiet residential wing on the top floor. Annie marveled at its size as she explored the high-ceilinged rooms — a master bedroom, marble-floored bath, guest room (in case any of her sisters came visiting from Hawaii, the Captain explained) and a beautifully proportioned living room with fireplace and tall windows facing south and west to catch the most sunshine. From the south windows was a distant view of Rincon Hill in the lee of which lay the new Pacific Mail docks.

"It's perfect, Jack, absolutely perfect!" She threw off her bonnet and ran into his arms. "Can we afford it?" she whispered. "I could have done with less . . ."

He stopped her with a kiss. Then he said, "You listen to me — there's nothing on God's earth that's too good for my little Annie. *Nothing,* do you hear?"

In his week ashore he took her out on what he called "trial runs" about the city, showing her the streets where a lady could walk alone and those it was best to avoid, the restaurants called "Three-for-Twos" (three dishes for two bits or twenty-five cents, their substantial foods displayed through plate-glass windows) where she could go unescorted if she ever wearied of the hotel's famous fare, the locations of theaters, concert halls and library and the horsecar lines that would take her to them. On his last night he got tickets for the Metropolitan so Annie could see the famous Adah Isaacs Menken who had once sailed on his ship. She was playing the lead role in *Mazeppa* and was dressed in the first tights seen on a serious San Francisco stage, which shocked some of the ladies in the audience, but not Annie who knew the star was supposed to be a Cossack chief. The final death-ride scene, with Menken strapped to the back of a live white horse that swept her up a planked hill to vanish in the wings, left Annie so breathless and spent that she had no strength to applaud.

The Captain beamed at her pleasure and, later in the hotel, beamed even more at the incredible prospect of seeing her again in just five weeks' time (six, if they had to wait cargo in some port en route) and promised letters for her by the upbound ship he would meet in Acapulco. Thus launched in her new life ("like a frail vessel," she wrote to her father, "with all courses charted in advance, shoals and reefs red-starred and safe harbors for fuelling circled") Annie proceeded to explore the city for her own secret purpose which was to find a reputable doctor who could tell her why, at the age of twenty-five after five years of eager, if somewhat discontinuous, married life, she was still childless. She thought once to ask the hotel manager for a recommendation, but he was too good a friend of her husband to be counted on to keep her confidence.

Her search for a doctor carried her to seamy corners of San Francisco far from the safe thoroughfares the Captain had charted for her. From the swarming foreign colonies of Italians, Greeks, Russians, Germans and French around the waterfronts, through the dramatic alleyways of Chinatown whose herb doctors served many a nervous stockbroker, down the broad expanses of Market Street (now paved with basalt blocks sunk into the shifting sands) Annie roamed each day, looking at the façades of every "doctor's residence" she had found listed in the newspapers that gave columns to their advertisements. San Francisco appeared to be the world's capital of medical charlatans.

Their office fronts, emblazoned with placards — A CURE FOR YOUTHFUL INDISCRETIONS. INFALLIBLE REMEDY FOR CATARRH, THE BANE OF SAN FRANCISCO. SPECIALIST IN MALE FERN TREATMENT FOR TAPEWORM — told her at a glance where the quacks resided. If she ran out of addresses from newspapers, she could always have picked up new ones in the streets. Medical pamphlets fluttered from lampposts, drifted along curbs, tossed from the open carriages into which enterprising runners had thrown them.

One ballyhoo that fascinated her was a wondrous equipage drawn by four horses, its liveried coachman and single passenger (the latter reclining with chalky face on satin cushions) appearing on the Monday of each week. The following Saturday the same coach and four would reappear with the same passenger who was now a man in buoyant health waving a gold-fringed banner that proclaimed WORLD RELIEF. Every few blocks a stop was made for a spiel about a certain doctor who was "scientist, naturalist, botanist and graduate of the most noted medical college in Paris" and who, during his world travels, had found the Balm of Gilead, a proven cure-all for anything afflicting the human race.

Seeking always the small, discreet shingle with only a man's name followed by M.D., Annie explored much of San Francisco before the Captain's return and, with her true ear, she became an inimitable imitator of its street cries. The razor grinder pushing his grindstone on wheels, with jingling bell suspended over his clumsy cart, sang *O-ho, get your razors ground!* The collector of rags, bottles and sacks driving his broken-down horse had a cry that sounded like *Wags-socks-bottells* and when you heard a lovely Italian tenor voice singing out *Wah-gee . . . Wah-gee!* you were sure to run into the peddler of wild geese, hunted and shot by himself over in the marshes of the Marin shore. These all became Annie's familiars in the narrow lanes off the main streets where there were still private homes not yet converted into boardinghouses.

Once the appearance of an advertised doctor's residence was so auspicious that she found courage to ring its doorbell. But the young man with Macassar-oiled hair dressed in puffs and curls who smiled through the parted curtains so startled her that she fled before he could open the door. Not a whisker on his face, not a wrinkle of experience about his shiny eyes, he was anything but prepossessing.

The morning after this scare, the Captain arrived. Waiting on the pier for his ship to come in to its mooring, Annie resolved to tell him nothing of her adventures, though she knew she could make him laugh with her description of the face she had seen through that so-called doctor's door instead of the one she had hoped to see. She pulled straight the seams of her new red gloves. With a touch of white in her navy blue bonnet and dark blue cape, she was the lady of fashion dressed in red, white and blue like all the young matrons of San Francisco in that last year of the Civil War. She doubted her husband would notice her red gloves, but if he did, he would think she had spent her time strolling through shops.

The Captain came down the gangway chatting with the last of his passengers. He had changed from uniform into shore togs — frock coat, quilted vest and beaver hat — and looked a little like a prosperous tourist from down East who had sailed out to see if the Far West was all that it was cracked up to be and if, perchance, a little fling in the Mining Stock Exchange might not be worth a try.

Annie smiled at the improbable thought of her canny husband risking even a dollar on that most volatile exchange. James Lick who had made his money in real estate was the only one of the city's many millionaires the Captain truly respected — a man with an eye for real values, not fly-by-night stuff. Her smile opened a path for her across the crowded pier.

The Captain did not expect her to meet him. He stared at her with a mixture of delight and dismay, embraced and scolded her in the same breath. What in God's name was she thinking of, coming alone to the docks? Unescorted through those saloon alleys, past all those crimp houses?

"I'll *always* be here, Jack." Her eyes danced as she looked up at him, remembering the streets she had explored in far more questionable quarters than the familiar wharfside. "Every time your ship comes in," she added, thrusting out her chin.

"And she will too, by heaven!" said the Captain to his companion. "Just as I told you, Mack, all spunk and independence!"

He swung her about, holding her in the curve of his arm as he presented the passenger he had shepherded ashore. The man was a doctor. She blinked as if the Captain had pulled a rabbit from his beaver hat and shook hands with a tall lean man with brown eyes, sandy gray sideburns and a gates-ajar collar with sober silk cravat such as every doctor she had ever known had worn and which had come to mean for her the sure outward sign of professional rectitude.

"Dr. McDougall," she said. Laughter rippled behind her words of greeting. Even the name was reassuring, one she would have moved toward trustfully (thinking Edinburgh University, of course) had she seen it over a door.

"From the land of your favorite Robert Burns," said the Captain happily. "We're taking Doctor Mack to the Lick House until he gets his bearings."

In later years, the Captain was to bring to port many a rare and (after the China runs) even exotic personality, but none was ever so cherished by Annie as the Scottish doctor in search of a place to hang his shingle. She helped him find a suitable location, interviewed female help to keep it in order and eventually chose the sort of solid elderly housekeeper who would lend tone to his bachelor establishment. Then, when at last he hung out his sign, she became his first patient.

In her private thoughts it was Dr. McDougall who laid the

cornerstone of her family life with his simple assurance that she could of course bear children. She had only to relax, he said, cease blaming herself for not yet having made the Captain a father and, above all, erase from her thoughts the quaint notion that a miscarriage at sea five years before might have left some permanent impairment. She had better enjoy life now before children started coming because if past experience had made him any judge (and it should have after, say, two or three hundred accouchements) once they started coming, they'd keep on coming.

She flew from his office, wheeling in delight over the city she seemed to be seeing for the first time, its streets strung with bunting for the Jubilee to celebrate Grant's victories before Petersburg and Richmond, and Lincoln's second inauguration. Everything sparkled, there was a feeling of freshness in the air. Even the Captain, somewhere off Mexico at the helm of a new command, was beginning something new which she clearly saw as the inevitable upward climb, from smaller to larger vessels, for the Pacific Mail had already laid the keels of two 4000-ton wooden side-wheelers back East, destined for the China run.

But she would have a child by the time he reached command of one of those monsters, and his months-long absences then would probably seem no more than her present five-week waiting spells that scarcely gave her time to look over the lots for sale he had marked in the real estate columns for her appraisal.

If she had not had long acquaintance with the Captain's passion for perfection, Annie might have suspected that the protracted hunt for a home site was his calculated way of keeping her busy while he was at sea. He expected her to report on each lot's exposure to the foggy trades, to afternoon sunshine and, most important, the extent of its view over the Bay.

In that happy spring, Annie saw San Francisco's funereal procession for the assassinated President Lincoln. She had gone off to the hills that day, to escape the gloating of some Southerners in the hotel. Through tears she watched the dark cortege wind slowly through the streets below, past crape-draped shops that had been bright with victory bunting just a few days before. The roll of muffled drums sounded like a mournful wind blowing over the city.

A few days later, on the morning of "Steamer Day," the Lick House clerk handed her a black-bordered letter. She saw the New London postmark and fled up the marble staircase to read it alone. *To Captain and Mrs. John Mansfield Cavarly* — her mother-in-law's angular handwriting. A small sepia photo, cut circular as if removed from a locket it had fitted, fell from the envelope. She looked at the thin pointed face of her husband's brother Phillip with his dark hair, like a poet's, brushed back curled and long behind his ears. He had died four weeks before, after a hemorrhage brought on, it was thought, by a drive to town to fetch new books from the library. Mother Cavarly wanted son John and daughter Annie to know that there had been no pain, that he had died with the same small smile on his lips they could see in this locket photo taken just after Annie's last visit. They had read the Forty-sixth Psalm at the funeral because Phillip had loved its mention of the mountains being carried into the sea. *His brother's sea* . . . Mother Cavarly underscored.

Tears almost blinded her as she groped through the desk for the Captain's Bible, purposely left home this trip to keep his duffel light; Corwine was transferring him to a new steamer on arrival in Panama. Annie had brought the Bible to him when she had come from the East, his name and the name of his first command inscribed on its flyleaf. Beneath her inscription she pasted Phillip's tender photo, then sought Psalm XLVI and drew a trembling pencil mark about it: *God is our refuge and strength, a very present help in trouble. Therefore will we not fear, though the earth be removed, and though the mountains be carried into the midst of the sea* . . .

For the first time, she dreaded the Captain's return. She covered the black-bordered letter with the brown-backed seaman's Bible and walked back and forth before the desk, wondering how

she could ever begin to tell him. In the end, she told him directly
— "all square yards," as she knew he would want it.

Then, with an arm about his shaking shoulders, she read him
the eleven verses, her voice low and measured like an echo from
the faraway burial ground she used to drive past on her way to the
New London farm . . . *There is a river, the streams whereof
make glad* . . . She could never take the place of that brother
in her husband's heart, she thought, never assuage his tender
fraternal love, the emotion of the strong for the weak, of the
fighter for the peacemaker . . . *He maketh wars to cease unto
the end of the earth; he breaketh the bow, he cutteth the spear
in sunder* . . . But she could, God willing, *put* something in its
place. She thought prayerfully of a son as she finished the psalm
with a whispered *Selah.*

Brass bands and exultant crowds welcomed every ship that arrived in San Francisco throughout the summer and fall of '65.
The "boys in blue" were coming home. High society entertained
the generals, pavement nymphs the enlisted men. The doctor advised Annie to keep off the streets on the Fourth of July which
promised to be a roof-raiser. Thanks to the flow of forty-rod
whiskey, he had stitched more scalps in the past month than in
his entire thirty-one years of practice.

But nothing kept Annie away from the docks when the Captain's ship came in. The arms of the semaphore on Telegraph
Hill, wigwagging that a steamer was entering the Gate, were her
signal to start dressing prettily to meet him, and she rode to the
docks on horsecars flying small flags that proclaimed *U. S. Mail.*
"Steamer Day" was not just her personal holiday; it was like a national holiday when mail from the East came in. The whole city
turned out — to queue up at the post office for tidings from far-
off homes and friends, to crowd the docks when friends or relatives themselves were expected, and there was always the moment, breath-takingly lovely, when the huge paddler made her

appearance around the point and swung her prow toward the Pacific Mail wharves. And now, by prearrangement, as he swept his
ship down Bay to get room for the turn before entering the dock,
the Captain ordered sounded for Annie's ears alone three blasts
from his steam whistle which told her what kind of a trip he had
had — three identically timed toots for an average voyage, two
short and one long for an exceptional voyage.

Occasionally, he sailed out of San Francisco in one ship and returned from Panama in command of another, usually bigger
and newer. David Corwine was fulfilling his promise to keep a
weather eye on "Captain Jack," thrusting him forward as fast as
opportunities developed. Thus in September he was given command of a boisterous cargo of artillerymen on transfer from the
East to reinforce the Presidio overlooking the Golden Gate.

As usual, for her scrapbook, the Captain sent Annie a copy of
his instruction letter. The assignment, he remarked laconically,
was "somewhat of a challenge." Annie knew from her newspapers what had happened with the previous shipment of artillerymen to whom the skipper of the New York-Aspinwall steamer
had unwisely given shore leave a few hours before train time at
the Atlantic end of the Isthmus. They had literally torn up the
grogshops of the port and had made of their Isthmus crossing
one of the wildest in history, dwarfing anything on record since
the lusty days of the Forty-niners.

The Captain devoted most of his letter to remarks on the number of laundresses traveling with the soldiers. I remember, he
wrote, when there wasn't a washerwoman or man, white or Chinese, in the whole of San Francisco and the big trade to Honolulu
was dirty linen to be washed! Copra and sugar to the mainland,
bags of laundry as return cargo, just fancy. Tell Doctor Mack I'm
bringing up the laundresses. Last trip I heard him storming about
his Chinese laundryman who sprinkles his rough dries with spit
— maybe he can charm one of these buxom Irish ladies away
from her officer.

The copy of his instruction letter evoked the Kentuckian who had written it, thorough to the last detail, almost fatherly in his concern that all would go well for the Captain:

Agency, Pacific Mail SS Co.
Panama, Sept. 1, 1865

Capt. J. M. Cavarly
Commanding S. S. SONORA
Bay of Panama
CAPTAIN:

You will receive herewith copy of contract for the transportation of:

 38 officers
 524 enlisted men
 22 officers' servants
 41 laundresses

all of the 2nd United States Artillery, and who will be accompanied by

 11 officers' wives
 14   ”   children
 8 female servants and
 29 laundresses' children —

these last all to be carried free, as well as entire luggage amounting to 33 tons, more or less, for which please make provision.

The Officers with their wives and Children go as First Class passengers and are to be provided with First Cabin Fare but are not to be furnished with Wines, Spirits or Malt Liquors unless they pay for same at regular rates. The Enlisted Men, Laundresses with their Children and the Officers' Servants all go as Steerage Passengers and are to be accommodated as such: the U. S. Government, however, provides them with rations which we are to prepare and cook for them. On no consideration is this class of passenger to be provided with intoxicating drink whether they are willing to pay for it or not. You will also see that the soldiers are disarmed as soon as they come on board, and that the arms are secured beyond their reach should they feel inclined to possess themselves of them. The Ship's arms must be in perfect order for immediate use should the occasion require, and accessible only to yourself and your Officers — and you will be expected to take stringent measures to preserve the utmost cleanliness, order and discipline on board during the voyage.

On the arrival on board of these Passengers, you will proceed on your voyage to San Francisco as soon thereafter as practicable, conforming as nearly as possible to the usual schedule time of 13½ to 14 days from port to port but on no account pressing the ship to unusual speed, or such as endangers her safety, which must be considered as of paramount importance. You will touch at Acapulco, receiving your supply of coal there, taking in not only enough for consumption during the remainder of the trip, but sufficient to keep the ship in proper trim during the voyage. You will take the inshore route crossing the Gulf of Tehuantepec and keep well in sight of land, giving all headlands and islands a wide berth, and avoiding strange sails in view of current reports respecting the pirate ship *Shenandoah.* I would ask that in assigning quarters to the U. S. Army Officers, you will be governed by the order of their rank.

Trusting, Captain, that you will make this a successful trip for the interests of the Company, and wishing you a safe and pleasant voyage, I remain,

Yours very truly,
D. M. CORWINE, *Ag't*

The Captain had not only followed to the letter but had improved upon Corwine's instructions. He urged their colonel to have the troops ready in formation on the decks, the most spruce and starchy outfit the city had yet seen. Annie guessed rightly that he had kept the forty-one laundresses busy all the way up, steaming and pressing the faded blue uniforms, putting sharp creases in every sleeve and trouser. She fluttered her handkerchief with deep sympathy as the scrubbed and sober veterans marched past her, grumbling their relief for having escaped "that hell-ship skippered by a temperance maniac."

For that arrival which set an example of how a passenger ship loaded with war veterans could arrive in port, without wreckage to saloon furnishings and no stretcher cases carried off, the Captain was given his first regular command in the company's service — the S.S. *Sacramento*, 2683 tons of trim sidewheeler elegance, the queen of the Panama service.

This was his third command of the twenty-two Pacific Mail ships he would eventually skipper over the Pacific without loss of a single hull. In later years when Annie was to name his ships for her children, from sail to wooden side-wheelers and thence to his screw-driven iron steamers, her voice always faltered over the *Sacramento,* long since wrecked on a reef off Geronimo Island in Lower California. It was as if she and that ship had had something together like a secret bond that required no more than a glance from a distance to keep it alive. I never actually sailed in her, Annie would say, but I always loved her . . . Yes, I think even more than the *Anglo-Saxon.*

The *Sacramento* was racy, responsive to helm and, in her passages to and from the Isthmus, as regular as Annie's chatelaine watch. For her it was the ideal time, the ideal command, in which to discover that she was pregnant. "Jack will be here when my time comes," she told the doctor. "By the law of averages he couldn't possibly miss."

On an August afternoon in '66 she went to meet his ship, eager to tell him her happy news which she had purposely not told in letters. She must see his face. She was unaware that he had on board the Dowager Queen Emma, widow of Kamehameha IV of Hawaii, who was returning via the Isthmus to her home in the Islands after a tour of England where Queen Victoria had entertained her and Oxford University had honored her. Annie knew, as did all San Francisco, that the Queen was due shortly. Preparations for the reception of the first Queen ever to set foot in California had been headline news for many weeks. But Annie had missed the issue saying this was the day and the *Sacramento* the ship. She had bigger news for her husband than any to be found in print.

The dense crowd on the dock, the many flags and brass bands

seemed appropriate to her occasion. The twenty-one-gun salute heard booming as the *Sacramento* sailed past the Presidio suggested some important passenger on board.

She worked her way to the company office where everyone was on tiptoe watching the point around which the *Sacramento* would appear. Captain Eldridge, the agent, swept off his hat and made a place for her at the window, complimenting her on her stylish appearance for the reception of Her Majesty.

"Jack's bringing her?" Annie exclaimed.

"But of course," Eldridge said. "And what's more, Her Majesty has been sitting in the pilot house much of the trip up, taking a lesson on the winds and tides, no doubt, from our master mariner."

The *Sacramento,* strung with pennants from bow to stern, with the royal Hawaiian standard floating from her mainmast, sailed around the point dazzling as a lighted Christmas tree. Every bit of brass on her shone. Her white deck trim was scoured to the sparkle of driven snow. Her varnished paddle-wheels flashed against her black hull. As she swept down the Bay, the Captain sounded his private signal for an exceptional voyage. *Hoo . . . Hoo . . . Hoo-ooh-ooh!* The steam whistle sang over the water as the great side wheels went into reverse, kicking up clouds of spray in which rainbows danced. Even with a Queen on board, the Captain had not forgotten his steamy salute to her, Annie thought. With her head held high she walked up the gangplank on the arm of Captain Eldridge to meet the Queen.

Queen Emma was in the pilot house surrounded by notables who had gone down the Bay in tugs to give the royal welcome. Annie would have lingered on the edge of the attentive circle to savor the sight of her husband paying court to the beautiful woman whose dark tragic eyes and melodious voice had charmed all Europe. But the Captain saw her at once and brought her forward.

"Your Majesty . . . may I present my wife!"

The Queen had obviously heard a great deal about the Captain's wife during her visits to the pilot house. She clasped Annie's hand as she spoke of her father and the good example of thrift and godliness he set in her kingdom. She thought it most appropriate that Annie had been married aboard a sailing ship right there in the Bay. And as for those two trips around the Horn with such a skipper, she was frankly envious.

Captivated by Queen Emma's charm and simplicity, Annie completely forgot her own news. In the carriage driving to the hotel and all during the reunion dinner, she questioned her husband eagerly about his royal passenger. Though he seldom gossiped of his passengers he was willingly expansive about this one.

She was, he declared, a fine Christian gentlewoman, so naturally democratic she might have been born in Connecticut. She had come often to the pilot house for chats. No, she had never spoken of the loss of her only child four years previously, nor of her husband's death the following year. But once she did show him the son's picture, His Royal Highness the Prince of Hawaii, a duplicate, he supposed, of the photograph she had presented to Queen Victoria who was the child's godmother. She had told him the lad's full name as he studied the photo of a dusky little lad in pantaloons and high buttoned shoes with a small white dog beside him. Albert Edward Kauikeaouli Leiopapa a Kamehameha — he would never forget that moment. Queen Emma's voice then had made him think of ships' bells tolling in a fog . . .

Suddenly Annie remembered her own news.

"We'll call ours simply John, after you my dearest," she said. "He'll be an April child." She smiled across the table at her thunderstruck husband.

Chapter 9

EIGHT MONTHS LATER, giving birth to her first child in the stark loneliness of a strange house, attended only by Dr. McDougall and his Irish midwife Maggie McLatchie, Annie was to relive the days of her "Queen Emma shore leave" when the Captain had made her feel like a reigning queen, showering her with a diamond ring from Shreve's whose size would have embarrassed her New England soul in any other city but San Francisco where diamonds were common as buttons around the Stock Exchange and often quite as large.

In their victoria, they had followed Queen Emma's barouche drawn by four white horses, from the dock to the Occidental Hotel, to which the royal Hawaiian standard had already been transferred from the *Sacramento's* mainmast. The Captain, holding Annie's hand in his during the parade ride, smiled as he heard the salvos of cheers from spectators and said, They're as much for *you* as for her! And that, Annie recalled, was before she had told him she was with child.

In their own hotel when she had finally remembered her own good tidings, he had knocked over his wineglass in his wild excitement as he rose abruptly from the dining table and came around to her chair to embrace her. When he had calmed down, he began immediately to plan ahead. Swiftly he had projected every *Sacramento* voyage from that moment until April of '67. Then he had suggested inviting Julia to come up from the Islands but she had vetoed that; Julia was "keeping company" just then, a courtship which by latest reports from her family was very fair and promising. *He* would be there for her event, she said. Even if she hadn't been able to follow chronologically his sailing computations, she had faith in them. And at last he had said, "If I had the least doubt, I'd ask a layover of one voyage, but I won't have to — I can be here in plenty of time."

His assurance had sustained her through the early months of her pregnancy, through and beyond the crucial fifth. She did everything Dr. McDougall and the Captain prescribed. She took no more carriages for hire (reckless drivers, runaway horses!) but rode instead the horsecars whenever the weather was fair, to give herself the healthy outings advocated. On each arrival in Panama, she had a message awaiting her husband in Corwine's office — *All well, love, Annie* — though this reassurance she considered slightly extravagant since he was home every sixth week to appraise with his own eyes her blooming state of health.

On only one point had she set her foot down decisively. Their first child was *not* going to be born in a hotel, even in such a family-like place as the Lick House where every provision was made for such eventualities, including nurses' quarters adjoining the upper floor suites and a children's dining room. "No, Jack, absolutely not here," she had said. "I'll find a place, just for a fortnight, nearby."

And, with the help of a doctor, she had. She found Mrs. Gelston's exclusive boardinghouse on the corner of Stockton and Geary, just a hop and a jump from the hotel. The Captain had inspected it on his next port leave, pacing off the room she could have on short notice, which was kept in reserve, said Mrs. Gelston, for just such fastidious people as Mrs. Cavarly who preferred not to have *all* the world know when the labor pains begin. He had arranged for Maggie McLatchie to sleep in the Lick House during the final fortnight so that Annie need not depend on a hotel messenger to get word to Dr. McDougall.

He deliberately played down his departure for Panama seven weeks before the child was due. "It's Captain's orders that you're *not* to be on the docks when I return," he said with a grin. "Neither you nor Maggie; I've told her the same thing. I'll have my First Officer clear the ship through customs so I can come directly here — or there. Doctor Mack has my port calls. You don't have to think of a thing, Annie. I've got everything arranged."

Everything, as it turned out, except the Pacific Mail fleet. As he had sailed out the Golden Gate on that trip, one of their veteran side-wheelers, the S.S. *Golden Age,* was limping into Acapulco with an engine breakdown that could be repaired only in the home yards of San Francisco Bay. David Corwine had already named the Captain for the honor of towing her two thousand tons of inert weight up the Coast; but he was not to know this until he arrived in Panama.

What had happened to him when Corwine had delivered his homebound sailing instructions, Annie could only imagine. His telegraphic message was written after composure was regained. *Must tow home disabled ship. Duty, I have no choice. Cannot be there for our event. Be brave, my darling, will arrive soon after.* When she had first read it her tears were for him.

"He'll go crazy with worry," she said to the doctor, and Dr. McDougall had stared at her, plucking at his sideburns thoughtfully as if she had suddenly revealed to him a depth and breadth of marital love beyond his bachelor's imagining. He called at the hotel every day after that, usually at the tea hour.

He made his final instructions sound like teacup talk. The first pain would be the signal that her time was near. She must tell Maggie at once. Right after, she would go to Mrs. Gelston's, on her own two feet would be best. Maggie would carry the bags. Labor pains had a rhythm like a certain music with the beat far apart at first, then shortening its intervals between — a sort of crescendo. He would count on her to bear the pains as best she could and she could count on him to have the *anaesthésie à la reine* ready for the last ones. A few drops of chloroform through cotton, that was all it was. *À la reine* — named for Queen Victoria who had accepted this help for the birth of Prince Leopold in '53, just six years after Sir James Simpson had begun its use in Edinburgh University's infirmary.

Knowing what would happen made everything sound easier for Annie as long as she was on her feet. But once she entered the quiet boardinghouse, every fear she had ever known returned with intensity. She went right to bed on Maggie's orders. Beneath her pillow she put the Captain's message. In the night when her labor started, she imagined she could feel his words *Be brave,* pressing firm, round and reminding against the back of her head. I'll try, she whispered, seeing him then so clearly, he might have come sailing through the shuttered room. His eyes were fixed on the tension of his towline.

"Jack's not using chain," she said once to the doctor. "Chain has no give to it, it snaps under the strain. He's using a coir hawser played out long . . ." Her back arched for a pain and her breath whistled between tight lips. Afterwards, she tried to go on about coir, but the doctor told her not to talk. "You have several more hours of this," he said, looking at his gold watch.

Coir, a sailor's Anglicizing of the Tamil *kayiru,* fancy that, the Captain said. He unraveled an end of the tow rope and showed her its composition of tough coconut fiber. They were using these hawsers on Indian Ocean dhows before Columbus discovered America and we *still* use them. He grinned at her and added, *Nothing can beat it for give!*

Her eyes opened to see Maggie McLatchie calmly arranging instruments and graniteware basins on the table across the room. With her eyes wide open, it was more difficult to make the Captain materialize, but Annie tried desperately to keep his presence between her and those dreadful preparations. *Be brave . . .*

As long as she kept him there, she could fend off the certainty that she would never come out of this alive. Twice, as the pains quickened, she lost him but her cries of anguish brought him back. Then, abruptly, she lost him altogether. She was alone in her agony rising and sinking on waves of pain that tore loose every towline attaching her to memory.

Two strangers worked over her in a strange room. A man with sandy sideburns said, *Bear down, lassie, as hard as ever you can,* and a woman in a starched cap held a paper cornucopia stuffed with cotton and a bottle poised over it. *Give it!* Annie shrieked, but the man shook his head. Somewhere then there seemed to be a stricken animal crying in the room. The chloroform dripped down through the cotton just as she sucked in her breath for the last terrible pain that seemed to tear her asunder.

From far away she heard a faint cry like that of a sea gull wheeling aloft. Hours later, still deep in lethargy, Annie saw her child for the first time. A bonnie lassie nine and one-quarter pounds, the doctor said as Maggie laid the flannel-wrapped infant in her arms. She looked down on the small red oval of her daughter's face with a fringe of damp hair standing straight up from the fragile forehead, her own blondness reproduced in faultless miniature. "Jack will love her . . . nevertheless," Annie whispered. She smiled at the Scottish face bending over her and shut her eyes.

Nevertheless. Her last word spurred the thought that set her small chin determinedly as she seemed to sleep. Though I didn't produce a sailor this time, I shall, I shall.

Dr. McDougall saw a tear run out from the corner of the closed eye that lay against the golden fuzz of her daughter's head. He touched the pulse of the hand lying outside the coverlet, counted for a moment, then nodded reassuringly to Maggie McLatchie.

"She's just relieved that it's all over," he said professionally.

By the time the Captain steamed slowly through the Golden Gate with the S.S. *Golden Age* in laborious tow, Annie was back in the Lick House. She had a Swedish baby nurse, Christine, whom the doctor had found and hired for her, installed in the servant quarters of the hotel, and she had turned the guest room of their suite into an efficient nursery with a ruffled crib, a clothes rack and a small tin tub set up on two wooden stools. She debated meeting the Captain's ship as usual but, remembering his words, finally asked the doctor to go in her stead.

She was sitting on the sofa with one knee drawn up to make a wider lap for her sewing when the Captain stealthily entered the door of the apartment with his own house key, on tiptoe, hat in hand. She had thrust into her chignon one of the hummingbird combs that were then the rage of San Francisco. The two stuffed green birds with gold beaks and ruby eyes appeared to be hovering over her blond head as if attracted by her flowerlike grace as she stitched and snipped, smiling with private pleasure over her handiwork.

He stood still in the hallway for a moment. This was how he would see her henceforth, busy and birdlike, with a smile of secret satisfaction playing about her tender mouth. This was the vision he would superimpose at will upon every fogbank, every lonely expanse of moving sea that would stand between them for the rest of his days. He called to her, *Ahoy there — anybody on board?*

She flew up from the sofa and ran into his outstretched arms, leaving behind her a trail of baby dress makings, bits of lace and narrow pink ribbons that fluttered to the floor.

That night he hovered over the crib waiting for the baby to awake from her nap. He had refused to pick her up, fearful that "something might snap." Later, he had taken her over from Christine and had walked the floor with her, warbling a peculiar off-key chantey. Annie had long since discovered that he couldn't carry a tune, not even a sailor's chantey, but she had never realized until this attempt at sustained singing how completely tone-deaf he was. She kept her face straight as he paced and warbled. A daughter, he declared between stanzas, was what he had hoped for all along. He nodded at her with unfeigned delight and continued his mournful lullaby.

Then there had been the inspection of their child from head to toe as he watched Annie undress the baby before bedtime. The tiny perfect fingernails and toenails astonished him the most. They were like the small pink shells you scuffed up in the sands of tropical beaches, he whispered, counting them. And, for the twentieth time, he exclaimed, "I don't know *how* you did it all alone!" His admiration for her bravery sent a glow of happiness through her. It was a new kind of tribute from him. It was a payment in full for all the terrors of her lonely ordeal.

When at last he took up his seaman's Bible, she stood behind his chair while he opened the book to the middle section between Old and New Testament. Here were the pages captioned *Family Record,* two for *Births,* two for *Deaths.* He paused a moment over the entry of his sister Elizabeth's death, four months after Phillip's at the age of twenty-three, and he looked up at Annie with glistening eyes. *Elizabeth,* he whispered, it's as if you've given her back to me. He smoothed flat the blank pages for the born, then slanted his pen and wrote into the space at the top:

> At 108 Stockton Street, San Francisco, April 4th, 1867.
> Elizabeth Cavarly, first daughter of J. M. and Annie E.
> Cavarly. Weighed at birth 9¼ pounds.

As she watched his moving hand, Annie wondered how many of those spaces must be filled before the words "first son" would be written down. How many girls' names before *John* would appear in the strong flowing handwriting that always looked like pennants in a breeze when a special happiness impelled the Captain's pen?

On the day before he sailed again, he told Annie that he needed her presence for a little business to be transacted, and he led her forth, wonderingly, to the Office of H. S. Homans on Montgomery Street, Pacific Coast agent for The Mutual Life Insurance Company of New York. He was taking out, in her name, a policy of $10,000 on his life and had the first payment of

$1110.20 in his pocket. Annie was so horrified at the idea that she balked at signing the application. Twice she read the conditions — *Ten thousand dollars on the life of John M. Cavarly, premiums paid for 10-year policy, payable at Death or in Fifteen Years.*

"That'll be a nice windfall fifteen years from now when I'm fifty," the Captain coaxed. He gave her a grin of connivance and added, "Mebbe we can take one out for each child!" She signed then, shakily, and watched Mr. Homans lick and paste onto the form a 5-cent Inter-Revenue Express stamp, brown, with a portrait of George Washington in its medallion. But she refused to touch the paper the agent extended to her with a bow; the Captain accepted it for her.

Outside the office he pointed up to the gold lettering over its show window — CASH ASSETS $25,000,000. "It's the safest investment I could think of, Annie dear," he said gently; but it would take her a long time to uproot from her mind the dreadful idea that he had sold himself, for her sake, to Davy Jones's locker.

While the Captain planned protectively for his domestic future, his company was already well launched in its transpacific expansion. In that spring of '67 the immense wooden side-wheel steamer *Colorado* returned to San Francisco from her eighty-day wonder trip to Yokohama, Nagasaki and Hong Kong. The Captain had followed the progress of the great steamer from the day she had sailed, filled with notables whom he called "ship's cousins" — Allan McLane, the Pacific Mail's president, Captain James Watkins, the company's fleet commodore, and a new investor in the transpacific enterprise, Mr. A. A. Low, president of the New York Chamber of Commerce. He had escorted Annie to the bunting-hung pier to meet these good-will emissaries, to view the splendors of the first Pacific paddler and to watch its riotous New Year's Day send-off. The glint in his eyes told plainly of his desire to be at the helm of one like that.

News stories of the returning travelers momentarily dimmed

the brilliance of the city's society columns. There had been banquets in Yokohama, charming geisha girls serving and entertaining and daylight fireworks which the Yankees had never seen before. In the granite-ribbed British crown colony of Hong Kong, there had been more heroic wining and dining and more cargo offered for the return voyage than the 3800-ton steamer could carry. Future reservations aboard her were clamored for. In Tokyo the new Mikado, Emperor Mutsihito, had arranged to have the *Colorado,* on a future sailing, carry the first official Japanese delegation to Washington.

What life for ordinary passengers aboard such a floating palace was like Annie was to learn later, when the published work of a round-the-world traveler who had sailed on the *Colorado* would appear — *Pekin, Jeddo and San Francisco,* by the Marquis de Beauvoir.

> We lead a sort of country-club life, except that the country house moves along with us, 300 miles every 24 hours, seemingly effortlessly. One converses with travellers from all parts of the world. . . . The passing of the 180th parallel excites all. . . . Yesterday was Monday, today is Monday. . . . Twice daily the Captain makes a thorough inspection of the ship, entering every cabin, pantry, kitchen. . . . The vessel shines like a mirror. For meals aboard, a gong vibrates calling all to table. Six tables are dressed and a whole army of waiters stands ready to serve. The head steward is a Negro, but his white waiters obey him as if they were black! The steward rings a bell. Forward is the word. The waiters advance a step; two rings they place the plates; three rings they step back. Then they advance in rank and step, platters in hand. The whole meal is served this way. . . . Once at dinner a sudden shock broke all the glassware on the table. All rushed to top deck to see a whale the ship had struck — we saw him going off leaving a trail of blood stains on the blue ocean. . . .

Meanwhile, Annie began sewing again for her next child. With calm determination, as if weaving a spell, she embroidered a floral J on every small bib and dress yoke, J for John. She told herself she was not trying to force the Lord's hand, merely showing Him how deeply she desired a son.

To the Captain she explained her handiwork as the essence of practicality. There would be no necessity to rip out the lettering later, since they had both agreed that a second daughter would be named for her favorite sister in the Islands. "J for Julia," she said. "Or J for John. I'm simply initialing in advance. What time will I have afterwards, with two babies to care for?" Only to Mrs. Farnsworth would she confess her fierce hopes to have a boy.

Ever since Captain Farnsworth had given to her husband his first post aboard the old side-wheeler *Orizaba,* the bond between the two families had grown closer. Mrs. Farnsworth was like a wise elder sister to Annie, and when they had first been reunited in San Francisco they had made between them the kind of pact that knits all sea wives together in ports far from their families — an agreement of mutual support in time of trouble. She reminded the Captain now that she was no longer alone in the city; she had a solid Downeaster to stand by when the baby would come.

This time, no planning could make his steamer's schedule coincide with her delivery; he would have to relinquish his command for the space of one round trip to Panama to be with her then. This she refused to allow him to do, just at the time he was next in line for a major command in the Pacific Mail's new service to the Orient.

"A second child is a very different affair from a first-born," she reassured, smiling. Moreover, for this time she had decided to remain in the hotel, a known ground, friendly and comfortable. She sent him off to Panama in mid-August of '68, proud as Punch of her courage. And ten days later she went down to her bed of pain.

The J for John turned out to be J for Julia. When the doctor laid her second daughter beside her, she looked up from the small wrinkled face to his and said, "We have to go through this yet again, don't we, my friend." She murmured something incomprehensible to him about going on with the jays and fell into a doze.

Julia was three weeks old when the Captain returned on September 24th. He took it for granted that Annie was again on her feet looking trim and lovely as ever and that his new child was a confection of pink and gold. And how could it have been otherwise? Annie asked herself. He had never seen her in the sweating disarray of childbirth nor an infant as it first appeared, red, wrinkled and slightly repulsive with its damp hair plastered in points about its domelike forehead.

He approved of girls, he told her stoutly. He was glad she had a second one. His daughters would be company for her, something no boy could ever be. He acted as if he had planned it this way, for her sake exclusively, so she wouldn't be lonely when he started on the China runs in January. But Annie observed, when he entered Julia in his seaman's Bible, he omitted her weight at birth. Did he care less for this one? Or was he getting so used to girls that he no longer considered such a detail important? "Eight and three-quarters pounds is nothing to sneeze at!" she told Mrs. Farnsworth with a little toss of her head.

Nevertheless, his pride in her remained undiminished. He had to show her off to his fellow officers whom he invited to the hotel for a glass of Madeira. As Annie passed the babies from bony knee to bony knee of the shy circle, the Captain taxed them for their "celibacy." A sailor did not have to stay single, he said, brushing up his whiskers. If *he* had had the luck to find a wife like Annie, why couldn't they? Most women had courage enough for two. You take Annie, now . . .

Annie fled the room to put the children into their cribs, in a fluster of embarrassment, before her husband was well launched on his favorite theme of her courage. She was to remember his trumpeting voice four weeks later, on the day she made her first acquaintance with the San Andreas Fault.

The courage the Captain bragged about was severely tested on the morning of October 28th, 1868 — a date she would remember for the rest of her life. That morning she lay in the middle of the double bed, staring at the plaster ceiling, pleasantly drowsy after her 6 A.M. nursing of Julia. She heard Christine moving about in the apartment. In a week the Captain would be home again, probably at that moment he was swinging his helm toward Manzanillo. She stared dreamlike at the ceiling as if she saw written on it the text of her last message to her husband — *Lizzie first molar; Julia ten pounds, all well fore and aft, love, Annie.*

The plaster ceiling seemed to tremble and a crack curved across it just as the bed began to rock. For the first seconds of the earthquake, Annie stared straight up unbelieving. She had never experienced an earthquake and could not believe that this was one. Then, without knowing how she had moved, she was in the nursery snatching Julia from her crib and crying to Christine to take Lizzie. The floor moved beneath her bare feet as she looked about wildly for a place to go. The idea of running outdoors in her nightgown never even occurred to her and, if it had, the clatter of brick chimneys cascading into the street would have stopped her. With the whole earth in convulsion, there *was* no place to go. The horror of it dawned as she paused in the nursery doorway watching vases and candlesticks pitch off the living-room mantelpiece and pictures on the wall swinging crazily. There were screams from the hotel corridors and crashing of cornices from the streets below but those sounds rode the great wave of subterranean rumbling like surface debris, inconsequential.

The big stone hotel swayed like a ship on the shaking earth, up and down, sideways, but all in one piece still. *She'll ride it out, Christine — quick, quick!* Annie ran back to the huge bed whose weight held it riveted to the unsteady floor. She got the two babies under the covers before the plaster started to fall. It fell first in flakes, then in ragged flat chunks as the shocks sharpened and bared parts of the ceiling to its slats.

The first temblor lasted for thirty seconds. Long after it was over Annie lay in her bed in a trance of terror hugging her babies to her. Christine rose from the floor where the 'quake had thrown her and stood staring at the opposite wall from which, with no perceptible shaking to loosen it, a single brick fell in a cloud of mortar dust. Annie pantomimed that she was going to be sick.

She vomited at intervals through the second and third earthquakes. The last two were less severe but more frightening because of the minor tremors between them which seemed to make them continuous. At 11:20 that morning the earth at last stood still. Christine took the babies from her and announced in a thin voice she was going to dress them. Annie stared at her; she shook her head when Christine suggested that she get up and dress. Her limbs had gone dead.

The hotel manager made a room check at noon, promised that all debris would be swept up by nightfall. Various ladies in the hotel, with whom Annie had made friends, came by to see if the babies were well, and the Pacific Mail agent called to get Annie's contribution to an omnibus message they were going to try to telegraph down the coast to catch all their steamers in the various ports. Annie dictated *Babies both well, myself slightly seasick as usual,* and smiled her thanks for the company's service. She tried to get a hotel messenger to send word to Mrs. Farnsworth on Rincon Hill, since her husband was also at sea; but no boy appeared in answer to her ringing.

In the afternoon Dr. McDougall called and encouraged Christine with the remark that San Francisco knew how to stand up and take her medicine. He had a special edition of the new daily *Chronicle* to prove it — an extra that had appeared on the street, by Jove, just two hours after the final shake. He was astonished to find Annie still in bed — "It wasn't *that* bad, lassie," he said as he took her pulse.

He tried to make her smile by reading squibs from his paper. Loss of life had been remarkably low, no more than six persons known dead thus far. Lots of broken legs suffered by fools who lost their heads and jumped from windows. Two runaway horses had dashed through the plate-glass of a drygoods store on the corner of Fifth and Folsom and the spire of the Sutter Street synagogue had toppled — a possible blessing, that, considering its atrocious architecture. The only people who refused to go back to work were the Chinese sorters in the Pacific Woolen Mills. Everywhere else, business was now going on as usual.

"In a week's time," said the doctor, "you'll never know anything happened."

"*I* will," Annie whispered. A dray rumbling past the hotel made the walls vibrate ever so slightly and her blood stopped for an instant. The earthquake had put its mark upon her. The awareness of this new menace seemed to bring to a head her resentment against the long, long hours in this unfamiliar place. A sudden fury against the city that sat so precariously on an earthquake fault made her clench her fists as if she would pummel to dust what remained of it. Raw, brash, boasting — and now dangerous.

"I *hate* this place," she moaned. "*I want to go home.*" And quite suddenly with hot relief the tears came. A flood of pent-up longings poured forth with her tears. It seemed to the doctor as if her cry for home had inadvertently knocked loose the stout shorings of her spirit. Often she had talked about her family in the Islands but never like this, crying out as it were for a lost paradise of kinsfolk who never asked her to be brave, who knew how much she needed others.

He listened attentively as she sobbed about home. Singing, she wept, there's always singing in my family, my sisters and I, after supper . . . She drew in her breath sharply and closed her eyes as if hearing a faraway music in which she no longer participated. Actually, she was hearing her own voice crying for the moon like a hysterical child. Presently she looked up at the man who was listening.

"Droll, isn't it," she said calmly, "what an earthquake shakes out of one?" She sniffed the smelling salts he handed her, staring at him steadily over the top of the vial. Then she said, "Doctor Mack, I don't wish Jack to know about this absurd little *crise,* promise me?"

"I promise you, lassie. But there's nothing shameful about being afraid in your first earthquake, ye know," he said smiling.

She was herself again and even stretched her neck a bit in pride when the Captain, on his return, admitted he had never experienced an earthquake, which had added considerably to his wild worries until he got her telegraph message in Manzanillo. She told him it was quite impossible to describe an earthquake to one who had never been in one. A Cape Horn storm, she said, was only half as dreadful. Even a Force Eleven gale, she added nautically, remembering her lessons from their sailing days.

Deeply impressed, he read the clippings she had saved for him. The earthquake lore that turned up in newspapers gave him the same comfort it had provided her. According to old-timer geologists, the San Andreas Fault had never cut up more frequently than every forty years, more or less. The Indians had said this, the Spanish *Californios* after them. As far back as the Coast's recorded history went, this had seemed to be the case. The next one would be in 1908 or thereabouts — in another century actually, a long time away. The Captain remarked that if that was so, it would be safe to leave his little family in San Francisco when he would be appointed to the China service. San Francisco or Yokohama — it had to be one or the other.

"San Francisco, of course!" Annie said.

But she would never learn to call it home. Home would be the heart-cry of Hawaii that her girls were to hear in later years each time she started packing for trips to the Islands on Dr. McDougall's advice.

Chapter 10

T HE LONG-HOPED-FOR COMMAND in the China line was given to the Captain at the end of '68. He was to sail for the Orient on January 4th, '69 at the helm of the side-wheeler *Great Rupublic.* For her Christmas and New Year holidays, Annie wrote to her father, she had had the *Great Republic* for breakfast, lunch and dinner daily and she could tell him, if he were interested, the weight of her crank (eight tons), the circumference of her paddle-wheels (120 feet) and how many furnaces each of her four marine boilers had (six each). Her Captain had received as a present the log of the *Great Republic's* '67 maiden voyage. This he had read as raptly as if it were a "penny dreadful," memorizing each day's run, coal consumption and compass course. But she *was* proud, she confessed to her family. Her husband was the youngest of the fleet's skippers to be given command of one of those monsters, responsibility for her 250 cabin-class lives and the thousand to twelve hundred in her Oriental steerage.

In the two weeks of the *Great Republic's* layover from her previous voyage, the Captain went every day to his new steamer, taking Annie with him when the weather was fair. He wanted her to know every corner of his new command — from the peach-blossom bridal suites, through pantries, post office, barbershop,

cow and ice houses to the steerage cabins aft which were doorless
and had standee berths easily cleared away to give space for eating. She followed him eagerly, knowing that once he would be at
sea and writing letters to her from his handsome quarters he
would never think to describe his domestic surroundings, especially those of first-cabin which entranced her the most. She
clasped her hands in admiration for the walnut woodwork and
furnitures throughout the first-cabin domain, for the beautiful
floorings of light spruce and black walnut laid in zebra pattern
and exclaimed over the silk drapes and upholsteries in color combinations of peach, lavender, pea-green and purple blending
perfectly with the frescoed walls of saloons and ballroom.

The Captain told her happily that he could write to her even
outbound. His letters would be picked up mid-ocean by one of
the *Great Republic's* ships — the S.S. *China* or S.S. *Japan,* then
making their record runs in the new service — meeting, pausing
and exchanging mails at prearranged points in watery space, one
ship westbound from San Francisco every month, one eastbound
from Yokohama. Skippers of the passing ships made it a point
of pride to encounter one another in the middle of an ocean
that dwarfed its islands to dots in a seascape six thousand miles
wide. Annie was slightly shocked to learn that the Pacific Mail
executives actually bet that their ships would meet midway,
such was their faith in their navigators.

He gave a small private party in his quarters the day before
sailing, for Annie and the doctor, the Farnsworths and Captain
Seth Doane whom he had succeeded to the command of the
Great Republic. For the first time, Annie saw in action the famous "blue-gowned boys" of the Pacific Mail, the Chinese stewards whose hiring had occasioned such an outcry in the press
when they had first appeared, supplanting white and Negro
stewards, soon after the inauguration of the China line.

Dressed in black silk caps, dark blue tunics and wide trousers,
with their pigtails hanging down almost to the heels of their
white-soled black felt slippers, they moved soundless over the

zebra-wood floors with trays of champagne and cakes, serving each guest with a respectful bow and tiny slant-eyed smile. It seemed to Annie then that the worst risk her husband would face on his two months' voyage, waited on hand and foot by those fluttering little Celestials, was that of being spoiled for life.

The Captain kissed her and the babies good-by the night before sailing, and went aboard ship as was the custom. Though he had ordered her not to come to the docks next noon to see him off, because of rainy January weather, she slipped away anyhow, unable to resist giving him a secret send-off on his maiden command in the China line. The crowds on the dock seemed composed of people ten feet tall and all she actually saw from her unreserved place were the tops of the *Great Republic's* masts, funnel and the giant walking-beam starting its slow motion back and forth. A man beside her said to his companion, That danged contraption ain't gonna stop seesawin' till they reach Yokohama! The year-old service was still a wonder to San Franciscans.

Even a greater wonder was the return of the mammoth from the Orient. If Annie had not had a pass to the company's wharf behind gates, she would have been trampled to death. Accustomed to meeting the smaller paddlers of the Panama line, she was unprepared for the city-wide hullabaloo that greeted the arrival of the *Great Republic* in early March. The lookout on the Heads at the entrance to the Bay telegraphed her approach to the Golden Gate. A messenger from the Merchant's Exchange galloped through the streets with the news. Every hack in town, express wagon, truck and dray pounded off to the docks bearing crowds of excited welcomers — boardinghouse runners, restaurant touts, baggage hustlers, Chinese merchants expecting cargo and suave representatives of the "Six Companies," the city's regional organizations of Chinese, who would shepherd the thousand Oriental immigrants coming in. Riding through the *mêlée* in a private carriage, Annie thanked God that she had not brought Lizzie with her as she had first thought of doing. The docks were a believable replica of the Tower of Babel. By the time she had fought her way across them to the fenced-off wharf-side for pass-holders only, the *Great Republic* had already rounded Rincon Point and was headed downstream toward San José at the south end of the Bay. She turned gracefully a half mile away, then came in toward the wharf, full speed against the strong tide, beating the Bay into a foam as she reversed her wheels and stopped within hawser toss of her berth. A moment after she ceased to move, the Captain came forth from the pilot house and stood apart from his officers, as he had promised, so she could see him clearly from below. She whispered, Beautiful, beautiful, my dearest, as she stared up at her mariner with the March wind parting his beard.

In the summer of that year, Annie's father sailed up from the Islands to see his first grandchildren and to try to tempt her to rejoin her family. Her lonely months during the Captain's voyages struck him as an unnecessary hardship when she had family just ten days away by schooner. He had moved from Lahaina to Honolulu and now had a rambling white house midway up toward the Pali on Nuuanu Road, big enough to include her, the two babies and the nurse. Before too long, he said, the Pacific Mail would certainly be entering the Australia trade with stops at Honolulu going and coming, and he was willing to bet that her skipper husband would be one of the first to command those longer runs to the Antipodes.

Annie shook her head, loyally hiding her regrets. "As long as Jack is on the China run, I've *got* to be here," she said. She read aloud some of the Captain's recent letters to help her father understand why, after a thirteen-thousand mile round trip, the home port had to mean something more for her husband than just the docks at the foot of Brannan Street.

The Captain made no attempt to conceal the hazards of the twenty-two-day non-stop voyage to Yokohama, then on through the typhoon-ridden China Sea to Hong Kong. Anything could happen and often did — broken shafts or paddle-wheels en route, running out of coal (which the company meted out so sparingly to its skippers that once he had returned to San Francisco with barely enough for a day's steaming left in his bunkers) and, most dreaded of all — fire. Meat for the passengers' table was carried alive on the hoof, which meant that vast quantities of inflammable hay were stored in the holds near the coal bunkers. On every crossing the Captain wrote something about the coal. It was like a special passenger to him, a black temperamental presence aboard, liable at any time to flare in spontaneous combustion, given often to brooding heats which required frequent shovelings over to keep it dry.

"Every day he makes a sniffing inspection of holds and bunkers," Annie said. "He has developed his olfactory nerves to such a sensitivity that he can smell smoke when it's no more than an invisible thread buried beneath tons of cargo. Swain, his quartermaster, told me he has twice saved his paddler from catching afire mid-ocean . . ." she paused, then went on in a gayer vein, "That's why they call him the Fire Fiend, all through the service! You can see now, can't you, why the children and I must be here when that Fire Fiend docks? He comes home, oh! so weary each time." She patted her stack of letters into a neat bundle and tied a ribbon about it.

"Yes, Annie dear, I see," said her father, looking at the letters she lived for whose envelopes bore stamps with rising suns and flying dragons and all manner of forwarding instructions in columnar Chinese inscriptions down the backs of them. He asked her if she was starting a stamp collection. Not yet, she laughed, but she planned to when Lizzie would be old enough to appreciate them. Lizzie was just like her father, a collector of odd objects, a little spitfire sometimes.

"And Julia takes after you, that I can see," said her father, wrapping his arms about the baby that never cried.

Annie begged him again to stay over until the *Great Republic* returned, to see her Captain, his ship and all the docking excitement. "It's a real hallelujah, Father — you'd love it!" He reminded her that her brother Frank was still pretty young to be running Bolles & Company chandlery singlehanded; he must leave within the fortnight.

He sowed one seed, however, before he left. She had confided her hopes for a boy next time and promised him that when *that* duty to her husband was accomplished, she would come to the Islands for a long visit. He had gazed at her with his bushy eyebrows lifted in yearning peaks of hope and had said, "I've got even a better idea, Annie. When you know for certain that the lad is on the way, why not come then? Have him with us? Wouldn't that be wonderful for all concerned?"

It was so wonderful she hardly dared think about it, for fear of flying apart with joy. But the seed sprouted in her mind like a magic beanstalk. What could be more nautically auspicious than to have a son born in the middle of the vastest ocean on earth? She imagined every detail down to the crib ruffled in blue. And around that crib, like the good fairies she believed every newborn babe should have, she saw her mother bending, with a slight creak of whalebone, to see whose eyes the child had, whose nose, whose chin — and her gay younger sisters all in summery white with hibiscus flowers in their hair.

She told the Captain of her Hawaiian dreams during his Christmas weeks ashore, at the same time she revealed she was pregnant again. His relief for the sure knowledge that she would have her own folks about her for the third birth told her how deeply and continuously he worried about her while at sea.

"By God, I should have thought of Hawaii myself, Annie dearest," he said apologetically. "Probably would have, given enough time. Sailors' minds work slow on land."

Figuring her date to be August 1870, he suggested she sail for the Islands in the spring, have her final months with her family and he, meanwhile, would hope and pray that his Pacific voyaging would carry him into the Australia runs so that he might be in her same latitude in time for the birth. He didn't say outright "for the birth of our son," but this was the hope he celebrated that Christmas, turning the holiday ashore into a double festival — for the new baby and his new command.

On New Year's Day of 1870 he was to sail in the S.S. *China,* a sister ship of the *Great Republic* and of the other two China paddlers in the luxury transpacific fleet — S.S. *Japan* and S.S. *America.* Since all four steamers were identical in elegance of furnishings and perfection of service by the "blue-gowned boys," Annie didn't understand his jubilation for the "new command" until he explained to her that the *China* had one great superiority over her sisters — double outside plankings and internal watertight bulkheads which would considerably lessen his worries at sea with a thousand lives in his care.

After rounds of Christmas parties for his new officers, the Captain wound up on New Year's Eve by making a radical departure from his fixed custom of being aboard ship the night before sailing, and, instead, took Annie to the California Theater to see John McCullough starring in *Richelieu.* For a year since its gala opening, Annie had lived for the moment when one of the Captain's shore leaves would coincide with a production in this famous theater to which she would never have dreamed of going alone, or even with Mrs. Farnsworth who shared her views on unescorted ladies seen at night in the streets of San Francisco.

But she knew through wistful readings of the society columns exactly what lay behind the impressive Corinthian portals of the California Theater — the tessellated marble floor of the vast foyer, the big Bay mural with clipper ships painted so that the viewer seemed to be standing on the Bar looking at the *Western Continent* going out the Heads towed by the *Lookout,* and the *Challenge* standing off the Cliff House making for port, with yachts and fishing boats midway in the background and Alcatraz off to the left. She could recite the names of notable boxholders and knew the location of their boxes — the Billy Ralstons, the Crockers, the Coits, the Leland Stanfords, the Hall McAllisters and the Donahues — and what the wives had worn in the way of jewels and furs at each opening.

She dressed excitedly for her theatrical debut with her husband, pinching cheeks and ear lobes to give them the pink she refused to apply with vulgar rouge, trying out every kind of coiffure ornament, feathered, flowered and spangled, until at last she decided to make with her fingers a pair of the new-fashioned *crève-coeur* curls in the crown of her coiled braids. She had Christine check every hook and bow on her gown before going into the living room where the Captain paced with his watch in one hand and her New Year's present in the other — an elegant little ivory fan he had found for her in Hong Kong.

Behind the rustling of silk and the visible splendor of that New Year's Eve, Annie saw the whole of the bright new decade of the '70s opening out in carved story, like the ivory fan she fluttered excitedly in her small gloved hand. The Captain was so proud of her clear-cut New England beauty in the crowds of bare-bosomed, diamond-encrusted society ladies that he almost burst his buttons. Not once during the whole evening did he so much as mention the S.S. *China* tied up at the foot of Brannan Street, loading seven hundred homebound Chinese into its steerage and California flour and silver ingots into its holds. During the intermission he introduced her to gentlemen in white ties and tails who had sailed with him to the Orient to make more millions from their connections in Japan and China. The "Bonanza Boys," he called them genially, without a trace of envy for their visible affluence. One of them had a stickpin in his silk cravat, a Gothic J made of fire-spitting diamonds at which Annie stared with delight, matching it up in her mind with the J she was already embroidering on small garments in the Lick House — J for John, this time surely.

The '70s she was certain would give her the son she desired more than a Comstock Lode. They were also to give her a home of her own in the city where housing for newcomers ranked second to the comfortable family hotels and, eventually, the culture she hungered for, in the persons of Edwin Booth, Madame Modjeska, Lotta Crabtree, Lillie Langtry, Melba and Paderewski who were to come later to this same theater. But none of these extra dividends could she guess that night. All thought stopped with the good omen of the diamond stickpin and her emotional memory crystallized around one single picture she saw — her sea-captain husband reflected in a great gold-framed mirror beneath a gasolier with a dozen jets and scores of sparkling cut-glass pendants. She was on his arm but she did not see herself — only her Captain with his combed and gleaming beard, his barrel chest clothed in black satin vest and his rolling gait that made all other men's in the foyer look like the mincing struts of pigeons.

Next day at noon Annie waved the Captain off for the Orient aboard the S.S. *China* with a capacity load of Chinese in its steerage and some fifty American and European globe-trotters, plus a few missionaries, in its First Class. As the steamer backed away from the dock with her great walking-beam tilting like an iron seesaw against the sky, the Chinese tossed overboard bright bits of prayer paper to placate the spirits of the sea and assure a safe passage. Annie whispered her own prayer for a safe return as she watched the joss paper fluttering down in flecks of gold, silver and vermilion that looked like clouds of small butterflies swarming and settling, to perish at last in the paddle-wheel's foam.

The Captain signaled with a long pull at his steam whistle as he swung the *China* around and headed majestically toward the Golden Gate. Annie knew he ordered that whistle especially for her, to make the steamy blast say *Hawaii, Hawaii in the Spring.* It was all arranged. When he returned in March he would take her to Hawaii, letting Doane or Watkins command the *China* for one voyage. He planned to remain with her in the Islands for a month, taking the first vacation he had ever allowed himself since he went to sea as a boy of fourteen.

Consciously and conscientiously Annie began her New Year as he had prescribed. She took long healthy breaths of fresh air for

John's sake and refrained from putting her muff to her cheeks as a shield against the January winds. Feeling just a little bit heathen in her belief in omens and portents, she watched for J's on signboards as the little dummy car rocked along its narrow tracks, over which, when the sand had blown, it seemed to grope swaying as on a sea, until its iron wheels connected again with iron rails.

Two months later a letter from her father demolished Annie's dream of Hawaii, though his intention had been quite the opposite when he wrote it. He was fearful only that news of the first scarlet fever in the Islands might have reached San Francisco in exaggerated form.

"People out here make such a to-do about any disease new to the natives," he wrote, "always expecting repetition of the small-pox epidemics of the '50's and '60's which cut down large numbers before vaccination was made compulsory." He would not even have mentioned the scarlet fever, he explained, but for a report published in the *Hawaiian Gazette* of February 16th which put the current mortality at 179. If San Francisco papers had copied that story, he hoped they also copied the correct name of the Island whence it came — Maui. The epidemic was there, *not* on Oahu. Honolulu's few cases had been swiftly quarantined by the Board of Health. "No matter *what* you may read in your papers, don't be alarmed. Don't get any ideas in your fanciful little head that Lizzie or Julia could catch anything here on Oahu."

Before she finished her father's letter, Annie knew she would not go to Hawaii. Even one case would have given her pause. She had seen scarlet fever as a child in New London, when her sister Mary was struck down by it and almost died. Forbidden to enter the nursery for more than two months, she had spied, from outside the window, on the progress of the disease — the vomiting, the tossing fever and then the "strawberry tongue" swollen and inflamed, frightening to see when Mary opened her mouth and wailed. Almost more fearful had been the vigil for complications her mother had kept after the contagious stage was passed — complications with maiming names like mastoiditis, encephalitis and meningitis. It had been like a deathwatch that went on for days on end and left her mother as wasted-looking as the child she surveyed.

Annie picked up her pen and wrote off Hawaii in a series of small swift strokes without having to pause for word or phrase, her decision formulated and instantaneous as always when the welfare of her children was concerned. "I can't risk it, Father dear. I know myself too well. *I remember Mary.* The fright from her scarlet fever has never been outgrown. Even if that dreadful epidemic were completely over by the time we'd arrive, I'd *still* be looking for it, expecting it to strike again and who else but one of the Captain's daughters? I know I'd be fearful all the time. I simply *must not* have fear about me while carrying John. He must be born brave like his father, not the coward I'd make him if I came down and trembled every time a friend or relative stepped off the Maui boat and came at me with open arms. I know that you don't believe in prenatal influences, but I do. So you see, it's not only for the sake of the girls' health that I renounce our happy plans, but for the boy's sake also. I'm putting a letter aboard the *America* to catch Jack mid-Pacific on his return from Yokohama. He'll agree with my decision without question. In some ways he is more cautious than I about contagious diseases."

Cautious was a mild way of putting it. The Captain was actually a maniac about disease, as Annie well knew. Many times on the Panama runs he had refused to allow passengers ashore because of rumored smallpox or yellow fever in one of the tropical ports. It was always a blow to his sight-seeing tourists when he ordered no communication with land beyond the exchange of mail and specie, not even permitting them to purchase from the greeter canoes the shell baskets, colored corals and tortoise-shell curios the natives held up temptingly. He never cared how unpopular he became with his irate passengers, nor that some refused to speak to him for the remainder of the voyage.

It fortified Annie to remember these things as she sealed the letter that ended not only her Hawaiian dreams, but also presaged another lonely confinement in San Francisco. She would earn a hearty *Well done* from her husband for having made a decision he himself would doubtless have made, though for reasons less personal than hers. He remembered the Islands from his whaler days when the first tuberculosis and the first venereal diseases had been brought to the natives by the whaling schooners. He had seen how those new diseases had run like wildfire through a race in which no immunities had been established, a race as innocent of disease as had been the children in the Garden of Eden.

"You did the right thing," he would say, "as always, Annie dearest . . ."

The extent of the sacrifice of her holiday in Hawaii did not begin to strike until she had put on bonnet and cape and was ready to go forth to post her letters — one for the racy little Honolulu packet and one for the big side-wheeler due to sail that noon for the Orient. Her three-year-old Lizzie tagged at her skirts, begging to be taken along. Annie shook her head, it was raining hard outside. She bent to kiss the child good-by and heard the fluty voice say very correctly the words she herself had taught her, in preparation for the Hawaiian trip.

Aloha, mama, Lizzie piped. *Aloha nui!*

She managed to hold back her tears until she had hurried through the Lick House lobby, but once out in the rainy street she let them flow freely. It made no difference then. Everyone had a wet face, even the pedestrians like herself who slanted umbrellas ineffectually against the veering rain-soaked winds.

She had to clutch her umbrella with both hands to keep it from blowing inside out as she rounded the corner of Montgomery and Post. It was like a flying jib in a gale. Wrestling with it was an act of survival that took her mind off Hawaii. She would get to the post office without furling it. I've got enough lead in my keel to stand up to it, she told herself as she ran before the gale down the rain-slashed street.

The Captain came to port with the *China* in mid-March, his request for transfer to the Panama service already composed. Halfway across the Pacific he had met the westbound *America* that brought him his wife's determined letter. Since Hong Kong he had been expecting it. There he had picked up a January issue of the *Pacific Commercial Advertiser* reporting the scarlet fever scourge in parts of the Islands and a new outbreak on the windward side of Maui.

To compensate her for the sacrifice he knew she would make he had almost bought out the bazaars of Hong Kong, selecting furnishings for the home they now must promptly find in San Francisco since, with one more baby, they would outgrow their comfortable quarters in the Lick House. He had teak tables, carved high-backed Chinese chairs and a Canton ware dinner service for twenty-four stowed away in the *China*'s hold. In his pocket was a necklace of flawless jade that a mandarin friend in Hong Kong had helped him select.

Annie put her foot down and said no to the transfer, but lost her case this time. The Captain insisted the transfer was as much for his sake as for hers. A year and a quarter on the wooden Pacific paddlers was enough for any skipper at a single stretch, he said. The longer hours on the bridge (especially during the summer monsoon when navigation in the Japan and China Seas was always a lottery), the nervous watchfulness for fire and the constant calculations of coal consumption would wear him out before his time, if he didn't give himself such a break now and then. A season on the Panama run would be just the "resting up" he needed; that coastal course he could sail with eyes closed.

The company, understanding why he wanted to be closer to home, assigned him to command his old *Constitution*, which was still the largest side-wheeler on the Panama run and actually only some 520 tons lighter than the S.S. *China,* a fact which he pointed out to Annie as if to prove that he suffered no loss of prestige in making the change.

Thus, he could be near her in August when her time would come again. Though he remembered now and again to mention his weariness with transpacific voyaging, as if to underline his contention that he needed a spell of easier sailing, he never deceived Annie for an instant. Under her loving eyes, he was as transparent as glass.

Before he had completed his second round trip to Panama, she had found a house which suited them down to the ground. During the Civil War, Rincon Hill and its adjoining South Park had been peopled mainly by the Southern clique but it had lost its anti-Union character and had since become a residential section for Yankees as well, notably sea captain families like the Farnsworths, and Forty-niners turned into respectable stockbrokers who now (as the Captain put it) gambled on the Mining Stock Exchange for the gold they had formerly panned from Sierra creeks.

The house she found was a two-storied cottage at the end of a short private lane, safe for the children since no carriages entered there. The rear windows looked out over the busy panorama of San Francisco Bay and directly down on the Pacific Mail docks. She leased it at once, knowing no prior parley with her husband would be necessary. The Captain could see the house from the bridge of his ship each time he sailed in, and its proximity to the company docks would permit him to come home for lunch when in port.

He was delighted with her choice which he assumed she had made because of the sight of the Bay from its windows, rather than (as was actually the case) because of its nearness to the beautiful South Park which was copied after London's Berkeley Square, its trees and central fountain surrounded by dignified houses of brick full of nostalgic reminders for her. The Captain turned his back to the park and looked out over the Bay, stroking his beard with pleasure. He spoke indirectly of the son he hoped she was carrying.

He himself had been born within sight of the sea, when his father was still skippering out of New London, he told her. It was the proper way for a sailor to begin life, breathing in salt air from the first. He arranged for a series of signals she could show from the back parlor windows, colored cloths to be hung out like flags which he could spot with his spyglass the moment he rounded North Point. White for the good health of all on board, red for any infant malady like mumps or measles and a strip of blue gingham just in case the stork beat the *Constitution* to port a few months hence, a possibility he was positive would not happen.

In August when he came around North Point, five days later than schedule, his spyglass picked up the red-and-white checked cloth from the kitchen table, the nearest thing to pink for which he had made no preparation when setting up his home-system of signal flags. But it looked like pink from a distance.

J for Jane. While Annie had been crying out for deliverance from her pain, he had been fighting a tropical storm in the Gulf of California. It had stood him up for three days. He had finally saved his ship by jettisoning cargo, casting overboard tons of baled dyes that had stained the rearing waters carmine and indigo and had inspired a lady poet among his passengers to write him a poem captioned "S.S. *Constitution* in a Storm Crossing the Gulf of California":

> *Successive waves in madness rolled,*
> *The winds their fury gave;*
> *The trembling vessel plainly told*
> *'Twas yielding to the wave.*
>
> *The gallant Captain bravely stood*
> *Close by the Pilot's wheel*

> *And watched his ship plunge through flood,*
> *Trembling from mast to keel.*
>
> *And as the storm grew fiercer still,*
> *A stern command was heard:*
> *To cast away with greatest skill*
> *The cargo overboard.*

It was his first real fan mail from a passenger and, while laboring up the coast with a damaged rudder case, believing that with luck he might yet arrive in time for Annie's delivery, he had thought how the poem would amuse her, take her mind off the travail to come, even prompt her maybe to set it to music with her rolling bass chords that so aptly imitated angry seas.

But all such thoughts stopped short when he came around North Point and swung his spyglass toward his home. The pinkish cloth flying from the rear window confused him for an instant, then with a pang he understood its message. "Another girl, by God," he muttered. Then, "Ah, my poor little Annie." He was too late to help. All she needed from him now was his booming reassurance that there could *never* be too many girls in a sailorman's family. And that, very likely, she needed in a hurry.

He made ready to leave the ship as soon as she tied up. He removed from his ditty bag the box of fine Havana cigars he had bought in Panama and stowed them away in his cabin. Annie must not see those. Not a jot of his own keen disappointment visible anywhere.

He thought of a cheering phrase as he hurried up the shortcut from the docks to the hilltop house, but it sounded unaccountably hollow. He was nervous; he had never seen Annie so soon after a birth; it must have occurred just two or three days before. Lizzie and Julia, he remembered, had been three weeks old when he saw them first, and Annie tripping about happy as a bird.

His heart beat fast when he entered the house, and almost

stopped when he saw Annie's face. The exhaustion from her labor was still written plainly upon it. All the blue in her eyes seemed to have drained into the dark purple circles beneath them and her small pointed chin, chiseled to strength like a clipper's bow, trembled with the wave of emotion that swept over her as she whispered from the bed, "I've done it again, Jack . . . a girl."

He dropped to his knees beside the bed and blew up with rage against himself. He used language of the fo'c'sle never before uttered in her presence. He cursed himself for always coming home to her "loaded like a gun" with unspent desire. He babbled of places his sailors went, even some of his officers occasionally, but never himself because he simply *couldn't*, never had, never would. "But oh my God, Annie," he cried, "I never before saw the ends of our loving, I never thought . . ." He stared at her and caught her hand moving toward his face, thrusting it away. "So help me God, I'll *never* do this again to you. Oh, my poor darling." He buried his face in the coverlets.

Presently she spoke, in a small voice but very clear and determined. "Oh yes, you will, Jack," she said. "You'll come to me *every time*. If I ever caught you going any place else . . ." Her hand played for a moment in his thick dark hair. Then she said softly, "Don't you want to see our little Jane? She has dark hair and eyes like yours, Jack, the spitting image. We're coming nearer the *exact* reproduction each time, my darling. I take heart from this. Can't you?"

Chapter 11

THE CAPTAIN REMAINED on the Panama run for the next four years, until the birth of his first son in '74. They were strange years for him, sailing that familiar coast with a monotony he had never known in his life until then. Occasionally he said that he felt like an old ferry-boat captain steering his paddler across the Bay, up the river to Sacramento and back again. But Annie's radiant happiness at his regular return was his compensation and, as she recovered from the difficult birth of Jane, he dared once more to hope that time would bring them the son they longed for.

Annie was happy with her girls. She became a familiar figure in South Park, strolling on fair days with the three of them — Jane in a buggy with Julia perched aboard it when her little legs wearied and Lizzie trotting alongside, clinging to her long full skirts. Big families were still a rare sight in that upper-crust section and often occasioned admiring comments from passers-by, one of which became a family joke. A lady new to the quarter, who had evidently heard about her, stopped her one day and asked, "Are *you* the little lady who has so many babies?" As Mrs. Farnsworth told it later to Lizzie, Annie gazed with her wide blue eyes at the questioner, who she thought had lumped her in with the free-spawning immigrants down around the waterfronts, and said with a toss of her head, "Oh no! *I* never have more than *two* babies in diapers at the same time!"

On port days she dressed them identically in the frilly white clothes she made for them and lined them up for the Captain's inspection. She could see from his face that he noted the changes. Lizzie, the princess-like firstborn, was the boss of the trio, the first to run at him and rummage through his pockets to see what surprises he brought this time from down Mexico way. Julia always thoughtfully selected from among the little painted clay figurines the one that portrayed an Indian woman with a child slung in blue *rebozo* over her shoulder. A born mother like you, the Captain said to Annie. Jane was given only shells to play with, which the Captain himself had cleaned thoroughly, since she was still in the tasting age.

He adored them. With the three on his lap, looking slightly submerged in the bouquets of ruffles and ribbons his long arms enfolded, he would forget the sea, concerned with nothing but his armful; but sooner or later he would again begin talking about it over the tops of their heads.

In October of '72 he relived the agony of the S.S. *America* which had gone up in flames in Yokohama two months before. Details of the investigation before a Consular Court in Yokohama, and of the concluding inquiry of Captain Doane in San Francisco, were appearing in the local papers. He grieved for his colleague Seth Doane and reminded Annie of the party they had had aboard the *America's* sister ship — the *Great Republic* — when he had taken over command of that China paddler from him.

It was the kind of nightmare that had always haunted him on the China runs of those inflammable wooden ships. It might have happened to him, he told Annie thoughtfully. Though Doane had been exonerated of responsibility for the fire (apparently set by arsonists) the Captain knew that his friend would never forget the sight of his million-dollar side-wheeler in flames and of his Chinese steerage passengers jumping wildly overboard with all their California-earned treasure in money-bags lashed to their bodies — thousands of dollars in gold and silver which dragged them immediately to the bottom of Yokohama Bay. Fifty-three of the fifty-nine lives lost had been gold-laden coolies.

On his next shore leave, he brought home a letter from the company's officers which he presented to Annie with only a glimmer of the pride he would ordinarily have taken in such a salary boost:

> *Agency, Pacific Mail S. S. Company*
> *San Francisco, Nov. 27th, 1872*
>
> *Capt. J. M. Cavarly*
> *Commanding Str.* CONSTITUTION
>
> DEAR SIR:
>
> In recognition of the skill, energy and good judgment displayed by you in towing the disabled Str. *Arizona* from Acapulco to this port, we take pleasure in informing you that we have advanced your pay to $4500.00 per annum, this being the highest rate of pay allowed by the Company to any of its Commanders.
>
> This increase to take effect from the commencement of your last voyage, say, October 7, 1872.
>
> Very respectfully,
> ELDRIDGE & IRWIN

Forty-five hundred a year in those days had the equivalent purchasing power of some twenty-five thousand today, but the Captain treated it as peanuts. The Big Bonanza at Pioche, Nevada, was making new millionaires in the city every month, via the Stock Exchange, many of them sailing on his ships for their victorious return back East, laden with more possessions than the overland railroad could cope with. Once the Captain had exclaimed to Annie about a certain passenger who had come out to the Coast with a cuspidor and, one year later, had gone home with a museum of Chinese art. Now, as he began figuring what he could do with his new income, he made it sound pitiful by comparison with that of the "Bonanza Boys."

But it did not seem the least pitiful to Annie as she assisted at computations that increased her household allowance to $2500 a year. Rent, wages of nurse and cook also to come out of that, said her husband gravely. With frugal management of such a sum, she knew she could emerge with a handsome annual savings. The Captain roughly estimated that eight hundred dollars a year would amply cover his own few personal expenses — uniforms, cigars and pipe tobacco and all entertainment when in port. The prospect of having something better than a thousand dollars annually to save or invest cheered him somewhat, especially after Annie reminded him that on his previous salary he had managed to purchase a life insurance, several lots in the new Western Addition and all the furniture they would ever need for the home they planned to build on one of those lots.

His moodiness about being only "an average provider" was spurred of course by the spectacle of San Francisco in the midst of her Silver Era, drunk on speculation in Nevada mining stocks with everyone from kitchen to pulpit gambling, theaters and music halls booming and the streets around the Stock Exchange so congested as to be nearly impassable when the market was open. The magic words heard in the streets — *California Mines . . . Consolidated Virginia* — must surely have taunted him with the desire to take a flyer just once; but his Yankee prudence just as surely forbade such speculation, especially for a man turning forty, with a wife and three girls to provide for and hopes for a son or two to come. That he read every news item about the "Silver Upstarts" is evident from his scrapbooks conserving them. Doubtless he allowed each one to madden him. There was the story of one stockbroker who had 365 pairs of pantaloons, one for each day of the year, all in fawn and pastel tints, all with satin stripes down the outsides of the trouser legs. There was another about a Nob Hill cook who entered her mistress's mansion each morning and hung up her shawl weighted down with a brooch holding a diamond as big as a Boston bean. It must have been a difficult time to be a sea captain on a fixed salary, however ample. That he was to leave his children so well provided for that dividends from his real-estate holdings would continue to trickle through to his grandchildren into the middle of the twentieth century was never dreamed of by him as he brooded over his sandlot holdings and watched them creep up in value against the high-leaping charts of the mining exchange.

He was to see, however, a few years later, the bursting of the beautiful silver bubble when the Comstock, after having produced one hundred and ninety million dollars in almost pure silver, was to start petering out in '77 and with it the curbside speculation that could lift a man from rags to riches overnight. Leidesdorf Street with its bucketshops and free-lunch saloons, and its back-door entrance into the Pacific Stock Exchange, was to become known as "Pauper Alley." The Captain would stroll there once or twice, with Annie on his arm, to gaze at the broken-down men and bedraggled women still haunting the narrow pavement, still dreaming of fortunes never to be made again. He would feel very well off indeed, then, with his regular pay coming in from the sea. Only in the interim between boom and bust was he sometimes a bit difficult for Annie to understand.

She believed that it was the stagnation of the Panama run that had depressed his spirits. Recently she had been reading about the wider horizons of the China run. To brush up on her French she had bought the memoir of one Baron de Hübner who had sailed on her husband's former command, the S.S. *China*. In the Baron's diary pages describing the passage from San Francisco to Yokohama, her husband had emerged full-length and three-dimensional in the domestic activities of a transpacific paddler:

> Every day at 11 in the morning and at 8 in the evening, the Captain, followed by his purser, makes his inspection of all

cabins (respecting those of the ladies in the morning) . . . but as soon as they leave their cabins, the eye of Providence, that is to say the Captain, enters. Any matches found are confiscated without pity. . . . Over the whole ship absolute cleanliness reigns. Nothing is more appetizing than to see the kitchens. The chefs do the honors here. Everywhere, the employees are found at their posts, eager to show their visitors every little corner and cubby-hole. The pantries are admirable; everything is classified, ticketed like drugs in a pharmacy. In the Oriental steerage there is a little cubby-hole reserved for opium smokers. We saw several of these victims of the deathly habit — some puffing avidly their poison, others lying out, feeling the effects of it. . . .

7 July — Instead of being somnolent, we are all the prey of great excitement. The *China* has arrived at the point where she will meet the *America* . . . the Chinese on deck look with wide eyes. The Captain and his officers are on the bridge, spy-glasses at the eye. No *America*. The Captain is in disgrace. He consults his maps. A sad dinner, we are all preoccupied for the same reason as the Captain. It appears that the Directors of the Company bet that their ships will meet. It is for them a proof that their Captains have exactly followed the route and that the ship coming from San Francisco has run without accident a third of the Pacific. For the Captain, it is a matter of personal prestige. . . .

8 July — At 5 o'clock in the morning, the *America* comes in sight. Salutes are exchanged, and a gig from the *America* brings us an extract of her log and the passenger list. Also papers from Hong Kong, Shanghai and Yokohama. But what is most essential, they take aboard the letters for the United States and Europe. . . .

Through the Frenchman's eyes, Yokohama was revealed in color and detail, in contrast to the Captain's descriptions which had generally recorded no more than the worrisome presence, or lucky absence, of fog in that distant harbor:

To right and left land is in view. Wooded hills, carpeted in grass or rice paddies — all of a green worthy of Holland. The contours of mountains suddenly revealed through the steam seem to spring out of a pot — a 1400-foot volcano floating there above. . . . Coming toward land we now see numerous little creeks under big trees, bordered by houses and filled with junks, some at anchor, some moving, sailing with enormous sails made of yellow reeds. Several of these strange ships recall the galleys that once upon a time passed by China. Standing at their bows, naked men with only a *pagne,* thrust at their poles, accompanied by chants; their supple bodies are bronzed, tattooed and their gestures develop the real beauty of their muscles. Before 8 o'clock, we are opposite the bluffs of Yokohama. At 8 o'clock exact, the *China* throws her anchor. Exactly at 9 o'clock, as we were promised in San Francisco 24 days ago, we put foot on this mysterious soil.

Annie was certain that her husband secretly longed to be back on the China run — not because of the Oriental scenery on the Far East shore, but for the challenge to his seamanship of meeting midway the opposite-traveling steamer, and the even greater challenge of arriving in Yokohama at an exact hour on an exact day, named nearly a month before on the docks of San Francisco with a Yankee nonchalance that dumfounded the passengers. "An assurance that gives a slight *frisson* . . ." the French writer had described it.

Once or twice Annie suggested to her husband that he request a transfer back to the China line, but he always shook his head. For one thing, he said, David Corwine would never relinquish him, now that he had demonstrated his ability to tow disabled steamers up the coast. More were sure to break down and Corwine liked having him in Panama ready to take over when they did. These wooden ships wore out fast; he could actually *feel* their aging when occasionally he took the helm of one he had commanded only a few years back. Beam engines and paddle wheels were much too hard on a ship's timbers. The British had discovered that the Cunard hadn't launched a paddler since '62; but the Pacific Mail went right on building its wooden side-wheelers as if iron screw steamers had never been heard of.

That's what they should have if they expected to hang on to their monopoly of the Pacific Ocean passenger and freight trade.

His worries about the condition of the fleet proved justified when the company announced it was chartering three British screw steamers to double the frequency of its sailings in response to popular demand, and was at last beginning to build its own modernized iron screw steamers. In late '73, the first of these — *Acapulco, City of Guatemala, Colima* and *Granada* — appeared in Pacific waters and the Captain had a hand at the helm of each. He began to smile again. Tensions in the Rincon Hill house relaxed. The new ships were like yachts, sturdy on their stems and brave as all get-out when they screwed their stern propellers into rough seas and drove ahead, almost, said the Captain, with the smooth feel of sail propulsion.

He was commanding the *Granada* in early '74 when Annie told him a new baby was on the way. Her blue eyes flamed with conviction when she declared that this one would be a son. It *had* to be. Things go in threes, she said positively. They had their three girls, now they were entering the era of boys!

The Captain began bringing his spyglass home to look raptly at the scenes his son would see, sometime after November, when his eyes would learn to focus on the world beyond his crib. He taught his girls to differentiate between the sloops, schooners, scows and ferries that passed back and forth over the gleaming waterway of the busy Bay. He treated the house like a crow's nest, naming every ship that passed, whether sail, side-wheeler or screw-propelled, and when he spied a clipper in tow with the pilot boat he reminded them proudly of his own early days on the clippers when he had navigated the treacherous Golden Gate currents without benefit of bar-pilots, skimming in under full sail ahead of the wind.

He ignored the pile-drivers down on the waterfront, stealing land for the city's rapid growth from the Bay itself, piling down, filling in, extending waterfront streets into mud flats where formerly only sandpipers walked. Always he directed his gaze, and that of his daughters, to the forests of masts and funnels below their windows. On sunny days, when four-masters moored in the lee of Goat Island and shook out their sails to dry, he swept his glass excitedly that way, focused it to bring up the men on the yardarms and made each of his girls look at them.

"When your baby brother arrives," he said, "you can use all this for his first picture book. *All this,*" he repeated with a sigh of deepest satisfaction.

Throughout the spring and summer of '74, with one exception, the S.S. *Granada* with the Captain at her helm bowed out the Golden Gate, sailed to Panama, discharged her passengers for the S.S. *Acapulco* waiting at the opposite end of the Isthmus, took aboard the *Acapulco's* westbound passengers and returned to San Francisco within the six weeks' period, to the day, to the dot. The exception came on March 20th when the Captain learned, in Panama, that he had been transferred to the *Acapulco* for the space of one voyage, Aspinwall to New York, replacing the Atlantic-side skipper who had fallen ill.

He saw no portent in the sudden switch that interrupted his close-to-home sailing of the past four years, a schedule he had sworn to keep until after Annie's ordeal in November. But Annie felt a flicker of premonition as she read his letter from Panama: "It's just for one voyage, my dearest, an emergency replacement. Thank God it came now instead of later."

Emergency, she whispered. One here, one there, like monsters of the deep they rose out of the sea, always, so it seemed, athwart the bows of the Pacific Mail ships. In the past year two more had gone down — the *Relief* wrecked in the Sea of Japan and the *Ariel* off Honshu in Japan. As always, there had been a wild scramble on the part of the company to find spare ships and spare captains to throw into the breach. Even from her windows she could see another costly wreck, the S.S. *Costa Rica* propped up in drydock at the Hunter's Point repair yards. Her husband

had towed her up from Acapulco with engine breakdown just
two years before; subsequently she had run ashore on Lime
Point at the entrance to San Francisco Bay, ending the Pacific
Mail's service to the Sandwich Islands after only six months of
regular sailings. Spare ships always needed and spare captains,
and now Jack, she thought. Was he the *only* skipper Corwine
could find in Panama who knew the Atlantic currents? The only
one the company could trust to run the stormy gamut off Cape
Hatteras?

"Dearest Jack," she murmured as she folded his letter. *"You*
think you'll be here in November, but I don't . . ."

Dr. McDougall nearly lost her during the birth of John, but
Maggie McLatchie withheld this fact from her announcement
telegraph to Panama in the belief that the Captain himself
would read it between the lines. A ten-pound boy delivered
from a woman normally weighing one hundred pounds would
have told the story to anyone but him, looking at the word *son*
in his message. He was ready to cast off for Acapulco when it
reached him, charged with the duty of towing back from that
port another disabled side-wheeler and a Pacific Mail coal launch
as well.

His first shock of joy so thickened his speech that his officers
thought he was drunk when he returned to his ship from the
agent's office. All they could gather at first was that ten pounds
of solid sailor had struck him amidships — ten pounds, probably
eleven by now and what did they think of *that,* by God? He
ordered rum for all hands, passed out Havana cigars to his
officers and wigwagged his happy news to every ship anchored
in Panama Bay.

In Acapulco he picked up his tow and a prim block-printed
letter from Lizzie amplifying Maggie McLatchie's message to
Panama. The new brother had yellow hair and blue eyes. He
seldom cried but when he did his voice was a foghorn. Their
mother was very tired. Doctor Mack said she must stay in bed

for at least three weeks and let herself be waited on hand and foot. She and Julia were doing just that and he was not to worry. Their mother sent her love and said for him to read *Numbers VI*.

He opened his salt-stained Bible to the book and chapter Lizzie mentioned, though he knew by heart every word of it. There in the margin in Annie's small fine handwriting was the message that always brought her close to him: *Your wife's blessing, my dear husband — Jan. 30th 1864*. She had circled the 24th, 25th and 26th verses:

> *The Lord bless thee and keep thee:*
> *The Lord make His face shine upon thee and be gracious unto thee:*
> *The Lord lift up His countenance upon thee and give thee peace.*

He read her words for him and wiped his eyes. She was telling him through their daughter that she understood the emergency that had kept him at sea despite all their earnest hope and planning; she forgave him everything, including the desolating fact that he would not be home for Christmas that year, nor would he see his son until the baby would be almost two months old.

He looked at her inscription to him on the flyleaf bearing the same date as her blessing, and remembered how, when she had presented the Bible to him, she had told him to hunt for the marked verses, the transcript of her thought for him every day and hour when he was at sea. Since then the Bible had accompanied him on every voyage and it was now marked up like an old memory book. Every allusion to the sea he had underscored in red — Solomon's Navy in *Kings*, Paul's voyages in *Acts* and all the Psalms that sang of the Lord's wonders in the deep. The Hebraic food laws in *Leviticus* were marked; from them he had learned the distinction of meats that could be offered to his strictly Orthodox passengers. Down the margins of the Second Book of *Chronicles,* he had written "Masonic," after a Freemason passenger had told him that some of the building-stones of their secret order lay in certain of those chapters. The souvenir of his passage with Queen Emma was conserved in *Ecclesiastes,* over which he had written *Steamer Sacramento, July 1866, From Panama to San Francisco,* with underscorings of Her Majesty's favorites, the chapters subcaptioned "A Time for All Things," "The Vanities of Riches Without Use," "Remedies Against Vanity, etc.," and "Rulers Are to be Respected." He turned to the Family Record and looked longingly at the blank page where the birth of his son would be inscribed; but he must wait to do that until he got home. He and Annie always made these entries together.

After a while he went up on the bridge and looked out over the beautiful bay of Acapulco through which his dauntless *Granada* labored slowly with an old side-wheeler and a coal launch in tow. He was going to try to take the two together to San Francisco so as not to have to sail down again and repeat one of these tortoise-slow trips back to the home port. His First Officer looked at him with lifted eyebrows as he studied the tension on his long towline. He told the officer to put a couple of oil bags over the stern to ease the sea on the tow, and stood watching the maneuver with his legs planted far apart, moving with his laboring ship like a part of it as he thought how one day he would tell John about that oil-bag trick, so useful in a wicked sea when towing. It fairly made his head swim to think of how much he had to pass on to that boy.

During the three-day passage from Acapulco to Manzanillo, a three hundred miles ordinarily achieved with a screw steamer in a day, he decided the double-salvage operation was too risky, and swung his helm in to Manzanillo to drop off the coal launch. The Manzanillo agent had no personal letters for him (Annie knew the towing routine, straight up the coast, no stops en route) but he had a piece of news which momentarily took the Captain's mind off the son he was crawling toward with such infuriating slowness. The great old side-wheeler, the S.S. *Japan*, had gone down off the China coast on December 11th, just six weeks ago and exactly eleven days after John's birth. By exchange of mail mid-ocean, between the remaining side-wheelers, and then by telegraph line from port to port, the grim news had at last reached Manzanillo.

The S.S. *Japan* had been on her way from Yokohama to Hong Kong under command of Captain Warsaw, heading through a rough sea when fire had broken out in the forward coal bunkers. The Manzanillo agent who had once been a Mate on the China run guessed that it had been raining in Yokohama when the *Japan* took on her coal. Stowed damp, it made a perfect medium for spontaneous combustion. More than four hundred Chinese passengers, loaded as usual with their California savings in coin and bullion, had leaped from the burning ship in the middle of the night and drowned. Twenty-three officers and crew had been lost, a diminution of the Pacific Mail family more costly, in the Captain's eyes, than the loss of all cargo, half a million in treasure and the great steamer herself. "And Captain Warsaw?" he asked tensely.

"The last to leave the burning ship," said the agent. "He's probably now in Hong Kong, facing a Board of Inquiry."

They both looked out over the water grieving, as all Pacific Mail men grieved as this somber news reached them, whether on land or at sea or passing through some tiny port like Manzanillo where you had to fire a gun to rouse the natives from their tropical torpor. The Captain wiped the sweat from his forehead and, after a long silence, said, "If the Board finds negligence, that's the end of Captain Warsaw, too, poor man." Lose your ship, lose your job was the unwritten rule of the Pacific Mail.

As he sailed on with agonizing slowness up the coast, the Captain thought of Annie reading with horror the details of the *Japan's* loss, doubtless already appearing in the San Francisco newspapers. The merciless inquiries of the ill-fated captains who lost their ships always shocked her; this one with its appalling loss of lives would be doubly shocking. It was as if a curtain were dropping down on the days of the side-wheeler after little more than a decade of pioneering the vast waters of the Pacific. The few old wooden paddlers left were being retired as fast as iron steamers could be built and brought around the Horn to take their places. And now, public opinion would clamor for a faster retirement.

For one thing he thanked God fervently. His son would never know the peculiar anxieties of a wooden side-wheeler command. By the time he would be of age, everything on the great ocean would be iron-hulled. As he gazed at the old side-wheeler at the end of his towline, with her paddles dismounted and shrouds furled, he saw her debut in the Pacific trade barely six years before — a thing of wonder then, 2700 tons of roomy side-wheeler elegance. She had come from her New York yards via the Suez Canal and Yokohama, churning her way across two oceans to reach her rendezvous in the Panama line. Over the stern of his sleek screw-propelled *Granada* she looked like a lumbering old river craft never meant for the briny deeps. John would doubtless one day look at the engraving of the S.S. *China* framed on the wall at home and ask what kind of hero or madman would take a thing like that to sea.

By the time the Captain reached San Francisco, John was the laughing plaything of his three admiring sisters, and for Annie a constant source of joy and thanksgiving. She had at last produced a son. That she had almost lost her life during the breech-presentation birth was only faintly evident now, two months later. She had to pinch her cheeks harder to bring spots of color to them and her frail body wearied quickly, but these were hidden results the Captain's eyes would never see.

"We'll pass muster with our old Fire Fiend," she whispered to her baby, staring with delight at her welcome-home present for the Captain. That John was created in her image, fair-haired, blue-eyed, with not a visible trace of the darkly handsome Cavarly traits that bespoke pride, passion and temper, would make him doubly dear to her husband, she was certain.

The first meeting of father and son was something to remember. Christine, spruce and starchy, sailed into the living room like a Valkyrie and laid the baby in its father's arms. The air suddenly grew electric with emotion. A flush of pleasure sent a ruddy glow up through the Captain's whiskers to stain more darkly his wind-tanned cheeks. A vein in his temple sprang into relief, pulsing rapidly as his black eyes explored feature by feature the small pink and white replica of Annie's face. The baby stared back at him unafraid, seemingly unmoved by his strangeness, its blue eyes round with interest. Presently it broke the silence with a series of moist chuckles and abruptly blew a big viscous bubble straight up into its father's face.

"He *spit* at me!" the Captain cried, hoarse with joy. "The lad's got spunk, by God! What a sailor *he'll* make when the time comes."

The time was already there mirrored in his dark proud eyes. As he handed the baby back to the nurse, he stretched out its two curled legs for a final glance of approval which seemed to lengthen and strengthen them so that you could imagine them already running up riggings with catlike power and agility.

The next day, overriding all their protests because it was stormy, he bundled up his son and carried him down to Kearney Street himself, to have his picture taken in Morse's gallery. He could hardly wait to show his shellback friends in every port the spunky chip off the old block who thought nothing of spitting in the Old Man's face. He pretended to Annie that the picture was for her family in the Islands and his folks in New London, and he had a poem he had clipped from the *Australian News* to back this pretension. It was entitled *The Baby's Picture*, and it read:

> *We must carry our beautiful baby to town,*
> *Some day when the weather is fair, we said,*

> *We must dress him up in the prettiest gown,*
> *And weave his hair on the top of his head;*
> *For all his cousins and all his aunts,*
> *And both his grandmothers proud and dear,*
> *Declare it's shameful and every way blameful,*
> *To have had no picture of him this year.*

And so he went to town with his boy. Annie delegated Lizzie to accompany him. "Bring him right home after the photographer," she whispered, as if confiding to her daughter the care of a drunken father.

Chapter 12

THE ONLY SHADOW over the Captain's joy was Annie's peculiar nervousness, an aftermath of childbearing he had never seen before. Queried gently about her ordeal, she became quite flighty. Whole days seemed to have dropped from her reckoning, especially after the birth, which was most unusual.

"You're not holding back anything?" he asked again and again, his brow lifting in furrows of worry. He noticed that she never looked him in the eye when she said No.

What she was holding back from him was a confession for which she could not find the right words, though she tried out different formulations each day when he went off to the docks. The one that seemed safest began, "Actually, Jack, it was on the doctor's orders . . ."

The week before John's birth, she had listened to Doctor Mack talking about a fling he was going to take in California Mines. One of his clients had just returned from Silver City in Nevada. This enterprising individual had gone down into one of the mines to see if the Big Bonanza really existed in a form more substantial than the paper certificates that flew from hand to hand in the Kearney Street exchange. Nine hundred feet beneath the surface, he had found himself standing in an immense gallery whose walls, floor and vaulted ceiling were striped with shining silver veins that flashed in the lantern light and made the whole cavern look like one of the imagined halls of King Midas. The doctor had suggested that if she had any savings from the Captain's liberal household allowance, it might not be a bad idea for her to join him in a modest speculation. It would give her, said Doctor Mack, something else to think about besides the sad news that the Captain would not be home for the birth.

In her private hoard the Captain called her "bunnit money" she actually had $900 — a sum too vast to have lying about the house at that particular time. Since she could no longer go out to place it in the bank, she put it in the doctor's hands to invest as he saw fit. "But of course we must never tell Jack," she had said. "He'd consider it treason if I looked any place else but to the sea for a little profit."

The doctor had bought ten shares of California for her, at $90 the share, on November 17th. A fortnight later, after the birth of John, it had risen to $160 a share and by December 23rd, when at last Annie was able to sit up and take notice, her stock was selling at $400 the share. The doctor's prescription of "something else to think about" proved as efficacious as an earthquake. Annie refused at first to believe that such things could happen. "It's almost immoral!" she cried, with the first spark of laughter the doctor had seen in many a week. "I'd not dare be caught with it when Jack comes home." She sold out a few days before the Captain steamed through the Golden Gate on January 17th, at $790 per share which just happened to be the top for that well manipulated swing of the fantastic mining stocks.

Though she was not in the market when she greeted her husband, she did have hidden away in her bureau drawer what seemed the total fortune of the Mining Stock Exchange — her original $900 "bunnit money," plus the profit of $7000 it had earned for her in exactly two months — the equivalent of nearly two years of the Captain's own high salary with the Pacific Mail.

And exactly how could she tell him that without hurting his pride as a good provider?

But, on the eve of his sailing, her secret became unbearable. From the day they had been married they had always been "all square yards" with each other, concealing nothing except minor health discomforts soon to pass, like throat colds on her part and twinges of rheumatism on his. He made it easy for her with his statement that she must go to Hawaii in the summer. She had certainly earned that long-postponed vacation with her family and he proposed sending her there with all the children, their nurse, and even Maggie the cook if she wished. He wanted her to travel in style as befitted the wife of a sea captain. He had the funds.

"The funds, Jack . . ." She brushed back with fluttering hands her impeccably groomed hair and began her confession. Before she was halfway through, he was roaring with laughter. That the stock she had bought at $90 the share and had sold at $790 was, that very day in February of '75, down to $50 the share was for him the cream on the cake, too rich to be swallowed without choking. He crushed the newspaper she had nervously shown him, dropped it to the floor and opened his arms to her.

"Only my little Annie could get in and out of a thing like that without losing her feathers," he cried. "And *that's* what my girl has had under her bunnit all this time!" His chest heaved with his sigh of relief. He tilted up her chin and studied her face chuckling. "Woman's intuition . . . Holy mackerel!"

She let him believe she had sold out, not through fear of his judgment of her gambling, but on a hunch, because that, she saw, was the story he could hardly wait to tell tomorrow when he would sail again to Panama, with his usual complement of suckers from back East, wiped out clean as a whistle by their plunging in mining stocks.

Next morning, with a sigh as if the weight of the world had been lifted from her shoulders, she gave him her stack of twenty-dollar gold pieces, 350 in all, to be dropped off in the bank on the way to his ship. She had them in her satin slipper-bag drawn in at the top with a pink ribbon tied in a bowknot.

"I'm keeping the original $900 to start the children's wardrobe for the Islands," she said. "This is just the profit. But I'd like the slipper-bag back, please." The Captain kept his face straight while kissing her good-by, but once out the door he loosed his stifled laughter and strode down the hill muttering, "'Well, I'll be blowed . . . By God I'll be blowed."

Preparations for the Islands turned the house upside down for the next months, sewing going on in every room, paper patterns adrift on every chair, fittings for the girls in continuous relays and Annie singing "No more San Francisco woolies!" as she snipped and pinned and handed to the dressmaker, for stitching up, the filmy white dresses, short-sleeved and low-necked such as her girls never wore except to a party, and that's how they imagined Hawaii. A gigantic party six months long. They got sick with excitement thinking about it.

Even the Captain joined in the dressmaking whirl. He had his sailmaker aboard ship tailor a sailor suit for Johnny, in white duck, with a miniature chevron on the left sleeve of the middy blouse and a real bo'sun's whistle to tuck into the middy pocket. The trousers with legs twelve inches long had bell-bottoms and a tiny flap in front that buttoned up squarely. That Johnny had not yet risen on his legs made no difference. "He'll be walking by the time he comes home," said the Captain, "I figgered the measurements accordingly."

Every mail packet from the Islands brought letters recounting progress on a new wing being added to her father's Honolulu house. Annie found herself singing Hawaiian songs again. The Pacific Mail inadvertently contributed to her joy by announcing an Australian service which would permit the Captain to visit her while in the Islands. For the first time in her sixteen years of married life the sea seemed to be cooperating in her private plans. Now she could take the long visit without any pangs of conscience that she would be depriving the Captain of the sight of his children, especially of his son, the apple of his eye.

Every news item on the Australian service confirmed her happy certainty. The mail subsidy that the Pacific Mail had obtained from the governments of New South Wales and New Zealand entailed a monthly steamer service from San Francisco to Auckland and Sydney by way of Honolulu and Fiji. Stops in Honolulu going and coming, and the contract was for ten years!

Three new steamers destined for both the Australia and China trade had already been launched from the yards of John Roach back East — the *City of San Francisco, City of New York* and *City of Sydney*. The Captain would most certainly win the helm of one of those when they arrived in Pacific waters. She saw ahead a decade of frequent reunions with her family and at a time, now, when it would be the most fun to have them. Both her sisters Mary and Julia had married and their first children had been born — to be compared, she thought laughingly, with her own incomparable four. The Islands swarmed with aunts, uncles and doting grandparents to enrich her children's lives which had always seemed so peculiarly lonely in San Francisco, relationless as seeds blown far from the family tree.

Uncle, aunt, cousin were indefinite words to Julia and Jane, who thought that all families ended with father and mother, like theirs. Annie showed them the relatives they were soon to see — "And *belong to,* mind you!" she said as she turned the pages of the family photograph album and pointed from beard and bustle of the people they were to meet. "Here's your Grandmother Bolles — she looks a little stern but that's only because she hates having pictures taken. Here's Grandfather Bolles, always with a little dog — you remember him when he visited us? Here's Julia's namesake, my sister Julia, a born singer . . . and dear little forthright sister Mary! And Frank, my handsome brother — he speaks Hawaiian, fancy that! I think he'll be your favorite uncle, so gentle and soft-spoken . . ." It sounded like singing as she described the natures, gifts and peculiarities of each.

The Captain added his own recommendation of people he wanted his children to know and respect. Their Uncle John by marriage, Aunt Julia's husband — they must never forget he was a Paty, a great name in the Pacific. Captain John Paty, his father, had been one of the finest skippers of his day. He had gone to sea as a lad of fifteen, won his first command at twenty-one and had settled in the Islands in 1834, to sail the Pacific waters for the remaining thirty-three years of his life. Between California and the Islands alone, he had skippered 168 voyages, more passages than any man had ever made, and all without loss. "You look at Captain Paty's picture when you visit your Aunt Julia's house," he said to his girls. *"There* was a man!"

He had booked passage for them on the packet line that Captain Paty had established. He sighed to think that the great old skipper himself was no longer at the helm. "John would have got something from him," he said wistfully. "Aye, aye . . . even at his tender age."

"When the time is ripe, Jack dearest, he'll get something from *you,"* Annie said. She could hardly bear to look at her husband on their last night at home, with the golden bundle of his son on his lap, his chin nuzzling the top of the baby's head. She lowered her eyes to the pile of children's socks she sorted. One more look at father and son and she'd have given up Hawaii on the instant.

Hawaii was the progressive house party the girls had imagined it would be. Their mother seemed to become younger than they had ever seen her, in her father's house, laughing and singing, her long white skirts swirling about her slender ankles when she danced with her brother Frank whom she obviously adored, and for whom she waged a pitched battle with her parents and swarms of visiting relatives after Frank announced he was going to marry a Hawaiian girl. "If any of you *dares* to be rude to her," she cried at them, "I'll have at you with tooth and nail — why, the very idea!" To start the ball rolling she herself invited the lovely dark-eyed girl to her father's house and introduced her to Lizzie, Julia and Jane as if she were a princess, which she was by hereditary right. Her Hawaiian name sounded like *lily* and they all fell in love with her, easy as falling off a log. "She'll be our new aunt in the spring," Lizzie told Julia and Jane. "Imagine having a Hawaiian aunt!"

Their Grandfather Bolles with his white spade beard and twinkling black eyes looked like God. He loved youngsters and would sometimes invite the children of Chinese merchants who would wade with them in the creek at the foot of the garden that had little lava-stone bridges arching across it and great flowering trees above, full of colored birds and queer seed pods.

Grandfather's house was named Kapena Place, for the waterfall in the tropical gorge behind it. Its front lawn, giving out on Nuuanu Road, was nearly as big as South Park back home, bisected by a long private driveway guarded by a dozen royal palms on each side — silver-gray sentinels, arrow-straight, capped with fronds like ragged umbrellas. It took the children days just to explore the gardens, under the watchful eye of Christine. Often their mother joined them, usually at the hour when Grandfather was due home from his chandlery. When he brought letters from the Captain, she read them to the girls under the monkey-pod tree. She laughed herself to tears over one of his descriptions of how he and Maggie were making out; he had taught Maggie how to make real Boston baked beans, simmering them slowly in warm water with molasses and mustard, then putting in the pork and baking them for a long time, with one small green onion added for proper flavor.

In the context of their own magical existence, their father's bleak life on Rincon Hill, eating Boston baked beans, seemed pitiful to the girls, living so much more bountifully. Any time they became thirsty, the Bolles' stableboy whose name was Jim, pronounced Kimo in Hawaiian, opened coconuts from which they sucked the delicious milk through straws. Pineapples, bananas and strawberries were always available in Grandmother's cooler. And when they went to town with Grandfather, they nibbled at many a strange delight in his big dim warehouse.

The Bolles chandlery was on Queen Street, down on the waterfront. Even Lizzie lost some of her poise the first time Grandfather took the sisters through it. The great warehouse was filled with ship's provisions and naval stores, horse and cattle feed and sacks of wheat and rice for human consumption, including Golden Gate Flour manufactured by Horace Davis & Co. of San Francisco (Julia read the labels to Jane) and pyramided tins of the Celebrated Pacific Rubber Paints, also manufactured in San Francisco. There were hogsheads of sperm oil, tins of kerosene and all manner of Chinese goods in bamboo crates. From the Chinese foodstuffs, Grandfather gave them samplings of candied watermelon sweet and oily, of coconut crisped into snowy white curls, of strange nuts he called *lee-chee* that had crinkled brown shells paper-thin and a chewy datelike meat inside surrounding a smooth black kernel they had to be careful not to swallow.

The whole Pacific seemed to be concentrated in the cool multi-odored warehouse. Teas and tallow, hides and honey, were identifiable both by sight and scent, but there were many strange edibles they had to guess at three times before Grandfather would enlighten them — *poi* in calabashes (which the Hawaiians ate), a dried fungus from decayed kokui trees (which the Chinese ate) and gourds of soy sauce (which the Japanese ate). Over all drifted the prevalent pungence of tar.

Driving home from the warehouse, Grandfather took roundabout ways to show them the sights of Honolulu town and to teach them something of the kingdom's history which he made to sound like Viennese operetta. The present King, Kalakaua, he called The Merry Monarch. His Highness could drink any man under the table, win the shoes off his feet at cards and had just returned from a triumphal tour of the United States in the palace car of President Grant who had received him in Washington with full honors. It was a storybook world Grandfather Bolles opened up for the girls. The royal household troops parading on Palace Walk looked like toy soldiers. The King's new boathouse on the waterfront was a play pavilion. His royal Hawaiian band, with its bandmaster Berger imported from Germany in '72 — "to lend style to the Hawaiian court," said Grandfather with a chuckle — was a scarlet and gold flash of splendor.

For Annie there was no strangeness. Honolulu seemed to her like an enchanting segment of New England set down on a tropical shore, and it actually was like that in the mid-Seventies. ". . . a very accurate reproduction of New England country scenery," Charles Nordoff had described it in his *Harper's Magazine* articles of 1873. "The white frame houses with green blinds, the picket-fences whitewashed until they shine, the stone walls, the small barns, the scanty pastures, the little white frame churches scattered about . . . are all New England, genuine and unadulterated. And you have only to eliminate the palms, the bananas and other tropical vegetation to have before you a fine bit of Vermont or the stonier parts of Massachusetts." Every home Annie visited had a piano and sewing machine, four-poster beds, hooked rugs, horsehair sofas and whatnots, all brought around the Horn by Puritan Yankees like her father who had changed nothing but their latitudes when they transplanted themselves to these coral shores.

By Thanksgiving, Annie was already picturing her Captain in the Fijis. As reports of the *Vasco da Gama's* maiden voyage on the new Australia run filtered into the Hawaiian papers, she read them aloud to her children, concentrating on the Fijis, the most romantic of the ports their father would soon be visiting. A passenger's letter from Kandavau described the anchorage inside the reef in the beautiful Ngaloa Bay fringed with breadfruit trees and coco palms and filled with native dugouts vending bananas, yams, pineapples, coconuts and Fijian crafts of all description. The local nobility in warrior canoes followed the native peddlers out to the ship — chiefs and princesses whom the Pacific Mail captain entertained aboard with elaborate dinners and flowery speeches. "The natives," wrote this globe-trotting reporter, "are generally large, well-fleshed, and symmetrically built, and possess a certain combination of manliness and modesty which conciliates the good opinion of the stranger." *Conciliates* — draws opposites together in friendship, Annie explained, since the natives went about nearly naked, save for a few ornaments of feathers and sharks' teeth. It was difficult for the girls to imagine their father at the head of the captain's table, surrounded by nearly naked brown bodies. But that, said their mother, was exactly what he would do on *his* voyage out.

Shortly after the turn of the year the harbor flags of Honolulu signaled the arrival of the S.S. *Granada* with the Captain at her helm. Grandfather Bolles said she had a large cargo for Honolulu and would probably lay over a week to discharge it and also to give its globe-trotting tourists a chance to see the sights — the Pali, the Punchbowl and Waikiki.

Lizzie and Julia, aged nine and seven, were old enough to take in and retain the impressions of their father's first real vacation with his family. In later years, they often described for the younger ones how the gay easy nature of the Islands had affected him, bringing out a kind of youthful playfulness they never had seen before. Even his quarterdeck voice changed to a mellower tone. "And the clothes he wore then!" Lizzie would say. "Like a happy old beachcomber, *really!*"

The prelude was his white ship coming into the harbor, dressed bow to stern with pennants — ripples of color against the bright blue sky soon matched below by eddies of pink and yellow hibiscus strewn over the waters by the greeter canoes. They were all on the dockside for the welcome, dressed in white, all wearing the plaited palm-leaf hats Lizzie and Julia had learned to make under the guiding hands of their Grandmother's Hawaiian house-keeper. Their mother picked up Johnny and held him high in her arms so that the figure on the bridge with spyglass at the eye could see at once her face and the boy's. Lizzie reminded her sisters that they were not to rush at their father with the news that Johnny could walk. The Captain was to discover that for himself. As a surprise, their mother had said.

A band aboard ship struck up a Strauss march as the gangway dropped over the side. The Captain leaped down, his eyes alight, his beard dark against his white duck tunic. He came straight through the crowd to Annie, kissed her first, then tried to take them all in his arms at once. There was a *mêlée* of palm-leaf hats, a transfer of burden and then Johnny was in his arms alone, staring up at the gold braid on his cap, with one fat brown hand clutching the beard beneath it.

"He *remembers* me!" the Captain said.

He swept their upturned faces with a look of gratitude, as if each one of his girls had had some mysterious hand in keeping Johnny's memory of him alive during the six-months separation. They knew it was the gold braid on him that kept his stranger-shy son plucking at him familiarly, but they smiled sweetly back at him, like the responsible elders his grateful glance had made of them.

Thus their holiday with their father began — "With no fog-horn howls from the brat and everything serene fore and aft," as Lizzie said afterward. Johnny had lit the first candle of joy in the Captain's heart. After his came the candles and Japanese lanterns of the Bolles' garden party the first night, the flaming native torches of the Patys' *luau* for him the second night, and every-where through it all was the firefly flash of their mother's dia-mond earrings, bright stabs of light that drew the Captain's eyes over lanterns and smoking torches and, once, even over the sizzling flares of Chinese fireworks, as if, for him, from those two discreet points of sparkle all other illumination originated.

One night the girls actually saw him dance. Impelled by the gaiety natural to Annie's family, and quite possibly lubricated by a Holland plum gin he had brought from his ship, the Captain flung into a sailor's hornpipe for the assembled guests. His daughters peering down from the upstairs landing could scarcely believe their eyes. Everyone clapped and their mother trilled the turns as he folded one arm over his midriff and one behind in the small of his back, and pranced like a young tar around and around the room, grinning at his bearded friends from town as they tapped their toes in remembrance of their own stints on British lime-juicers. He was light as a feather on his feet and apparently inexhaustible. Again and again he beckoned to a crony to join him but no man in the room would stand up to his pace.

Jane asked in a whisper why he wasn't like that at home, and Lizzie and Julia hissed her to silence. They knew they were seeing him as he used to be — a sailor boy before the mast who had picked up the hornpipe jig in English ports and had learned to dance it well to please his mates. That was long before the cares of command had taken all the dance out of him, long before he gained the quarterdeck and found himself mateless and alone.

In the lamplight below, steady and bright from clean wicks, their father's comical hornpipe suddenly turned into the loneliest performance they had ever seen. Looking like a boy prematurely bearded, a boy before the mast flinging up his arms and kicking his heels high, he seemed to be practicing for the later solitary pacing of a ship's bridge wherein all exuberance would be confined to springy steps back and forth, port to starboard, taut with watchfulness. Did their mother think the same thing just then? Was that why she suddenly put her handkerchief to her eyes and cried out, "Jack . . . Oh Jack, I can't stand another minute of it!"

He stopped short before her and put out his hand. Pulling her to her feet, he led her toward the French windows that gave out to the veranda. "We'll just take a little turn about the deck, Annie and I," he said to guests and relatives clapping for encores. "Keep the ship on course till we come back!"

The Hawaiian night shone star-bright through holes in the dark curtain of the porch vines. The girls waited until their parents vanished in the shadows, then Lizzie whispered, "Come on back to bed. There's nothing more to see."

Daytimes he dressed in old, easy clothes — cotton shirt open at the neck, cotton trousers uncreased and a white canvas hat with a beaten brim that drooped about his whiskered face. He drove them several times to town in this regalia, and once he drew up stylishly before the King's boathouse to which he had entree and the loan of any racing boats that pleased his fancy. He settled Annie under a parasol on the pavilion and took his children for a spin around the harbor in a catboat, handling tiller and sail himself, with Johnny clamped between his knees and the three girls jumping from starboard to port at his command on each tack. He brought them back to the boathouse bone-dry, as he had promised Annie he would do and when Johnny shrieked at being separated from the white sailboat, his day was made.

"Salt water in his veins, by God!" he exclaimed to Annie as he hoisted the boy to his shoulders and trotted down the beach to give him a look at the outrigger canoes drawn up on the sand.

He sailed for the Fijis and Australia two days later and they all wept to see him go. They had thought the beautiful life would go on forever. Their nurse Christine clucked sympathetically. She was already brown as a Kanaka for she was a Swede who believed in sun-bathing and, when sitting with them in the garden, exposed as much of her tall Viking body as decorum would allow.

"He won't be back here to pick us up for two months," Christine said. "That's more than sixty whole days. Let's all be happy with what we've got."

But how could sixty more days be enough? So much still to see, to do, and do again and again, like the afternoon rides with their grandfather. Usually around four, Kimo the stableboy hitched up the black stallion Zu-Zu for the long run down Nuuanu Road to the waterfront warehouse where Grandfather joined them (a bag of different sweetmeats in his hands each time) and took the reins. From the foot of Nuuanu all the way out to Diamond Head ran carriage tracks shaded by algaroba trees. These were the "plains" where he always let Zu-Zu go like the wind. Hawaiians living in grass houses along the way waved as they flew past. In the shadow of Diamond Head lay the coral crescent of Waikiki Beach, the King's domain, with his summer pavilions and a few beach houses set back from the water's edge, hardly enough civilization to disturb the feeling that you were alone on a tropical shore listening to breakers crash over the reef a half mile out. After the race to Waikiki, Zu-Zu would stop and look around at their grandfather, wrinkling his nose for sugar, and he would speak to the stallion as to a person. "So you think we've had enough? You think we should turn back, Zu-Zu? Well . . . perhaps you're right." And he would touch the whip to the black flank and bring Zu-Zu around for the long run home.

Back in Kapena Place, the house and garden always spilled over with visiting relatives finishing their tea — cousins from Maui, uncles from Kauai, a great-aunt maybe come up from the Big Island to see "Benjamin Bolles's famous grandchildren from the mainland." They were famous, and they belonged. When they had washed off the red dust and put on fresh dresses, they went to the parlor, grouped about their mother and sang "Over the Banister Leans a Face" or "When Irish Eyes Are Smiling" for their Island relatives. They had well-trained voices, Lizzie, Julia and Jane. Annie had seen to that.

In some ways the nights were best of all. Then their grandfather told stories, not just for his assembled grandchildren, but for his own grown-up children as well. He was an inimitable story-teller; his black eyebrows lifted like exclamation marks when he came to the climax of his yarns and he would always pause then, for a moment of agonizing suspense, and look around his listen-

ing circle with twinkling eyes. There was the story of the shark in
the Lahaina channel that an old fisherman had tamed to rise from
the deeps, when he drummed on the bottom of his boat, and take
a fish from his hand, yes-sirree. The shark waited for his friend to
come out each day to feed it; it wouldn't touch a fish not *handed*
to it by the old fisherman and once, when he lay ill, that old shark
practically starved to death swimming desolately about in schools
of fish. . . . Nobody of course believed the fisherman's story until the shark took to rising beneath other fishing boats, thumping
against their bottoms with the same signal his food-bearer had
used to summon him up, scaring the tar out of the unbelievers
you could bet your boots! Then there was the time when the good
missionaries first inveigled their female converts into wearing
Mother Hubbards — but Grandmother Bolles shushed him to silence on that one.

In the last week of March their mother started to pack the
trunks, slowly, a few garments at a time, mainly the summer
clothes that went in at the bottom. The top trays were for the
San Francisco woolens sunning out back after a half-year of being
closeted with moth balls. She smiled brightly at their stricken
faces.

"This was only the beginning of our visits," she said. "We'll
have many many more. Your father's on the Australia run now,
thank heavens. Maybe for ten years."

The girls looked at her doubtfully. Nothing with the Pacific
Mail had ever remained settled for ten years. Nothing in their
parents' lives had had such continuity. *Something* would happen
in San Francisco and they wouldn't be able to return to the
Islands for years.

Among themselves they discussed events that might delay the
return passage. If one of them became too sick to be moved, for
instance; but that seemed far-fetched when they looked at each
other's healthy faces. Even Lizzie whose frail health had always
been a family concern was brown as an Indian. Johnny listened

round-eyed as they switched from their own health to that of their father's ship. A slight disabling calling for prolonged repairs in Honolulu would be ideal. Then they'd have him with them also. Not a wreck, mind you, good gracious no! Just a minor break-down somewhere in the bowels of the ship in a place difficult to get to. Papa wrecked? Heavens-to-Betsy no!

"Papa wecked!" Johnny cried, picking up their words like a lit-tle parrot. None of them saw Annie's white face looking in the door; they were staring in stupefaction at their brother. "Papa wecked!" he trilled again, pleased at the attention he was getting. Annie flew like a fury into the nursery and snatched him up from the contamination of their talk. She held him against her crying, "Look what you've taught him — his first words, oh my God. How *could* you . . . oh, oh, how *could* you?" And she fled with him before one of them could open her mouth to explain.

They worked on him in the next days to undo the evil they had inadvertently wrought. They allowed him, for once, to pick the goldfish out of Grandmother's pond and almost squeeze them to death in his fat fist, while they cried, "Goldfish, Johnny, *gold-fish!*" It wouldn't take. He remained mum. "If we could just put another word into him," Lizzie said, "he might forget that w-r-e-c-k," she spelled. "Maybe he has already," Jane said. Julia shook her head and repeated her mother's maxim about infant intelligence: "Wax to receive, iron to retain."

Julia tried another tack; she talked to Johnny of the presents their father had promised from the Fijis. Never having seen any-thing of Fijian origin, she had to use her imagination. She pre-tended to weave feathers and sharks' teeth into necklaces and anklets and presented the imaginary gifts to her brother saying each time, "Look out for the teeth, Johnny. They're *sharp!*"

"Sarp" he repeated after her, rolling his eyes.

"He's got a word!" Julia whispered and proceeded to show him what sharp was. She took his small palm and pricked it lightly with her embroidery needle. "Sharp — like *this!*" then gave him a real jab. They stopped his howling by pricking themselves, each sister in turn. Julia brought a fleck of blood to the ball of her thumb and squeezed it up to a red bead before his delighted eyes. "Sharp . . . ooh!" she said, and they all heaved a sigh as he repeated again the new word planted in him to take the place, they hoped, of wreck.

"You have to draw blood to get him to remember anything," Lizzie remarked as a guide for future teaching.

Luckily, they had taught him the perfect word for the present the Captain brought to him a week later — a little Fiji war club carved of black wood with sharks' teeth set into its tip. Their father looked flabbergasted when Johnny patted the curved white teeth and said, "Sarp . . . ooh!" Until that moment all he had ever heard from his son was gibberish which only Jane could interpret.

"Did he say *sharp?*" the Captain asked, looking at his girls as if the sky had fallen. Oh yes, they replied in chorus. He picks up things fast, Papa. He probably heard us talking about our sewing scissors.

The radiant smile on the Captain's face washed away their feeling of guilt. He nodded approvingly, giving them full credit for having lifted their brother in one swoop into the realm of intelligible human speech.

"That's a real sailor's word, son," he said happily. He swung Johnny over his head and looked up at the cherubic face murmuring, "Look sharp aloft, son — keep a sharp eye on that war club!" And someday, said his proud eyes, you'll know how to keep a sharp lookout ahead.

In many ways, the trip home aboard their father's command was more revealing to the girls than had been their wonderful vacation with him in Honolulu. Here on the *Granada* he was in his element, master of all he surveyed. When he walked the decks with them, his sailor's gait that looked odd on land appeared so absolutely right that they tried to copy it so they might walk erect as he did, balanced and easy from swell to swell. They saw the enormous respect he commanded from his officers with whom he spoke as through a pane of glass, clear, cold and polished. Though his passengers looked ready to fall at his feet, especially the ladies, he gave them no more than a courteous nod when he encountered them during the daily constitutional around the promenade deck. He made the girls feel like princesses, walking with their father, the king. His evident rejoicing in their company made them think sometimes of all his voyages without them.

The loneliness of command which their mother had stressed so often became very apparent to Lizzie and Julia. They saw him then as he usually was, stalking alone, with eyes in the back of his head watching everything on board, and ears attuned exclusively to the normal running sounds of his ship. Evenings, in the privacy of his quarters, his huge delight that they were all on board with him seemed to underline still further the monkish life he customarily led when they were home on land.

After dinner (the children taking theirs in the cabin with Christine, and their mother hers in the dining saloon with the Captain) their father was like a genial and generous host throwing open to them his home on the high seas. He invited them to help themselves to sweets from his private pantry, to books from his shelves, and he always asked their mother, with a ceremonious bow and a twinkle in his eyes, just which liqueur Madame would prefer tonight.

Their mother, seated under a lamp with her embroidery, made his quarters seem a little less masculine. Though none of the furnishings belonged to him, they all somehow bore his stamp — the massive desk polished to mirror brightness, the leather armchairs built for big bodies, the thick carpet with ornate flowered design and the bracketed lamps with Bohemian-glass shades. Not a drape or flounce in the whole place, not a feminine touch anywhere unless you looked in the wardrobe of his adjoining bedroom and saw Annie's dresses and ruffled Victorian nightgown hanging beside his rows of immaculate uniforms.

For the first half-hour he always held Johnny on his knees,

watching the clock not to keep him up past his bedtime, while the three girls took turns occupying the wide arms of his leather chair. He would query them on their adventures of the day, what birds or sea beasts they had glimpsed over the ship's rails, what new quarters of the ship they had explored under the guidance of his steward. He corrected them gently when they said "downstairs" for *below* or "back" for *aft,* watching Johnny's face as it turned from sister to sister repeating the new words he taught. And hoping always, the girls knew, that his boy would murmur one after him, as once he had said "sharp."

The muted rhythm of the big ship churning through the night, the chimes of her bells telling nautical time and the occasional hoot of her steam whistle greeting a passing vessel, intruded faintly into their happy chatter — a lonely sort of background music when you stopped to think that if *you* were not there in the cabin, those hoots and bells would be all that the Captain would ever hear during the months of nights when he was at sea.

Julia stopped often to think. Inevitably, then, her tender gray eyes wandered to the built-in shelves opposite the big desk, whereon in neat rows stood all their photographs at every age — Lizzie's at the top, hers on the middle shelf and Jane's and Johnny's on the bottom shelf — only one of him to date. When the Captain sat writing his letters to them, that was what he looked at, a gallery of faces arranged chronologically. Julia had always wondered how he managed to keep track of them with such intimate precision. Now she knew.

Only their mother was not permitted to grow up, photographically. There was just one picture of her, in a double frame with his, which stood on the desk. It was the small full-length portrait he had rescued when the Rebels had sunk his last clipper ship, the *Anglo-Saxon.* She was a new bride when it was taken, aged twenty-one. But he really didn't need any subsequent photos, Julia concluded. Their little mother had hardly changed through all those years. Delicate, blonde and petite, the framed figure beneath the lamp might just have sat down among them aboard the S.S. *Granada.* Only a change in bodice and coiffure marked the passage of the intervening years. The wasp-waist and neck curls of the bridal days were no longer fashionable.

One night the Captain spoke to his girls as if Annie were not there, though his eyes followed her movements as she threaded colored silks in her needle and stitched them into a complicated tapestry that appeared to require her total concentration.

"Your mother turns out to be quite a sailor on these steamers," he said. "If my observations are correct, she hasn't missed a day on deck since we left Honolulu. Which, if I may say so, is quite a contrast to our days of sail, *quite* a contrast." He combed his beard up through his fingers, lifting his chin with satisfaction. "I'm mighty pleased that this is so. Now I know that my big wish can came true. I've never spoken to Mrs. Cavarly about this . . ." He tore his eyes from her and grinned at his daughters. This was the kind of play between their father and mother they adored. Annie wet a tip of silk at her lips and threaded it into her needle, stone-deaf as far as facial expression was concerned.

"What I've dreamed ever since Miss Annie Bolles stepped aboard my first command," their father continued, "was that one day she and I would sail around the world together. That would be, of course, after all you girls are married and Johnny an apprentice seaman aboard some ship. I want to show your mother every port, every coastline, every strait between oceans — all the wonders I've seen!" He shut his eyes and recited his favorite Psalm:

> *They that go down to the sea in ships, that do*
> *business in great waters:*
> *These see the works of the Lord, and his wonders*
> *in the deep . . .*

Then he squinted at his wife engrossed in her tapestry. "There are whole islands off yonder like those wreaths we saw floating in

Honolulu harbor. There are headlands that make Diamond Head look picayune. And ports — Yokohama, Hong Kong, Macao, Aden — friends in all of them who would receive your mother like a queen. That's my dream . . . to take her around the world when all you children are grown up and on your own." He tugged his beard and looked at their faces shining with approval. "Will Mrs. Cavarly consent, do you think?" he asked them wistfully.

Still playing his game that their mother was not in the cabin they cried, "Oh yes, Papa, she certainly will consent!" They saw the horizons of the seven seas opening out about her, as their father named ports to be touched on their Grand Tour.

It would probably, Annie thought, take years for him to show her everything he had seen, years of no child worries, no household cares; years of companionship coming to them both like bread upon the waters. That was the *real* reward — no more loneliness for him, no more anguish for her imagining him going down with his ship in some distant ocean. Annie looked up when the Captain finished, her mouth open but no words emerging. Her eyes spoke for her, flashing consent, amazement, anticipation, then she bent quickly to her work to hide the flush she felt creeping up above her high lace collar.

"Mrs. Cavarly consents!" said the Captain, striking his thigh. "And don't you girls ever let her forget it! You're my witnesses, do you hear? Lizzie? Julia? Jane?"

"Aye aye, Sir!" they replied to his voice of command.

They docked in San Francisco on the 15th of April in '76. One of the new Pacific Mail steamers, the S.S. *City of New York,* built the year before for the Australia trade, was tied up at the company docks. The Captain brought his family to the bridge to have a look at the three thousand tons of floating luxury. He had a surprise in store for them.

"That's my new command," he said. "I'm taking her to Australia two weeks from today."

He gave Annie his letter of reassignment which the pilot boat had brought out to the *Granada*. As she read it, the girls stood close to her, staring over the water at the huge white steamer — a three-decker with many outside staterooms and a permanent wooden awning over a part of the splendid promenade. On the hurricane deck there appeared to be an immense social hall well aired by plate-glass skylights mounted in heavy polished brass.

Their mother looked up from the appointment letter and said, "I'm *so* proud for you, Jack!" her smiling eyes cloudless as a summer sky. "She's a real leviathan." She nodded approval as she studied the powerful screw steamer, her glance running from spar deck aft, along the covered promenade beneath the deck house and forward to the sharp graceful bow, a scrutiny she made seem quite nautically professional when she added, "At least three hundred and fifty-five feet over all, I'd say."

The Captain beamed. "You almost hit it exact, Annie! Just two feet too many . . . she's three fifty-three feet long, forty wide on the beam." He grinned at his daughters. "Your little mother's got a wondrous sharp eye for ships," he said.

"Only for *your* ships," Lizzie corrected him under her breath.

Chapter 13

SIGHT-SEEING PASSES for the S.S. *City of New York* were at a premium during the fortnight she was tied up in San Francisco, taking on cargo for Australia. The Captain was irked by the strangers poking about his ship, the reporters with land-lubber questions and the photographers cluttering the saloons with their bulky paraphernalia. He waited until it was closed to the public, to show his own family his new command. "So we can have it all to ourselves," he said expansively.

And, if they had *not* had it all to themselves, Lizzie said afterwards, Annie would never have given the impromptu concert in the grand social hall — a concert that was like a wonderful musical charade, the high point of their steamer visit, most certainly.

They went aboard expecting luxury and were not disappointed. They followed their father over the immaculate decks, looking in at a Gentlemen's Smoking Room finished in black walnut, mahogany and blistered maple; at staterooms furnished with rosewood berths, marble-topped washstands, steam heaters, mirrors and plush sofas. In the stateroom hall they stood agape under the elegant skylight, staring at silver-plated handrails around the sides — "Aids to passengers' navigation in a heavy seaway," the Captain explained matter-of-factly. Johnny's restless feet could not tramp a sound from the miles of deep-piled velvet carpet they traversed. Annie's cries of delight quickened as they trooped down a solid mahogany staircase and entered the grand saloon and dining hall. The local reporter who had written, "We think this grand apartment is the richest one of its kind in existence," had not exaggerated.

There were velvet carpets on the floor, velvet seats along the sides, handsome wall lights set every four feet into elliptical recesses finished in choicest butternut, maple and ebony; elegant chandeliers overhead ("burning Mineral Sperm Oil" said their father) and eight polished mahogany tables to seat the one hundred first-class passengers the ship carried. They looked in wonder at the frescoed ceiling, the cornices of satinwood, amaranth and gilt and the huge plate mirrors gold-framed, set into the four corners of the saloon — quadrupling its glitter, quadrupling them standing spellbound, quadrupling Johnny making faces at himself in one of them — the only member of the family not momentarily knocked galley-west by all the glory.

The Captain said after a bit, "Come along, children, we've got more," and tucked Annie's arm under his for the climb back up the mahogany stairs, through the stateroom hall and aft toward another staircase that led up to what he called "our grand social hall" on the hurricane deck. The final staircase was a marvel of beauty with immense mahogany newel posts inlaid with walnut and striped with gold. It gave into a hall some forty-five feet long, crowned with a frescoed dome, carpeted in rich velvet with a black and gold design and lit by a series of crystal chandeliers. From the doorway Annie spied at once the Steinway grand at the far end and broke away from the Captain, to walk alone across the hall. Midway, she began bowing to imaginary passengers sitting to right and left on the crimson velvet sofas. The girls took their charade cue and entered the hall, no longer sight-seers gaping at unaccustomed grandeur.

They were passengers now; they had been weeks at sea on their way to the Antipodes and were a bit bored with each other's company. Haughty, slightly aloof one from the other, they took their places separately, each on a velvet sofa alone. There were enough for all the family, including Christine. She sat in her dark street uniform with Johnny beside her (obviously some rich man's son traveling with his governess). Annie stood before the lovely little Steinway and removed her gloves. She was the gifted passenger who just happened to be traveling with them that trip. She turned once and gave them a preoccupied little bow. Then she spun the velvet-tufted piano stool down so her small feet could reach the pedals without stretching. She didn't bother to tell them she would start with a Chopin Ballade. They knew; they had been there before . . . always this particular pianist began with Chopin.

The Captain remained in the doorway, just as he always did — simply looking in on his passengers whiling away another evening at sea. The lady pianist played two Ballades, looking up at the frescoed dome, playing, you would have said, not to those enchanted miniature women behind her, but to the mythological figures overhead, painted in purples, pearly grays and carmine, representing the four seasons. You knew from the Captain's rapt face that he was aware of an extra talent in this generous, most gifted passenger, and that he was waiting for it to be displayed. And presently it was. The pianist lifted her hands high from the keyboard, turned about on the velvet stool and said with a slight but cultivated Irish accent, "I will end as always with one little song, 'Macushla.' "

Her daughters exchanged enraptured glances as her lovely voice soared yearning to the painted ceiling . . . *Macushla, Macushla, your sweet voice is calling, Calling me softly, again and again* . . . This was how it would be on her round-the-world trip. In gilded and frescoed saloons like this one, soft lit by crystal lamps, velvet-soft underfoot, a hushed audience listening with delight to old songs, homesick-making on distant seas. Their happy eyes flashed signals — Jane's brown, to Julia's gray, to Lizzie's blue. The Grand Tour!

A low howl from Johnny broke the spell. The howl rose to a

shriek as he stared at his singing mother, his blue eyes round with fright. Jane got to him first, knelt before his sofa, wrapped arms about him and listened to his sobbing gibberish. No, no, Johnny! she murmured. She isn't, she *isn't* . . . and over her shoulder she said to her mother, Take your hat off, Mummy. He's never seen you sing with your hat on. He thinks you're going away!

So ended their sight-seeing tour of the S.S. *City of New York* on a gale of laughter, Annie with her hat in hand, the Captain wiping his eyes as he strode down the long hall to take Johnny on his shoulders and Christine babbling thankfully that it was only her mistress's new Easter bonnet and not the acute appendicitis she thought had struck her darling.

Johnny was not yet two when the Captain sailed for Australia three days later. He was to be nearly two years older when his father was reassigned to the China service. He saw the Captain at two- or three-month intervals between the Australia trips, but, thanks to the working over the sisters gave him just before the *City of New York* would dock, he appeared to remember his parent perfectly, which was all that was needed, as Lizzie said, "to make the Old Salt's homecoming cup run over with joy."

During those years there were certain events which the sisters hoped made no imprint on Johnny's memory, since they could hardly be calculated to instill a love for the sea. They were careful how they talked about them in his presence, afterwards. "Never say anything in front of him you'd not want the little parrot to repeat" was Lizzie's watchword to Julia and Jane.

In May of '77 the S.S. *City of San Francisco,* sister ship of the *City of New York,* struck a rock off Tartar Shoal on the Mexican coast and sank within one hour and ten minutes, a total loss. First news of it came out of New York, via telegraph from Mexico City, relayed to San Francisco. A Mexican gunboat allegedly had taken off all 137 passengers, Captain Waddell and his entire crew, and had landed them in Acapulco whence they would be brought to San Francisco by the S.S. *Costa Rica*. It was only a column-inch story buried in the maritime news and immediately beneath it a brief item, datelined San Francisco, said no word had as yet been received from the overdue steamer but that the local agents had no apprehensions; she was probably detained in some way port. Annie read the conflicting stories aloud to her daughters in a choked voice and said, *"What* this will do to your father, if true . . ."

The sister ship was identical with their father's *City of New York* — three decks of luxury, silver-plated handrails, frescos, velvet carpets, glistening chandeliers, even a Steinway in the domed social hall on the hurricane deck. It was impossible for any of them to imagine all the beauty lying on its side beneath the sea. The girls took turns reading again the small clipping. Julia whispered, "Let's all *will* it not to be true!"

But it was true. By the time the Captain returned from Australia, his desk was piled high with the subsequent newspapers confirming the loss. One story, Lizzie and Julia believed, would mitigate considerably their father's usual grief for a Pacific Mail loss. The wrecked steamer had been commanded by Captain James Waddell who, before joining the company, had sailed the Rebel privateer *Shenandoah* through the Pacific, decimating the last of the whaling fleet months after the Civil War had ended. They remembered that when Waddell had brought the *City of San Francisco* out to the Pacific two years before, direct from her launching back East, their father had refused to shake hands with the new addition to the Pacific Mail family and even their mother had been cool and haughty at Waddell's reception. Subsequently she had told her girls why. Now, in their eyes, Captain Waddell had got his comeuppance. "Papa will be glad for *that,*" Lizzie said. "Never at such a price," Annie said sadly and, of course, she was right. The Captain did grieve for the ship; Waddell he dismissed with a "Damned fool, went in too close —"

It was a somber shore leave for their preoccupied father — no carriage drives to the Cliff House, no outings in Woodward's

Gardens to look at the menagerie, the black swans on the lake and the sea-lion pond, not even a theater for their mother that time. Lizzie remarked petulantly to her mother and sisters that she didn't know why the whole house had to go in mourning, just because somebody *else's* ship had gone down.

"Somebody *else's?*" Annie cried. "There's *never* somebody else's — they're *all* his ships in a way." She flashed a look of dismay at her uncomprehending daughters and abruptly put aside her sewing. "I've not yet made you understand," she said as if to herself. "Come here, around my chair . . . the three of you," she added gently. And presently her storytelling voice captured them and changed their self-pity into a wider and more diffused emotion that seemed to encompass not only their father but the whole of his Pacific Mail family.

All the company's commanders, just like their father, had sailed the clipper ships before going into steam, Annie said. And a clipper ship you could prepare for a storm. You could clear her decks and batten down her hatches, furl her sails and heave her to, to ride it out . . . but not these monster steamers whose paddle-wheels or screw propellers simply *had* to keep going to prevent the foundering of their broad-beamed hulls, top-heavy with fancywork structures. Their father had once been caught in a China Sea typhoon with one of the Pacific Mail's floating hotels. When he had told her about it on his return, she had almost fainted with fright. The hurricane force had thrown his ship instantly almost upon her beam ends. Skylights had all been dashed in, saloon lamps extinguished and smashed to crystal bits. All the luxury furnishings — velvet sofas, potted palms, piano and plate-glass mirrors — were sent hurtling from wall to wall of the upper-deck saloons. He had herded his frightened passengers to small cabins on the lower decks and had bolted his Chinese into their steerage quarters to prevent them adding their blood-curdling panic to the general uproar. Then all he and his men had to do was to *keep the machinery going* — and that they did, even when one of the paddle-boxes would be completely under water giving such fearful strain to the shafts as to make the shuddering vessel seem to be flying apart beneath the feet.

"When news of that typhoon reached San Francisco," Annie said softly, "every Pacific Mail captain then in port called on me, and lived through it in anguished detail as if they had been in command, instead of your father." She cocked her head and gave them a queer small smile. "That's what your father is doing now," she said. And then they heard their father's footfalls in the room above them, pacing the floor in the shoes of the *City of San Francisco's* captain.

A month after the Captain sailed, a new danger to him began to take shape. For some time an ugly discontent had been brewing in San Francisco, the city's unemployed demonstrating in sympathy with the bloody railroad strike in the East. Previously "the sandlot agitators" had confined their activities to Nob Hill, threatening to burn the mansions of the "thieving millionaires . . . the bloated bondholders," but now in July of '77 they went into action below the windows of their Rincon Hill house.

They had watched the trouble building up, although none — not even their mother — had read the signs correctly. The children saw its beginnings like something happening on a stage. On a day when Christine was off duty, Maggie the cook had unlocked the door in the back fence which gave out on the Harrison Street Cut. She had allowed the girls to look down on what she called "the sin and depravity of them wharf rats."

Below was a row of saloons and sailors' boardinghouses which flanked the far end of the sandlots as far as the Bay. Gathered about were whiskered men in knit caps, men in bowler hats but without neckties, and an Irishman named Dennis Kearney who, said Maggie, had come to the city in a clipper in '68 and had gone into the dray business. He was a politician also, she said, like all Irishmen who could never let well enough alone. He had made up a slogan which they could hear if they sharpened their ears. As they peered and listened, hoarse angry cries — *The Chinese must go! Away with the heathen Chinee!* — drifted up to their lookout point.

It had startled the girls, especially Lizzie and Julia who clearly remembered their father's side-wheeler trips to the Orient on the *Great Republic* and the *China*. They knew he had many friends among the Chinese, that he respected their high culture, honesty and industry. It was as if the mob below were attacking gentlefolk like the Wah Sungs who had called upon them right there on Rincon Hill not long after the Captain made the last of his side-wheeler crossings. He had always bragged about his children and exhibited their photographs to anyone who would look. He had shown the latest to Mr. and Mrs. Wah Sung when they sailed back from Hong Kong with him on the *China*. In his lordly Yankee equality with all men, he had invited the wealthy mandarin to visit his home any time he would be in port. To his surprise, they had appeared one Sunday afternoon — two gorgeously attired Chinese in satin robes, accompanied by four black-gowned retainers. They had come up the lane soundless in their silk slippers and found Lizzie and Julia busy combing and braiding their father's beard into stiff little pigtails, which they adored to do and dared do only when he was in an expansive mood.

Nothing, they realized after, could have broken the ice more effectively. Since then, their mother had received many gifts of tea in caddies ornamented with gold-leaf appliqués, and jars of ginger in green ceramic pots webbed in nets of woven raffia. For the Captain's children, the Wah Sungs sent toys every Chinese New Year — birds suspended on silk threads from bamboo poles, dragon kites and Chinese puzzles carved intricately in balls of ivory.

Even if the threatening cry, *Away with the heathen Chinee!* referred only to the coolie laborers their father had brought in steerage loads to San Francisco to work in mines and on the railroads, it made no sense to the girls. Their father had often told them how gentle were his Chinese passengers, always staying peacefully below deck, cooking their own meals of rice and dried fish, playing games of chance with cards and copper tokens and slipping off from time to time for a quiet pipe of opium in the special curtained booths the ships maintained in the Oriental steerage. The Chinese traffic netted a good profit for the Pacific Mail, even at the small fare of $40 gold per person, Hong Kong to San Francisco. Moreover (and this was what made the mob's cry doubly unreasonable), it was a two-way traffic; the majority of the Chinese always returned to the homeland as soon as a little wealth was acquired.

There had been anti-coolie demonstrations for a long time before the sandlot outburst. During the Captain's service on the Australia run, the girls had been dutifully cutting from the papers the stories of outrages upon the Chinese and enclosing them in their letters to him while at sea. *Yesterday at the corner of Dupont and Jackson, someone threw sand in the eyes of a Chinaman . . . Two more Chinese laundries burned . . . Assailant ordered to pay fine of $40 for having been caught in the act of kicking a Chinaman at 2 o'clock yesterday morning as he was going to his wash-house near the corner of Market and Second.*

When they had first looked down on Kearney's mobs, they knew nothing about the thousands of unemployed in the white drifter population of the city. Nor that the Chinese were blamed for being cheap labor. Maggie called it all a "timpist in a taypot" and was ashamed for her countryman when the acts of violence increased.

On the night of July 23rd, William C. Coleman, the former vigilante chief, came out of retirement and offered his aid to the city police to suppress the mobs. Governor Irwin asked the Secretary of the Navy to send U.S. vessels from Mare Island to anchor off the city's wharves. From their windows, the children watched the *Pensacola* and the *Lackawanna*, accompanied by the Navy tug *Monterey*, steam over the Bay and anchor within gunshot range of the Pacific Mail docks. "It's a fine time for Papa to be at sea," Lizzie whispered to Julia, looking at her mother's white face.

The mobs grew larger in the next two nights. On July 25th they united into one — a sea of pitchpine torches dashing itself against the dark hulks of wooden warehouses. A lumber yard at the foot of Brannan Street burst into flames. The glow lit the white façades of the pier sheds so brightly you could read the lettering over the wide-arched doors — P.M.S.S. CO. — CHINA VIA JAPAN . . . NEW YORK VIA PANAMA . . .

Just as the police charged in, they heard the cry, *Down with the Pacific Mail. . . . Hang the Captains who bring in the coolies!* Their mother sobbed with fright, clutching the girls to her, unaware that Johnny had crept from bed and joined them. He was gazing down on the scene with fascinated eyes. A hundred voices vibrant with fury cried out from below for the hangings, naming the captains in a litany of hate. Would the torchlit streams of agitators, armed with clubs, swing about and surge uphill to storm the captains' homes? The children drew back from the window as shots rang out, all except their mother frozen in her tracks. She had heard her husband's name called.

For the next weeks it was like living in a sentinel's tower. The girls watched the docks every night until the Captain came home. Order was restored by then. The wharves were quiet, the burned lumber had been carted away. Annie recovered from her shock and confessed to her daughters that she had never been more frightened, not even during her first earthquake in the Lick House right after the birth of Julia. But, she warned them, they must not mention to their father how afraid they all had been. Fear was something he had never known and could never understand in others. He wasn't afraid of the devil himself, his crews always said.

They kept fear out of their voices when they gave the Captain their accounts of Kearney's mob incited against the Pacific Mail and her captains, including himself. Their father looked at them with a twinkle in his dark eyes and to their astonishment pooh-poohed the whole story. He was sure he knew that Irishman Dennis Kearney, that they had sailed together in the China trade in '54 in the clipper *Shooting Star*. He took the wind out of their sails completely with his final pontifical statement that former shipmates were like blood brothers who would never dream of plotting one against the other. Therefore, they must have imagined that they had heard his name called out as a candidate for hanging.

Annie shot a warning glance at her daughters which said quite plainly, "Let him have it *his* way."

He comforted them with the news that he had been reassigned from the Australia command to duty ashore as a "spare captain." For the next month, possibly longer, he would be a stay-at-home. A pensive expression came to Annie's face as he made his announcement. Lizzie, ever watchful, wondered what it meant.

By the end of the first week of shore duty, she knew. The discipline of the bridge became the rule of the Rincon Hill house. Having no ship beneath his feet, the Captain turned his home into one and, to the astonishment of his daughters seemed to grieve because it was going nowhere. A "spare captain" was actually an ace in the Pacific Mail's pocket, ready on the instant to take command of some supplementary steamer the company might have to throw into service when trade boomed suddenly in China, Japan or Central America. The Captain, however, didn't seem to think himself an ace in reserve; he grew morose and full of self-pity as his shore duty continued.

Lizzie said afterwards that if they had not been perched upon that hilltop with the whole of the Bay before them and ships their father commanded passing before his eyes every day, his transfer from active duty to spare captain ashore might not have been so hard to take. Though all Pacific Mail captains had turns at shore duty, their father secretly considered his change of status a demotion of sorts, despite the fact that he received full pay and, in addition, a handsome weekly sum called board money, in compensation for his food aboard a Pacific Mail steamer. It was this extra dividend that went to their mother for her special perquisites, on which no accounts were ever required.

All hands pitched in to help Annie in the tremendous task of trying to keep up the Captain's spirits. Lizzie companioned him to the Pacific Mail docks each time a ship came in, curtsied to their skippers as her father showed her off and listened to his hollow words of self-congratulation for having been accorded the post of spare captain which permitted him, for a change, to get acquainted with his family. Julia and Jane kept Johnny quiet when he was home reading. His morning *Chronicle* and *Alta California* were filled with stories of the booming Pacific trade in which the Pacific Mail with its virtual monopoly was reaping a harvest, along with the merchants of the city. Only their father (his face seemed to say) had been left out of it.

Annie slipped away to town one afternoon and bought for him out of her hoarded "bunnit money" an extraordinary book which they all thought would keep him engrossed for a month at least. It was Goodrich's *History of the Sea — A Graphic Description of Maritime Adventures, Achievements, Explorations, Discoveries and Inventions, From the Ark to the Present Time.* Between its handsome covers embossed with sailing ships and spouting whales were 266 steel-engraved illustrations and 775 pages of fine print. But the Captain put it aside when their mother presented it, saying he would save it until he was back on a ship where he could read it with the concentration her splendid gift merited.

By the end of the first month of waiting orders, the girls were all "walking on eggs" and Johnny had become their principal preoccupation. His sunny nature gave way to brooding, as if he resented his father's continued presence in the house. When the Captain tried to coax him into learning a few simple seaman's phrases, he hung his head and played dumb. Afterwards, in the nursery, he would mimic the Captain exactly in words and tone, planting his legs in a sailor's stance and piping out *"Ahoy there! Anybody on board?"*

"If *just once* he'd do that for Papa," Lizzie said in exasperation, "all the strain around here would let up."

Instead of letting up, it grew worse. One day the Captain discovered Johnny playing with a block of sulphur matches. They thought then that the roof would be blown off the house. Johnny flew to his mother's arms as the Captain haled all the sisters to the mat, plus the cook and nurse Christine, and interrogated them as to how the boy had got hold of the matches. Nobody knew, but before his lecture on the dangers of fire had ended, every Pacific Mail ship that had gone up in flames burned again before their eyes in language so vivid you smelled the smoke, saw the sparks and heard the plop of bodies diving to death in midnight seas.

Annie put her hands over Johnny's ears as the Captain raged, because it sounded as if the boy had set fire to all those side-wheelers flaming in the room and flaming from her husband's outraged eyes. She could feel the trembling of Johnny clasped tightly against her knees as the "Fire Fiend" concentrated his wrath on his single son, then ordered him in disgrace to his room, commanding Christine with an angry headshake to let him go alone. "High time he learns to walk the chalk!" he said.

Annie waited until the servants were dismissed before telling the Captain very quietly that it was his own matches Johnny had found, a block of them he himself had left within reach on his pipe-stand.

"If anyone's to blame, *I am,*" she said. "I should have confiscated them when I saw them there — as you used to do on the side-wheelers when you made the rounds of passengers' cabins." She essayed a smile for her nervous daughters, but her eldest was not to be mollified.

Lizzie turned on her father fearlessly, stamping her foot as she cried, "You should be ashamed, Papa — ashamed, *ashamed!*" Her spitfire temper rose with her voice as she told him what she thought of him raging around like a mad bull and all absolutely unjustly, letting their poor little mother take the blame just to keep peace. "Peace," she wept, "as if any such thing existed around here since your shore duty began . . ."

"That's enough, Lizzie," Annie said quickly. It was more than enough for the Captain. He stared confounded at his eleven-year-old daughter glaring at him, shaken with sobs of plain fury. His face worked oddly with mixed emotions — pride for the way she stood up to him, hurt for the things she said and remorse because he knew she was right.

"I reckon that reading of the riot act means I owe an apology to Johnny," he said slowly, looking from Lizzie to Annie, as if hoping to be contradicted. They all knew he loathed making apologies; he called it eating humble pie. Annie drew her daughters about her and said, "*We* think it would be the proper thing to do, Jack." We, the four of us . . . four against one. The Captain gave them a rueful glance and climbed the stairs to Johnny's room.

That night, when they were alone, Annie told her husband that she was again with child. This had been her contribution to the easing of the shore-duty tensions and she had made it with her blue eyes wide open and unafraid, against Dr. McDougall's advice not to have any more children. "One more boy to round out our little family . . . won't it be wonderful, Jack?" she whispered.

The appointment to the S.S. *Georgia* on the Panama line came most appropriately a few days later. It had come, as had all others from the company, quite suddenly and without any more forewarning than the letter itself conveyed. *You are hereby appointed. . . . You will assume charge of the vessel at once.*

They could see the *Georgia* from their windows. She was one of the five ships the Pacific Mail had recently purchased from the Panama Transit Steamship Company to end the threat of competition in the coastwise service. Trim in her white paint, already dressed for the tropics with deck awnings, she rode light as a sea gull at her moorings, flying for the first time the red, white and blue swallowtail flag of the Pacific Mail.

Their father remarked that under the new house flag it would be something like a maiden voyage, and he welcomed the challenge of making the faster runs he knew she was capable of with a seasoned Pacific Mail skipper on her bridge. They sighed with relief when he sailed away. The house seemed bigger. Johnny became again the center of his female circle and not only resumed talking a blue streak but began to join his mother and sisters around the piano for their evening singing of gospel hymns. When he threw back his blond head and shut his eyes, he soared to high C without a quaver.

"He has perfect pitch," Annie would whisper to the girls, her fingers rippling over the piano keys, lifting him octave by octave into the high soprano levels her own voice reached easily, drawing him after her with ecstatic little nods of approval. Higher . . . higher! Higher as a singer, Lizzie thought with a premonitory pang, than possibly he would ever climb as a sailor up riggings stretched like treble chords over the skysail spaces where his father always imagined him. Annie trained him to sing with his sisters, which he adored; but very often the girls' voices dropped out of the quartet one by one and they would listen to Johnny carrying on alone with his mother, their two faces so exactly alike, their two voices so perfectly matched that you could imagine one to be the echo of the other. Then the little pantalooned hellion became positively cherubic with eyes like bits of bright blue sky and the high notes issuing from his round red mouth were so heartbreakingly beautiful they would often weep. *When we gath-er at the riv-er* . . . he sang like an angel.

Between trips to Panama in the fall of '77 the Captain started building on a pair of lots he had bought far out in the Western Addition, on Sutter Street. He explained to Lizzie and Julia that Rincon Hill was getting a little run-down and that its proximity to the docks made it unsuitable for growing girls; but they knew better. They had only to cast experienced clinical eyes on their mother to know that he was building for the new addition to their family. New baby, new house . . .

He knew exactly the kind of house he wanted. With Lizzie in

tow he had inspected from bow to stern every domicile of pretension on San Francisco's hills, from the outside, of course, but (as Lizzie subsequently reported to her family) making such blustery comments about them that he might just as well have been standing in their entrance halls telling their owners what he thought about the gingerbread and gimcrackery defacing their portals. The home he admired was on the corner of Post and Fillmore next to the firehouse. He engaged the same architect who promised to copy exactly the false-front masterpiece, save for the addition of a few more bay windows since the Captain had a double lot on which to expand his sun-catching façade. The house must absolutely be completed by the following April, said the Captain, inadvertently informing his daughters of the date their mother would be expecting.

Annie gave them her news as a Christmas present that year, though Lizzie and Julia had long since begun their discreet hovering over her. It would be an April baby, she said, and she and Doctor Mack had decided to wait for it in the Rincon Hill house, then move shortly after to the new home their father was having built. She drew Johnny to her armchair and told him, like a secret, how she had asked God to give him a little brother to play with, so he wouldn't have to grow up all alone in a house full of girls. The new brother would be named Frank, after his Uncle Frank in Honolulu and he, Johnny, would be the principal custodian of his fellow playmate just as soon as he would be able to walk.

"Just think of all the things you'll have to teach him!" she said, searching his small face anxiously for signs of jealousy. Johnny gazed back at her with eyes popped wide with excitement. His mouth worked over the new name. He had difficulties with his r's. "Fank," he whispered, "Fank . . ." Suddenly he flung his arms about her knees and laid his head on her lap. "I want him *now,* mama — please, *please!*" he begged, looking up at her sideways with his most beguiling smile.

"Not now, my darling." She combed his bangs with her fingers and flashed a smile of relief at Lizzie. "Not now," she whispered. "Frank's not ready to come to us yet."

"You didn't bat an eye when you said *boy*," Lizzie said too quickly for Johnny to catch.

"Of course not!" her mother replied with sudden spirit. "Because that's what the outcome *must* be!" She looked down on her adored son burrowing his bright head in her lap. "For *his* sake," she said softly. "You're old enough, Lizzie, to understand why." She looked up at her eldest with a hint of pleading in her lovely eyes, too proud, too loyal, to speak the thoughts that clouded them momentarily.

Lizzie said them inwardly for her. . . . To take off Johnny's back the unconscionable load of his father's hopes and plans. To provide an alternate for that fierce drive toward the sea, in case one stumbles by the wayside or, heaven forbid, prefers to do something else than sail. Like singing, for instance. Not to have all our eggs in this one small basket, said Annie's hands smoothing the collar of Johnny's middy blouse. Lizzie blinked back tears as she looked at her valiant little mother, already so big, so early.

"I only hope *he* will still be on the Panama run when April comes," Lizzie said with a little flash of temper. She pulled Johnny from her mother's lap and sent him off to find Jane.

Annie studied her daughter for a moment as she sometimes looked at a sheet of new music, taking in the sharps and flats of its key, then its time, then reading the melody line, all in one swift comprehensive glance. She saw a thin, nervous, birdlike child, eleven going on twelve, who knew that babies didn't drop from the sky, who remembered surely the advent of Jane and John and, more recently, the warnings of Doctor Mack which she should never have been allowed to overhear, but had, because she was always hovering when the doctor came to the house. She put out her hand and said, "Come here, Lizzie dearest."

"First of all," Annie said gently, "I never again want to hear you call your father *he*. Next, I want you to stop your worrying. Everything's going to be all right. We'll get through this, my dearest, as we have all the others, with or without the skipper on the bridge." A smile flickered connivingly. "In some ways, it might be easier on all of us if your father were at sea, don't you think? Men are such babies!" Her laugh tinkled in the room like Chinese wind-bells. Then she was on her feet, without any help, and moving a little heavily toward the piano. Over her shoulder she said gaily, "*I* think we've had enough seriousness for one day! What do you say — shall I call the clan?"

She struck the first chords of the Blue Danube Waltz which always brought all children running from wherever they were in the house, from whatever they were doing. When she played that piece even the furniture seemed to dance. And you could imagine then, looking at her with head thrown back, eyes sparkling and throat vibrating like a singing canary's, that babies really did come out of Maggie McLatchie's suitcase (as Jane still believed) and that labor pains had never been heard or dreamed of, or even written about so gruesomely in the Old Testament. And that *that* was why the sisters were whirling with pigtails flying, round and round the room, ruffled skirts abloom like Shasta daisies, slippered feet prancing high but never fast enough to suit Annie who cried as she quickened her tempo, "*Come on, little slowpokes!*"

Dancing in the new baby, Lizzie thought, as if life came on like a touch of the taper to the gas-jet, easy and soundless, in her mother's gallant little game of let's-pretend.

Grandmother Bolles came visiting from the Islands two months before the baby was due. Annie, hearing that her youngest sister was also having a baby at her same time, begged her mother not to stay, since Mary had had great difficulties with her previous child and would be much more in need of motherly support than she. "I'll have Mrs. Farnsworth here, and with Jack on the Panama run, very likely he'll be here too," Annie said. Grandmother Bolles told Lizzie and Julia that their mother was the greatest convincer on the face of the earth. "Nobody has ever been able to stand up to her, once her mind is made up," she said. "She can even bully me," she added with a reflective smile. She drew them to her capacious bosom and made them promise to write with every packet.

Mrs. Farnsworth, being a South Park neighbor, came in every day during the final weeks, a double comfort to the girls since their father's sudden transfer to the China line the month before. Their mother's oldest friend was as musically gifted as Annie; she kept the sisters at their piano practice every afternoon, scales for Julia and Jane, a new piece for Lizzie — "There's a Ship on the Sea" — which, said she, they could all learn to sing since it had beautiful words about a ship with father aboard . . . *Sailing tonight, And the moon is all bright. . . . Oh follow the ship with your silvery light, As father sails over the sea.* The new piece with four sharps and 6-8 time was supposed to take Lizzie's mind off her brooding worries, but it did not succeed very well.

Lizzie observed to Julia that Doctor Mack came much more frequently than for Johnny's birth and that he put Maggie McLatchie on the job a whole week earlier. For the first time, too, the younger ones, Johnny and Jane, were moved out of the house on the morning when Annie had her first pain. They went with Christine to spend the night with her Alameda cousin. Mrs. Farnsworth wanted the older girls to go along too, but they refused categorically. "We're staying where we belong, near Mama," Lizzie said. "We've been through this before, Julie and I." She tossed her head with lofty assurance as if to say, One birth is like another . . . but a few hours later she was to discover how wrong she was.

Frank weighed eleven pounds at birth. He started into the world as Johnny had, feet first. Doctor Mack's every other word coming through the closed door to Annie's room seemed to be a curse, and every time Maggie McLatchie swept across the hall to the kitchen, her stone face drove Lizzie and Julia tighter into each other's arms and froze them there. Once they heard her say to the cook, "It's murr-rr-der, down-rrright murr-rrder. . . . Ah, the poorr-rr little thing!" But they couldn't cry. Tears, blood, breath and heartbeat seemed at a standstill in their shrinking forms.

The house was so quiet you could hear every gasping cry from the closed room, every comforting word from Mrs. Farnsworth and every rumbling curse and quick apology from the Doctor — "Forgive me, lassie, but ye done it again to me . . . *breech, by God!*" Lassie, he called their mother, as if she were a small girl. They cried then, thinking of someone their own age going through that ordeal.

"When he says *Bear down* it'll begin to be over," Lizzie whispered to Julia in a choked voice. Arms entwined, they sat like one body with twin minds thinking the same thoughts, reviewing the same past like drowning people.

Annie had predicted that the Captain would be at sea when her time would come, and he was. He was probably steaming at that moment somewhere between Yokohama and Hong Kong, pacing the bridge of the 5000-ton *City of Peking*. He would most certainly be studying his chronometer, figuring the difference of time between there and here, including the lost twenty-four hours at the 180th parallel, and deciding no doubt that all was now serene back home. Since nothing could shake his almanac-inspired belief that babies always came early in the morning, he'd consider Annie's labors about over if it was *yesterday* morning where he was. He had been so proud when he received his sudden orders to relieve the *Peking*'s former commander, a naval officer. They had watched him sail away thirty days before, all five of them crowded into the frame of the rear window to give him the last spyglass glimpse as he liked to see them, two on each side of their mother. "Clinging together like ivy on the garden wall," their mother had hummed, to make them all smile for his powerful monocular. The two girls directly next to her had felt again the pounding of her heart as when the Kearney mobs had howled for the heads of the coolie-bringing captains. The four-masted steamer, with space for a thousand coolies in her forward end, backed into the Bay with a stiff head wind flattening her flags against the sky — the Stars and Stripes, the swallowtail flag of the company and the yellow dragon of the Celestial Empire of China.

"It's *got* to be a boy," Lizzie whispered. "She just can't ever go through this again." Julia wanted to put her hands over her ears, but if she did she'd miss those magic words *Bear down* which Lizzie said would bring an end to her mother's cries. If they went on like that, quicker and quicker and weaker and weaker, she would never live to collect her reward of a trip around the world, Julia thought with panic. Even surviving her ordeal, the new son would set their mother back a full four years before realizing the beautiful dream. She counted on her fingers. This new one four years younger than Johnny, four years more, then, of growing care to his teens, before he too would be ready to shoulder a ditty box and go aboard some training ship. Only then would Annie be free to see Naples, the Barbary Coast, India and the Orient. Ah, how they had talked of that great round-the-world voyage, adding a new port, a new climate, a new civilization, each time their father came home and spun yarns of the far places. "Mama's trip around the world," Julia said softly, like a whistling in the dark.

The bedroom door opened and Doctor Mack, looking exhausted and disorderly, stood before them.

"Where's that coffee, you two?" he said hoarsely. "Thick and black I told ye, strong enough to stand up without a cup about it. *Where is it?*" He waggled his blond beard like a goat and glared at them with bloodshot eyes. "I bring ye a bonnie brother," he cried, "and here ye sit like bumps on logs!"

Then they could move. Lizzie collided with Maggie running in from the kitchen. The cook took one look at the doctor's face and said, "The saints be praised! . . ." Julia ran to her father's sacred liquor cabinet and took out the best brandy with shaking hands.

"Ay, lassie, *that's* the ticket!" The doctor dropped to the sofa and put out his hand for the glass she poured. Maggie came with coffee and Lizzie with a platter of Sctoch shortbread so rich with butter it crumbled to the touch. With crumbs on his beard he told them their mother was sleeping and they could see their brother just as soon as McLatchie and Mrs. Farnsworth got him cleaned up for inspection. "Eleven pounds, so help me," he said to the cook who crossed herself. He nodded, grinning. "Ye can well say the saints be praised!"

The doctor alternated gulps of brandy and coffee and dropped shortbread crumbs on the carpet. Then he squinted at Lizzie and Julia standing by with arms entwined, lending support one to the other. "He's got black eyes like your father," he said, smiling like a human now, gentle and reflective. "And the same white skin. A little dish of blackberries and cream, ye'd say. Yer mother knew she'd got a boy before I put her off to sleep. And now the little lass is dreaming sweetly. She's got herself a *pair* of sailors!"

There was a peace like that of sudden exhaustion. The words of one of her mother's favorites sang in Julia's mind. *Flow gently, sweet Afton, disturb not her dream* . . . And she thought for a moment she was going to cry.

Chapter 14

THE MOVE TO THE SUTTER STREET HOUSE was to begin a new life for the Captain's family. After a decade of gypsy years, living in hotels and rented houses, it would be, Annie said, like a coming to anchor at long last. The Captain, ashore three weeks before the actual move began, was almost beside himself with joy for his new son, for his new home and, most of all, for Annie's amazing recovery from a birth which the doctor told him must positively be the last. Possibly it was this understood fact, which was to condition the remainder of her wedded life, that put the wings to Annie's small feet. She had composed her little family like music, adding note after note, child after child, until balance and harmony were achieved; now she knew her composition wrought in pain was finished.

Several times during his shore leave she dressed her prettiest and drove forth with the Captain to inspect the new home, the schools in the neighborhood and the church that stood back-to-back with the Sutter Street house which her daughters wished to join. Between inspection trips with his wife, the Captain took his girls out to give them detailed instructions about the assignment of rooms, the placement of furnitures (which they must supervise, not letting their mother lift a finger) and suggestions about lawns and plants for front and rear gardens. Always, before leaving the grounds, he stood outside the house and gave it a long loving scrutiny from keel to mast tip, then gazed at others in the block with a deprecating smile as if they were shanties.

The wood-paved block of Sutter Street, between Buchanan and Webster, held only some six or eight houses in that summer of '78. These had sprung from the enveloping sandlots full-fledged, complete, established in their two-storied opulence of stone stairs leading up from fenced gardens to elaborate porticoes supported on wooden columns. They were all stamped with the style of the times — bay windows, false fronts and second-floor balconies — but there was variety in their exterior ornamentation, some tending more to the Doric, some to Ionic, some to combinations of the two. The Captain's home combined all three Greek styles. Its portico column began at the base with a section of fluted Doric that midway added fillets between flutings and became Ionic, and wound up in the capitals with a burst of wooden acanthus leaves to proclaim the Corinthian. The Captain would settle for nothing less.

On his final inspection trip with Lizzie and Julia, before sailing, he issued one order that left the girls speechless with dismay and gave them, as well, a foretaste of things to come concerning the neatness he would expect always to find in his first owned home. He looked down at the wooden planks of the sidewalk, told the girls they were split logs of Honduras mahogany — "Mebbe even some I brought up in the early days!" — then noted some clumps of weeds growing in the cracks between planks. "What's this?" he cried, glaring at the weeds as if they were baleful barnacles. "Everything must be shipshape around here," he told Lizzie. Those weeds must be rooted out just as soon as they moved, and kept out in future. The way to do it, he said, would be to drag fireplace pokers between the damp green cracks, easy if you catch them young.

"Out here *in public* — in front of *everybody?* Oh Papa!" Lizzie cried; but the Captain went right on as if she had not spoken. He appointed her chief of the weeding squad and set the price for the work — 25 cents per child each time the job was accomplished to his satisfaction. Johnny too, he said. Going on five the lad was certainly old enough to handle a poker.

And so "picking the sidewalk," as they called the onerous task, became a household watchword and, subsequently, a sort of calendar of the Captain's voyages. The weeds grew freely while he was at sea. You could judge the length of his absence by their height. They thrust up a good six inches when he was on the China run, barely two inches when he was on the Panama run. Once, when he was still commanding the *City of Peking*, there had been time for a few California poppies to come into bloom between the planks before their father's ship was sighted sailing through the Golden Gate homebound from Hong Kong.

In the fall of their first year in the new home, the Captain was reassigned to the S.S. *Granada* on the Panama run. Annie sang with joy when he announced not only his transfer, but also the amazing news that Crux had hove back over the horizon and would again be his steward on all future commands. She told her girls about the happy-natured Jamaican who had sailed with their father years before any of them were born, had been aboard the *Anglo-Saxon* on her own famous trip to London and had now come back into the Captain's life like a dark guardian angel who knew how to take care of him while at sea. "Bridge coat in the fogs, cap in the tropics, even," she laughed, her blue eyes brimming with memories, "the number of spoonfuls of sugar he takes in his tea!"

The children adored Crux on first sight. With his pointed *café au lait* face, laughing black eyes and thick curly hair bright with perfumed oils, he seemed like something out of the Arabian Nights. His advent in the family, moreover, made life richer and infinitely more predictable when their father was back on the Panama run. Crux became the herald of the Captain's return from the sea. Nobody had to run over to the Pacific Avenue hill to maintain lookout for the *Granada's* passage through the

Golden Gate. Crux always appeared first at the house after the Captain docked, like a musical prelude that prepared you for the more important matter to come.

The rumbling company dray, laden with loot to fill the new basement, back yard and the stomachs of five growing children, made a splendid drumming on the wood-block paving of Sutter Street. When Crux braked it to a halt before their house, it was as if the whole Pacific were a horn of plenty pouring its bounty upon their doorstep. Crates of oranges, mangoes and pineapples, and great stalks of bananas (in which sometimes a jade-green lizard lurked) were stacked in the wagon — the food of San Francisco's bonanza kings in those days . . . and of sea captains' families.

There might be live chickens from the Central American ports, crated in hand-woven baskets light and airy as bird cages, or a scrawny turkey which their frugal father believed could be fattened profitably in their back yard. The Captain's seachest of Honduras mahogany, handmade by a ship's carpenter from the clipper days and polished now to a patina that bespoke thirty years of service on almost as many ships, topped the crates, and on the high spring seat beside Crux reposed "the Captain's cake" baked by the ship's chef at the end of every voyage. This was a triple-layered confection frosted skillfully with pink and green icings that marked among hearts and flowers and sugary arabesques every date of importance to the family — children's birthdays, wedding anniversaries of their parents and, occasionally, a special cake with a sailing ship iced upon it, one of the commands their father had had before he "went into steam."

Always they had a good safe hour after Crux's arrival to prepare for the Captain's appearance, since he had to see his passengers debarked and his ship through customs. When weather prevented Annie from meeting him on the docks, the delay was even longer because then he took the horsecars instead of a carriage. The girls had time to inspect everything before he returned to the bridge of his home, including the flagpole that slanted out over the portico from the second-floor balcony. If the docking coincided with a national holiday, their father expected to see the Stars and Stripes flying. (What, most mercifully, he had never seen was the flag flying after one of his departures, as once it had when Johnny climbed out on the balcony and raised it in a salute to freedom again. Nobody in the house knew about it until a neighbor stopped by to ask what was the special celebration on that March day which was neither Washington's Birthday nor the Fourth of July.)

In the spring of 1880, Julia herself would have flown the flag for a private joy had Annie not placed it under lock and key since Johnny's prank. This was the trip when her father was bringing her the pet of her dreams. Months before she had asked the Captain for a parrot. He had promised to try to find her one down Panama way, but had run into difficulties in his search for one that had a clean vocabulary. Now it seemed he had found a bird whose language he approved. His last letter to her, date-marked S.S. *Granada, At Sea, March 26th, 1880* read:

MY DEAR JULIA:

I believe that I owe you a letter and I am seated in my room to write you a few words. We will be in Acapulco tomorrow morning, making a pleasant run down from San Francisco of less than six days. I am well and have been since I left home. The weather with us is very warm, but fine and pleasant and everything is working well fore and aft of the ship. I don't know what ship this letter will come to San Francisco on, but I will leave it at Acapulco for the first one bound up the coast. I hope you are a good child and help your mother all you can. Your mother has much to do for all you children, taking care of you when you are sick, making all your clothes and watching over you all the time. And what do you children do for all that kindness? I hope in return you are good to your mother, helpful and always obedient. I will on my return bring your parrot to you. And I hope it won't disturb the neighborhood and be complained of as Julia Cavarly's nuisance. I will write to your mother tomorrow. We have very pleasant passengers and the voyage is passing off thus far most pleasantly. Please remember me with love to your brothers and sisters and hoping you are all good children, I am ever your affectionate father,

J. M. CAVARLY

Between the lines Julia read the hint of speedy removal if the parrot did not behave. Their father's quick temper, which Annie forgivingly called "his Huguenot heritage — the French in the Cavarly blood," was as unpredictable as lightning. Even if Johnny misbehaved, that parental temper could conceivably strike at the parrot. She glanced at her brother, weeding the sidewalk with his sisters. Like Lizzie, who always hoped none of her beaux would catch her at the demeaning labor, Johnny hoped his Irish playmates, who lived as squatters in a sandlot shanty the other side of Webster Street, would stay off the scene. On a previous homecoming, they had called out "Hey Johnny — there's your old man drunk again!" when they had spied the Captain swinging with his peculiar rolling gait down the incline of Sutter Street, brown beard parted in the wind.

The western sky was the children's timepiece. The afternoon fog was just beginning to roll in from the Farallones. The Captain always sailed through the Golden Gate ahead of the fog, by careful calculation, to keep their mother from worrying. She must already be on the docks, Julia thought, probably sitting at that moment in the steamship agent's office warming her feet at his potbellied stove.

Presently she heard the drumming of the dray. It swung around the corner of Buchanan Street with Crux waving to them from the high seat and the plumed feet of the dray horses stamping hard on the wood-blocks as he reined them in, one-handed, for the incline to the house. The sight of a parrot in a steel-wired cage and of Crux jumping down, light as a genie with smoke beneath his feet, left Julia speechless with joy. Crux handed her the cage before giving the Captain's cake to Lizzie — a protocol she was glad her father was not there to see. Crux told her the parrot was to be left in its cage until the Captain arrived, then he caught up Johnny and swung him high in the air, making his blond bangs lift and drop . . . like the golden seaweed he'd seen at San Blas, he told them, where he had fished while the Captain coaled.

Julia's heart almost burst as she gazed at her parrot. It was a bright green bird with red crest and yellow eyes. The upper part of its great hooked beak was hinged to the skull by a wrinkled white skin that looked tough as parchment. The parrot opened its beak and waggled a rubbery black tongue at her as she peered into the cage, but she would not speak to it until the Captain gave the proper cue.

Excitement mounted as they helped Crux unload the dray. He told them it had been an easy passage — no head winds the *Granada* could not manage, no trouble with the crew, passengers all most amiable and well-behaving. There had been a man-eating shark caught while they lay at anchor in Acapulco which had had a section of tattooed arm in its belly still — but they must ask their father to tell them about it for it was too good a story to spoil. He hoisted the seachest on his shoulder and marched ahead of them into the house.

Like the trimmed sidewalk without, the house was in perfect order for the Captain's return. Just as if she were one of them and understood their feelings about some of the Captain's treasures, their mother had helped the girls to return to their places the objects they always hid when he went away.

The two stuffed macaws in gilded hoops were swinging again from the archway between front and rear parlors, just where their father had hung them when he brought them back from Ecuador a year ago. The Philippine bolo knives were again crossed above the mantelpiece and the Chinese screen, with padded dragons flying over pagodas of inset mother-of-pearl, had been returned to the front parlor leaving bare to the eye the curio cabinet their father had had built into the rear-parlor wall to house exceptional treasures like canes made from sharks' backbones, animal tusks of all sorts and sizes, bottles of pickled reptiles and insects from tropical shores, a Fiji war club and shoals of spiny shells that looked like pink spiders. The ivory figurine of a Chinese god with bulbous stomach and suggestive leer (which Lizzie said gave unmentionable thoughts to her girl friends) sat again on the piano on the runner of Chinese brocade they never removed.

Not everything the Captain brought back from foreign ports was "sailor bait." The sheen of lacquered trays, the carved sandalwood boxes, the Peking silks and Canton vases were a delight to the eye and the touch, textures the fingers slipped over with the same sort of love that had gone into their making. When you separated trash from the treasure, you had rarities that might very well have come from a mandarin's palace, as indeed some objects had — gifts to their father from wealthy Chinese who had sailed with him.

The only aspect of their unusual furnishings which troubled the conventional-minded girls was that so few San Francisco families had similar things. Unless you visited captains' homes, you seldom saw them at all, and these homes were all in another section, on hilltops overlooking the Bay where they themselves could not live because of their mother's susceptibility to fog. Moreover, the Pacific Mail captains were a small select minority among the city fathers, quite clannish in their social habits, not given to inviting landlubbers into their homes. Most of them were Downeasters from New England port towns where it was customary to see a whale's jawbone gaping on the front lawn, or, as in their own garden spaced among the calla lilies, objects like the three china garden seats from Nanking, which the girls always put away first on sailing day because they were such a public sign of their difference from other Western Addition families.

Lizzie and Julia made a quick inspection of the parlors before going upstairs. A fire was already burning in the basket-grate. Its bed of coals gave a steady heat — ship's coal provided by the Captain who always supervised all fuel purchases for his commands, choosing the coal that was free of the sand which could delay a passage by many hours and let a rival ship reach port first with news and mails. His leather armchair was drawn up before the fire, pipe and humidor on the teak table beside it. The Pacific Mail had accustomed him to such service.

The odor of fresh bread came from the kitchen where Maggie prepared the landing-day dinner, waging her private culinary war against the steamship chefs who knew how to concoct, and spoil the master with, every known delicacy except homemade bread. Julia looked for a place to put the parrot. Everything in its place and a place for everything was the Captain's most frequent advice to his children. But how could one know before formal introduction if the parrot was to be admitted to the parlor? She stood the cage in the undesignated common ground of the entrance hall, where Crux himself might have set a new acquisition not yet tagged with placement instructions.

They had just finished dressing when they heard the parrot speak. Jane had taken care of her charge, Frank, Julia of Johnny, and Lizzie had helped both sisters with the ribbons of Roman-striped silk which drew all the girls' hair straight back from their foreheads and secured it neatly behind the ears, when the perfect imitation of a bo'sun's whistle piped up the stairwell, followed by a raucous voice calling out *Hullo, hullo! The Captain's on deck!*

They rushed out to the stair-landing. Their father stood in the hallway with their mother on his arm. Out of uniform and in a silk top hat, he looked taller than the five feet nine inches he actually was. Their mother's bonnet, with height added by two Parisian pond lilies of pale pink silk, came exactly level with the ends of his luxuriant beard. Beside him she looked delicate as an hourglass. Above her tiny waist bloomed mutton-leg sleeves and a ruffled fichu, below, a full-gathered skirt of black silk trimmed at the hem with rows of shiny *soutache* braid. The parrot, who obviously loved their father, danced up and down on its perch, whistling and moaning with joy.

The Captain's black eyes shone with pride as he looked up at his children. He seemed to be counting them, as if unable to believe his good fortune. Then he gave them his greeting — the same three words charged with emotion which he had used ever since any of them could remember, whether returning from a voyage of months or from a single day on the docks supervising preparations for a voyage. *"Well, children . . . well!"* They flew down the stairs and flung themselves into his bearded embrace as if he had called them to him by the tenderest words he knew.

The first night ashore was always perfect, especially so when the Captain knew he would return to the same ship for her next trip and not be detained on land as a spare captain, awaiting some new ship coming out around the Horn to join the Pacific fleet. He grew restless on land, despite the delights and distractions of his growing family. This night he told them happily he was going back on the *Granada,* so they had to make every minute of his five-day shore leave count.

From the local papers they had forwarded to him, he knew everything he wished to do or see while in port. He laid out the activities of each day with nautical precision. His program began with a night in the Opera House (for their mother's sake), then the Tivoli Gardens for an *opéra bouffe* (which the children would enjoy), then one of the minstrel shows in Billy Emerson's theater on Bush Street, which, for him, could not be matched for thorough, all-round entertainment. Since he often carried actresses and opera singers as passengers aboard his ships, the Captain felt completely at home in the theater, so much so, indeed, that he habitually appeared there one full hour before curtain time, practically before the ushers finished dusting off the seats. This gave him time to read every word in his program, every advertisement on the asbestos curtain and to expound to his fidgeting daughters the virtues of promptness which he called the courtesy of kings. Actually, the girls did not mind too much his early-bird theater habits. They and their mother were being taken out; that was the thing. To see her delicate face alight with excitement as the orchestra tuned up was a whole opera in itself.

The nights disposed of, the Captain then scheduled their days together — visits to Woodward's Gardens to see the zoo and the flowers, and the inevitable round of calls on sea captain friends, from which the children were mercifully excluded. Then returns of hospitality in their own home were planned, when the sacred Canton service would be taken down from pantry shelves for formal dinners that entailed for Lizzie, Julia and Jane dreadful mornings-after of dishwashing, since no cook was ever permitted to handle the Export ware. But this was all part of the homecoming excitement that would turn the house upside down for a few days with so much to see, to do, to eat, that everyone would be a little ill afterwards, and their mother would trot out the bitter calomel powders folded in dosage-sized envelopes, to subdue the wave of biliousness in the children, the customary aftermath of port leaves.

Their mother flew about like a happy bird with one eye on the dinner table and one on Johnny who was behaving beautifully this evening, creating "the good atmosphere for Papa" she had implored of him. (Once Johnny had put flat pearl buttons before his eyes, like opaque monocles, and stared at his father through the small thread-holes in them, as if to shrink him down to comprehensize size; once he had stuffed beans in his ears to make the Captain's voice come to him as from a far distance.) Annie hummed as she gave last pats to the table setting and the Captain said to his daughters, "She's a fine figger of a woman."

The good atmosphere became even better after the huge landing-day dinner, the family arranged around the basket-grate with the firelight from sandless coal on their faces. Johnny and Frank were already in bed. The Captain was surrounded by "his girls" — Lizzie and Jane occupying the arms of his leather chair and their mother opposite, on her more elegant chair upholstered in the petit point she worked on during the long nights when he was away. She was sewing, as always, her head bent over yards of white lawn she gathered and tucked into a party dress for Jane. As he yarned about his days on the flying clippers, the Captain stared at the top of their mother's head with its four blond curls laid parallel to the hair-part, two on each side pinned snugly and neatly in place. The tender love which all the girls had sensed between their parents, from the very first time they began to take note of such things, seemed to have spun a golden web around them all. Even Julia's parrot, lying on its back on the carpet with eyes closed as she stroked its stomach feathers, had fallen under the spell of the Captain's voice. The diamonds in the pierced lobes of their mother's ears flashed like tiny beacons each time she nodded to confirm a date, or a harbor, or the lines of a ship's figurehead, which their father remembered perfectly but paused over deliberately, to see if she was attending.

An aging clipper he had seen in San José de Guatemala, taking on water and fresh fruits, had turned his thoughts to the ships of his heart, to their days of queenlike passage leaving scents of spices and sandalwood in their wakes, instead of the stink of guano that nowadays clung to their shabby shrouds. Their figureheads used to be touched up with paint at the end of every voyage.

The *Romance of the Sea* carried a full-length figure of an ancient mariner at her prow, with head bent forward and right hand raised to shade the eager eyes. The clipper *Nightingale* had a bust of Jenny Lind singing ahead into the winds and the *Gamecock* a fighting bird with head and neck outstretched for combat. And did Annie remember the *Sea Serpent* he had shown her once in Queenstown, with the long slender serpent at her prow picked out in green and gold? Aye, aye, she was a beauty! But the finest of all figureheads was that of *Champion of the Seas* which had been abandoned off Cape Horn just four years ago after nearly twenty-five years of running the westerlies down. That noble clipper had a square-built sailor at her prow, dressed in blue-and-white checkered shirt, skin-tight white trousers that flowed out to bell-bottoms and a shiny tarpaulin hat . . . and his hand waved aloft, did she remember? The earrings flashed assent and the Captain told his daughters that the hand was tattooed, a *tattooed* hand on a figurehead, fancy that!

He stroked his beard with his right hand. Lizzie held his left hand between her own two, rubbing its scar unobtrusively, not looking down at the two fingers crooked inward slightly on the tapered palm — the souvenir of the mutiny he had put down when he was a First Mate in those clipper days he recalled with nostalgia. Sometimes nowadays, when he stood the bridge through the Pacific fog belts, those curled-in fingers gave him a peculiar pain which he mentioned in his letters, along with weather reports, ship's miles logged and engine performance.

He sighed "Aye, aye" as he renewed the tobacco in his pipe. "Time for one more," he said, holding the match at arm's length until the sulphur burned off its tip. "And mebbe," he added gazing through the smoke at their mother, "time for one little piece before we all go to bed? Eh, Annie dear?"

And this was always the finale of landing-day, their mother at the piano with her head thrown back and eyes closed, fingers running exploringly over the keys, trying out chords of all their favorites — Chopin, Strauss, Schubert and Liszt, to see which fitted best the mood of that special moment. A waltz? A polonaise? A lied? The Captain puffed and winked at his daughters. "Let her show off a bit," said his dancing eyes, "she'll wind up with a singing piece, you'll see." And she always did because that, of course, was what he wanted to hear. And then, when she started to sing, her high sweet voice vibrant with meanings no words could have conveyed, her daughters always went back in thought to the one unanswered question about her marriage with their father — how in heaven's name she had ever come to accept a man who was completely tone-deaf, who could not carry the simplest tune, not even a sailor's chantey?

Using song for communication as naturally as a bird, she never had to tell anyone how she felt at any given moment. Her

choice of song was the informative key. This night it was pure
joy — because the Captain was home and Johnny had behaved
and she was being taken to the opera tomorrow night to hear *Il
Trovatore* which all San Francisco knew by heart, but not she,
who never went out nights when her husband was at sea.

Chapter 15

LETTERS WERE THE CONNECTING LINKS between the
Captain and his family. With four letter writers to keep him
informed, he never lacked for home news while at sea. After their
move to the Sutter Street house, he added that edifice to the list
of required subjects for comment, so that he could visualize in
minutest detail the atmosphere behind its false-front façade while
he gazed from his bridge at other men's homes — the paper
houses set among rice paddies back of Yokohama Bay, the
thatched platforms of the Fijian householders or, around Panama Bay, the natives' huts feebly lighted by wicks soaked in
coconut oil.

As Julia went from room to room with a thermometer in her
hand to record temperatures, on Captain's orders, so that he
could know, for example, that on September 8th 1879, the
weather readings at home were:

In the front room	74	degrees
In Lizzie's room	82	”
In the nursery	84	”
In the sun	96	”

(At one fifteen in the afternoon with all windows open)

her mother was making memoranda for *her* future letters to him
— "Doctor Mack gave me Brifonia in water every hour, then

Nux Vomica and Nat Sulph every hour in alteration, then Ferrous Phos."

Each time the Captain sailed, they all settled down to write letters to him. He always left explicit instructions concerning steamers that would be connecting with his, by which of course he would be expecting their news. Sometimes they had to write their letters on the very afternoon of his own sailing day, if, say, a vessel for the Orient were leaving on that same date, which he would meet, perhaps in Yokohama, coming the other way around to that port from Honolulu.

The mailing schedules he handed to them were written on small squares of paper, so many for each of his girls, so many for their mother. They gave names of vessels and sailing dates and, when the monthly bundle of newspapers was to be sent to him, the names of the ships' pursers in whose care they were to place them. Often, when they knew he must be well out beyond the Golden Gate, they received amended instructions in last-minute notes he had given to the pilot before casting off, having heard on the docks of some special sailing not regularly listed.

Lizzie always wrote her assigned letters in a single session and held them until their proper mailing days, not only to get the business over with at one clip, but also to free her mind of the dread that she might forget a future sailing and leave her father famished for home news in some distant port. Occasionally, she had to open her finished letters to add a paragraph or two when some event of unusual importance took place, upon which the Captain might expect her to comment, like the assassination of President Garfield in the summer of 1881.

But mainly what he wanted from his eldest daughters, and always received in fullest detail because they understood this, was news of their mother's health. Since the birth of Frank in '78, she seemed to be much more susceptible to the foggy summers of San Francisco and had had frequent bouts of grippe which she blamed for an occasional back pain of brief but peculiar intensity. Lizzie and Julia knew that their father had posted them to a permanent watch over their delicate mother, but they had to be exceedingly careful how they phrased any adverse health bulletins. These sometimes came back to Annie in the form of worried queries from the Captain, underscored with red crayon that indicated a clean-breasted reply was awaited.

Their mother never asked to see their letters, nor tried to censor them in any way, but, when her back was bothering her again, she would say casually that she had not mentioned this in *her* letter to their father and hoped that they had not, either. The only time she actually demanded secrecy from her daughters was after reading aloud to her assembled children a letter from her father in the Islands. From that point in the Pacific also there came vibrations of anxiety concerning her health. She began the reading in a gay confiding voice but, because her father, like the Captain, always came straight to the point, she could not stop, or rephrase, his worry about her:

"*Per Zealandia,* Honolulu H.I. Nov. 19th, 1880," she read, with a quick smile at Johnny who, in his first year in grade school, could follow without interpolation: "My dear Annie, Your mother has written and I suppose given all the news. She tells me that you are terribly run down and that your back troubles you very much. Your mother says she wrote you to come down and spend the winter, in which I join with her. I think a change from the winter there, to one here, will be a benefit to you, and perhaps save your life, for the present at least. We feel that you ought to have a change, and that soon. Think of this and write that you will come. We have plenty of room in the house for you all, and Maggie the cook, too, if she will come. Truly yours, B. F. Bolles."

Julia always remembered how Annie's hand flew to her throat, as if to choke herself for having read aloud a letter that worried them and frightened Johnny. "Are you going to die?" he asked in a withered voice. She pulled him close and gave him a quick squeeze of comfort. "Of course not," she said. "Fathers are always fuss budgets — mine is like yours, always worrying." But she leveled a glance at Lizzie and Julia and said, *"This* you leave out of your letters, understand?"

The girls obeyed her. They continued writing to the Captain as if that small curtain on anxiety had not been lifted, accidentally, momentarily, on some mysterious ailment their mother had confided to her mother in the Islands, expecting it to be buried there in secrecy. Later Julie would recall that morning's letter reading and would wonder miserably why she had obeyed Annie and told their father nothing about Grandfather Bolles's concern for his daughter. She would read back through all her cherished letters from the Captain and see that the same nameless anxiety resided in him, needing only a word from one of his daughters to spark it to action. He might have come home from the sea, then, for good, to be with their mother, to make up, as he had always promised, for the lonely years. As an adult, Julia saw the poignant frequency of his phrase *your mother*. It was in every letter, the brooding leitmotif of all thoughts of home . . .

Though their letters to the Captain were brimming with details of house, garden and the good behavior of the boys, his letters to them sounded, on first reading, dry as dust. But if you interpolated extracts from his Compass Books, that dealt with the ports from which he addressed them, then you could put a little background into his single-line descriptions and see something more than a solitary man given slightly to self-pity as he worked so hard to keep them all in comfort. Julia often made this adroit combination of letters and old Compass Book entries to lure Johnny into a deeper interest in his father's voyagings than the letters alone would have provoked:

S.S. *Granada*
La Libertad, *Nov. 4th, 1880*

MY DEAR DAUGHTER JULIA:

I am about to reply to your letter which I received at Acapulco on my way up last time. You write a very good letter for a child of twelve and I am always glad to hear from you. I like to think of you nicely domiciled in our new house. I hope that you will all be good children and take much comfort there. Goodness knows that I have worked hard enough for the money to pay for a home for you children, and all I ask in return is that you be a help and comfort to your mother. We are lying here at La Libertad, working and discharging cargo for this place. I hope to have it all out and be in readiness to leave here this afternoon for Punta Arenas. I am well and have been since I left San Francisco and the voyage thus far has not been a bad one. I shall send this to you by the "S.S. Colima" which will be here in a day or so. I shall write to your mother by way of New York, and I hope in a short time after you get this letter to see you all. With much love to yourself, sisters and brothers, and not forgetting a large share to your mother, I am as ever your affectionate father,

J. M. CAVARLY

"Now you take La Libertad," she said to Johnny. "It's one of those tiny Central American ports very tricky to get into. Here's how Papa described it, just for himself, mind you, in one of his old Compass Books." She showed Johnny the diary page of flowing handwriting captioned *Landmarks for Libertad* and began to read very slowly so the nautical terms would, hopefully, sink in:

"When the volcano peak of San Vincente bears N.E. and the surf on the beach is in sight, you should see the port of La Libertad bearing N.W. At this time you should see a strange looking ragged-topped peak down near the beach just forward of the beam, and still farther forward of the beam you will observe a white house or a white building of some sort. These are all good marks for Libertad. Salvador Peak from Anchor N. 1/2 E." He had not written the word anchor. He drew one with a little wiggly line of cable going down to his blue underlining. Johnny gazed at the cast anchor that ended the observations for La Libertad and asked why his father hadn't drawn the white house, as well. "Houses are easier," he said, in a backhanded tribute to the shaded hooks and tapered shank of the Captain's art work. But it was enough for Julia for that moment. Johnny would think about that anchor, maybe even try to draw one himself on the sly. Meanwhile, La Libertad was for him no longer an unpronounceable name. It had a volcano behind it and a ragged peak down near the beach on which sat a white house, and you came toward it bearing northwest. Fishing for Johnny's interest in anything that concerned the Captain had become her secret passion.

In the spring of '81 their father's activities captured all their imaginations. A telegram came from New York for the Captain, the first they had ever seen typewritten on a regular telegram form — METROPOLITAN TELEGRAPH — GOLD & STOCK TELEGRAPH COMPANY OF CALIFORNIA. It said, "Reach here by tenth May to take steamer to California." Signed Trevor W. Park. Annie said, "Oh my goodness, the Horn again!" and revived her memories of the Cape Horn Current tearing along past the black headlands of Tierra del Fuego. The Captain, packing for his overland train journey, laughed over his shoulder and said, "No no, Annie dear, I'll be bringing it through the Straits of Magellan. A steamer that size rounding Cape Stiff! Holy mackerel, have your senses flew the coop?"

And then he was off to bring the newest steamer for the Pacific Mail out to the Pacific from the yards back East where she had been purchased. He had graduated into the ranks of the company's senior skippers, Jefferson Maurey, William Cobb, Waddell and Seabury, all of whom at one time or another had brought new Pacific Mail ships out around the Horn to San Francisco.

"At forty-nine years of age," Annie said with a proud little toss of her head, "that's pretty young for your father to be classed with those graybeards!"

The steamer, S.S. *City of Rio de Janeiro,* was designed for the coastwise trade, though the Captain would take her on a run to the Orient, after her arrival in Pacific waters, to check her performance on that grueling stretch. Like the company's skippers, its steamers had to be, so to speak, ambivalent, capable of making both runs, to Panama or to China, as the shifting volumes of trade boomed or diminished.

Julia was next on the list for a letter from her father (he kept scrupulous tally of his communications with his daughters, so that none would feel slighted) and, after their mother had received and shared the first news from New York, she received hers:

> *Pacific Mail Steamship Co.*
> *Pier Foot of Canal Street, North R*
> *New York, July 1, 1881*

MY DEAR JULIA:

Your highly and much esteemed letter to me dated the 20th came to hand all right. I was delighted to hear that you are such a help to your mother during my absence from home. I hear that you are the gardener and attend to wetting down the lawn. You are a good girl and I am pleased. I wrote to your mother yesterday afternoon, and this morning I thought I would answer your letter to me before breakfast. I am very busy. Will go to the Custom House at 10 o'clock and clear the ship and at 12 o'clock we clear the wharf and go down the bay and anchor, and sail for our voyage around the Horn for Panama and San Francisco tomorrow July 2nd. I am well and all bids fair for a prosperous voyage out. I send my best love to your sisters and brothers, not forgetting your mother. And to you, Julia, you have my love and best wishes from your affectionate father,

J. M. CAVARLY

"How can Papa possibly think about our little lawn," Julia exclaimed, "when he has four thousand tons of new steamer to coax around the Horn!"

"He can think of everything, us, the house, the lawn — even my foolish love for jingle rhymes," Annie said. "My letter had a poem he clipped from the Boston *Gazette*. I've been saving it for some one of our bedtime readings." She went to her desk and took the newspaper clipping from the top envelope of her great stack of the Captain's letters. There was a twinkle in her eye as she settled down to read. "It is entitled 'He Never Has Been There.'" She paused to clear her throat for the proper poetry pitch, then read with a lilt of suppressed laughter:

> *"A life on the Ocean Wave!"*
> *The man who wrote it was green;*
> *He never has been at sea,*
> *And a storm he never has seen.*
>
> *He never has seen a wave,*
> *As it dashed o'er the vessel's deck;*
> *He never has seen a fire at sea,*
> *Or been floating upon a wreck.*
>
> *He never has seen a fat woman*
> *Growing thinner day by day*
> *And, leaning over the vessel's side,*
> *Throwing herself away,*
>
> *While people look carelessly on,*
> *Though in tears the woman may be,*
> *And unfeelingly say it is nothing at all —*
> Only *the roll of the sea.*
>
> *This man may have sailed in a boat,*
> *In some puddle or on a sound,*
> *But if he has been to sea and wrote*
> *Such a song he deserves to be drowned.*

"I've got to compose a little tune for that before he gets back," Annie said laughing. Johnny clamored for a second reading and Jane begged a loan of the poem so she could memorize it for a school function coming up. The young ones went to bed that night thinking of their father as a man of humor, a wit who clipped seasick verse from newspapers to make them laugh. But Lizzie and Julia, sitting up late with their mother, heard the real explanation of the Captain's intent, in their mother's low words addressed reflectively to the dying coals in the basket-grate: "Of course he sent me that silly jingle in the belief that I'd be so amused, I'd forget he was heading for the Horn again!"

There were weeks of silence from the Captain, following Julia's anchors-aweigh letter and Annie's communication in verse. Then a letter postmarked Rio de Janeiro, for California via New York, came for their mother. The Captain had had to put into Rio for adjustments in the stiff new machinery. "I'm fighting her all the way," he wrote. "It's as if she doesn't want to come out to the Pacific."

"Fighting her all the way," Annie whispered. She knew what that meant. She explained again, mainly for Johnny this time, how ships were like people in his father's eyes, endowed with particular willingnesses and stubbornnesses, sometimes as easy on the helm as the response of a friend walking hand in hand with you, sometimes as balky as the horn of a goat you might be grasping in the effort to lead. "That *Rio de Janeiro* just doesn't *want* to come out here," she said, "Heaven only knows why." As she tried to think why, her blue eyes became fixed like a medium's attempting to penetrate the future. But, though she could bring electricity to her, by walking about the room combing her crackling hair, she failed to draw anything to her out of the ethers, to explain the *Rio's* unwillingness to come West.

Years later, after the turn of the century, actually, Julia remembered how they had pondered their father's *I'm fighting her all the way*. She would have the answer then in the *Chronicle's* shouting headlines about the midnight sinking of the *Rio de Janeiro* in a dense fog in the middle of the Golden Gate, with 131 lives lost and nothing of her vast hull, or treasure, or passengers' bodies or effects ever found; only the decapitated head of her Captain discovered floating some days later on the Marin shore. And Julia always believed that *that* was why the *Rio* had fought her father every mile of the way coming out to the Coast — the knowledge she carried somewhere down in the bones of her beams that she was destined one day to give San Francisco its worst maritime disaster.

The *Rio*'s maiden voyage to the Orient in the fall of '81 had for the Captain's daughters the unique *raison d'être* of bringing to Annie a fur coat, destined to take the place of a winter in Hawaii which she was still valiantly refusing because it would interrupt the school terms of four of her children. The sealskin coat had been the subject of endless speculation ever since the Captain had extracted from their mother the confession of what she wanted most for her forty-third birthday which would fall on January 10, 1882. She admitted her longing for a full-length sealskin coat.

The Captain promised to bring her one from Hong Kong where, by some circuitous exchange of goods, sealskins from the Pribilof Islands wound up in small Chinese fur shops in the hands of Oriental fur workers who were, said their father, the most skillful matchers of fur on earth. Lizzie suggested helpfully that the local furriers might save him a lot of shopping around, and showed him the advertisement of H. Liebes and Company down on Montgomery Street:

SPECIALISTS FOR SEALSKIN GARMENTS

We have established an enviable reputation, not only in America but also in Europe, supplying leading Fur Houses in London, Paris, Leipzig and St. Petersburg, with skins hunted in Alaska and Siberia by our own fleet of six vessels.

That sounded good enough for their mother, but not for the Captain who was unimpressed. "Wait till you see what I bring her from Hong Kong!" he had said, and he sailed away with a glitter of conquest in his eyes.

But they could not wait. One day Lizzie and Julia slipped away to the Liebes furrier, opposite the Occidental Hotel, and brought back a set of *Fashion Plates and Rules for Self Measure-*

ment to show their mother what she was going to get. She plucked out the plate illustrating a rich rolled-collar model with dolman sleeves, which would cover her shoulder to heel in choicest sealskin and she made a little pirouette with the picture so that they actually saw the garment on her, wrapping her in a sheen of elegance.

About that time, the Captain, midway across the Pacific, was having one of his most earnest conversations with a woman passenger. She was French, a style expert, bound for Hong Kong to purchase silks and brocades for her dress business in New York, a walking fashion plate herself who changed costumes at least four times daily aboard ship, apparently for her own private pleasure. The purser had seated her at the Captain's right and eventually he told her about the sealskin coat he was going to purchase for his wife, asking her about the styles popular that winter in New York. She replied that all fur styles depended, but absolutely, on the lady's build, her shoulder slope and *taille*. Was his wife, for example, tall? He told her that his wife was a little thing, probably her own exact measurements if his eyes didn't deceive him. "*Petite, hein?*" the style expert shook her head. "But I would *nevair* box up ze small figure in sealskin, ah no!" she said. "Sealskin is so stiff, so heavy — No, no, *Capitaine,* I sink you make mistake."

He worried for two days, then showed the Frenchwoman Annie's portrait to help her visualize his problem. But it was no problem for her.

"For such delicate fine figure, I would buy exactly what I buy for myself," she said, and to his immense relief she agreed to do his shopping for him when they came to Hong Kong. She had a connection there, a fine, reliable house that would make up, during his layover in port, the garment of elegance that would be absolutely right for Madame Cavarly for sorties to opera and concert. He gave her the money he had planned to spend on a fur coat as trustingly as, later in Hong Kong, his sailors would hand over their port pay to the helpful Eurasian girls who knew exactly which shops had the prettiest fans, jades and silks for their girls back home. He returned to the bridge to do the one thing he knew expertly, grateful that Providence had put that little French stylist aboard his ship to prevent him from making the biggest mistake of his life. Annie in a stiff boxy sealskin, fancy that!

He returned home two days before her birthday, full of honors for the *Rio de Janeiro's* successful maiden run to the Orient, and with a huge wardrobe box tied with silk cords under his arm. Annie always made a special event of opening a present. First she admired the silk cord about the box — jade-green, her favorite color. She untied it with little cries of joy and wound it into a skein for future use. Her daughters looked at her glowing face while their father told them he had had the help of an expert in his selection, a real French stylist who said *zees* and *zat* and called him Cap-ee-*tenn*.

Without a change of expression Annie lifted from the rice paper tissue an opera suit of heavy grosgrain satin — first the jacket embroidered with twisted black-ribbon frogs for buttons, then the bare-necked gown with its bustle cunningly padded out with quilted satin, and a long train. Lizzie and Julia let out a gasp as she held the gown before her like a three-dimensional shadow built out to precision with slender ribs of whalebone.

"Oh Jack," she cried, "how *ever* in the world did you get the measurements so exactly!" Her blue eyes looked as if the sky had fallen into them as she pirouetted slowly, manipulating the elegant silk gown like a dancing partner. A gown she might wear maybe twice a year when taken to the opera, and never daytimes, a gown with a train to drag over the sandlots of the Western Addition! The girls took a lesson in concealment of disappointment as they watched her complete her dance turn, with a graceful little kick at the train as she swung about to face her husband with shining eyes of happy surprise.

Afterwards, alone with them, she laughed so hard she had to hold her sides. "Oh the poor dear," she cried. "Can't you just see him being wrapped around the finger of that Frenchwoman? And what a profit *she* must have got from the fur coat money he handed over to her so trustfully!" She put on the little opera jacket. It fitted her like a glove. "But we've got to admit that he carries my measurements *to the centimeter* in his mind's eye," she said, buttoning up the silken frogs over her small shapely bust. Every whalebone in it could have grown about her curves.

"I'll wear it," she whispered, "I'll wear it if it kills me!" She hushed Lizzie's expostulations of fury for the fleecing of their father. "Never let him know he was, Lizzie," she implored. "You, too, Julia, I beg of you." She stuffed the tissue back into the busty little opera jacket and patted it down in her wardrobe drawer. "There's one thing I want you both to know and always remember about your father," she said. "Whatever he does, he means well. He means well with the whole of his big sailor's heart!"

Julia tried to remember this when the Captain started on Johnny's nautical education. It began with a rhyme that he brought home from the ship one day for Johnny to memorize. He read it to his assembled family, in the sonorous voice of an oracle revealing one of the deepest secrets of navigation:

> *When both side lights you see ahead,*
> *Port your helm and show your red.*
> *Green to green, or red to red —*
> *Perfect safety — Go ahead!*
> *If to your starboard red appear,*
> *It is your duty to keep clear;*
> *To act as judgment says is proper:*
> *To Port or Starboard — Back, or stop her.*
>
> *But when upon your Port is seen*
> *A steamer's starboard light is green,*
> *There's not so much for you to do,*
> *For green to port keeps clear of you.*

> *Both in safety and in doubt*
> *Always keep a sharp lookout;*
> *In danger, with no room to turn,*
> EASE *her!* STOP *her!* GO ASTERN!

Johnny, leaning against Annie's knee, with one leg crossed over the other like a lounging faun, gazed at the Captain with round blue eyes identical with his mother's and with her same expression — a veiled merriment for his attempt to force the jingle into iambic meter by accenting with his hand on the downstroke. Johnny could memorize easily. He had scores of verses he recited or sang without error. But *this* thing with ruptured rhythm, his glance seemed to say, had no music in it and will therefore be very *very* difficult to learn.

Annie cleared her throat when the Captain finished and said, "Don't you think, Jack, it might be a little advanced for first grade?"

"*I* knew it by heart when I was Johnny's age." The Captain squinted at his son reflectively. "Even before, if memory serves me," he said. "Why, every lad about the New London docks would spout this at the drop of a hat, years before any of us ever put hand to a helm. This was the *rule.* This was what brought ships safely to port! We salted it away in our minds during the growing years. Aye, aye, son," he said to Johnny, "It's never too early to begin!"

He gave the poem to Julia and suggested that she and Jane take turns helping Johnny to read it. "When I come back from my next trip, maybe I'll have the pleasure of a little recitation, eh, son?"

He tugged his beard and looked very relaxed as he lit his pipe, shielding the bowl with his crippled hand. But you could feel the heat of his burning desire for his boy to go to sea, his impatience with the years that still intervened before he could begin to pass on to Johnny all the knowledge he had wrestled from waves and winds, not found in any books, transmissible only by word of mouth from father to son walking the same deck, feeling the same baffling winds above and the same tug of currents beneath and talking about these together in simple sailor terms bereft of mystery or apprehension.

Johnny looked at the curled-in fingers of his father's left hand as the Captain regarded him yearningly through the puffed smoke. His sisters knew what their brother was thinking in defiance of them all.

"I ain't going out to get bit by some crazy sailor. I like it here on land. I couldn't ever leave Mama for as long as you can. She'd die if I went away. You take Frankie. Frankie tells everyone — me, Maggie, even the lamplighter when he comes around — he's going to be a sailor like you someday. Not me, Papa. I like it fine here on land, the gang and all. Here we can build bonfires in the sandlots. Maggie gives us spuds to roast when you're gone away . . ."

And now, Julia thought, we've got two things to do before Papa comes home each time. Before the poem, there was only one — to scrub Johnny and Frankie clean of the smoke smells after their days with the Irish children in the sandlot caves out beyond Webster Street. She and Jane always corralled the boys the night before landing-day, stripped them to the skin and hung their smoky clothes to air in the basement. Now, in addition, they must get Johnny to memorize

When both side lights you see ahead
Port your helm and show your red . . .

and Johnny, she could tell from his expression, would pretend that the words were beyond him. She met Jane's eyes in a glance of quick communication. They had barely a month to grind that jingle into Johnny's memory. Their father was back on the Panama line, with a fast iron-screw steamer under him — the S.S. *Colima* whose average run to the Isthmus was fifteen days, 20 1/2 hours.

One encouraging omen for the future was that the *Colima* always put the Captain in a good mood. He never returned from a trip in her grumbling about her performance. Actually, he thought so highly and so personally about this ship that he had made entries about her on the flyleaf of his Bible, as if she were a member of the family. *Colima tonnage — 2905.54 tons gross, 2143.85 net. Colima steerage has 257 life preservers,* and so forth. When the first rubber stamps came on the market, he had had one made in bold block print — "COLIMA" — and thenceforth stamped it across the tops and bottoms of his letter sheets, not once, but as many times in a row as the width of the paper would take. Subsequently he ordered a *J. M. Cavarly* in soaring gothic print, but this he always stamped beneath the ship's stamp — a peculiar protocol which none of his daughters could fathom beyond the odd idea that it simply meant *Ladies first.*

In the end, it was Grandfather Bolles who taught Johnny to recite the Captain's navigation rules. He came to the mainland in that fall of '82, pretending business in San Francisco. "If the mountain won't come to Mohamet," he said to Annie as he took her in his arms, and that of course was his sole business in San Francisco — to visit with her, meet the newest grandson named after his own son and renew acquaintance with all the other children.

He brought a breath of the flowery isles with him in an oiled silk bag filled with ginger flowers. "Since these fancy new steamers have iceboxes good enough to keep strawberries and salmon fresh," he said with a twinkle, "I figgered they could keep these for my little Annie!" He winked at Lizzie and Julia as she floated the white blossoms in a Canton bowl, inhaling deeply their spicy sweetness. "If you two take up where those flowers leave off," he said, "maybe we'll get her home for a visit one of these fine days!"

He had come up on the S.S. *City of New York* and was booked to go back in her on her return trip to the Islands and Australia in a fortnight. The ginger flowers lasted for the whole two weeks (though slightly browned and waterlogged at the end) and their fragrance permeated the sitting room and became indelibly associated with the wonderful visit which, for the younger children, was almost like the advent of Santa Claus months before he was due.

Grandfather Bolles's spade beard was snow-white now and it set off the sparkle of his black eyes as he told his inimitable stories one after the other, an endless repertoire. The Island aunts, uncles and cousins came alive for them again, seemed to rustle about the room in summery cotton dresses and seersucker suits while he imitated to a T each one's tricks of speech and gesture. Every newborn, since their visit seven years before, was described, the rivalry of Annie's sisters to have their children declared the brightest or handsomest by him and the way he had to walk the chalkline of impartiality when they were all brought together for parties and put through their paces for him.

Annie cried again and again, "Oh, oh — I can just see it, Papa!" and she would sniff the ginger-fragrant air hungrily and whisper, "And smell it too . . . ah, so sweet, so unbearably sweet!"

Though San Francisco was offering that fall a theatrical fare that spanned just about everything from grand opera, through Billy Emerson's minstrels to Buffalo Bill Cody's Wild West Exhibitions, Annie and her father were not tempted to go forth once, during his visit. They were content to sit before the fire in the Sutter Street house, sipping tea and talking. Talking endlessly, Julia recalled afterwards, as if each must communicate to the other a whole life before parting. "Like ships that pass in the night," Julia wrote in her diary.

It was to be the beginning of a long night for Annie, though who could have guessed it then. Grandfather Bolles, so anxious to see with his own eyes how his favorite daughter was faring, never mentioned a small pain in his own back, resultant from a slip on the wet decks of the *City of New York* when he had been thrown on his chest against a ring bolt. Once or twice he had winced when laughing, but that was all the girls remembered afterwards. That, and the pervasive fragrance of the ginger flowers which their mother would never again smell without bursting into tears of remorse. . . .

"Oh if I had gone to him that year . . ."

Chapter 16

ANNIE SAILED FOR THE ISLANDS in early '84 with her youngest and eldest — Frank just turning six and Lizzie seventeen. It had taken almost half a year to perfect the arrangements to split a family that was part-time fatherless and would be totally motherless for the six months of the proposed visit. Plans, counter-plans and then their opposites had been discussed each time the Captain came to port.

Since Lizzie had to go, on doctor's orders for a change of climate (the teens seemed to have sent her into a decline), that left only the fifteen-year-old Julia as head of the house during the Captain's absences. Was she capable of handling such a responsibility? Annie thought so, but the Captain wavered as he looked at Johnny whose chief (though strictly forbidden) joy of the moment was driving the wagon of one of the Irish squatters who collected rags, bottles and sacks.

"I *must* try to locate Aunt Mary," said the Captain, referring to Miss Mary Gibson, an elderly Quaker spinster he had brought up from Panama a few years before to rejoin her widowed brother. To help her over her first lonely time in the strange city, he had invited Miss Gibson to the house to meet his wife and children; subsequently she had become a family friend and, during her occasional stints as governess when Annie was ill, the children had learned to call her Aunt Mary. Eventually, he traced the gentle Quaker lady and prevailed upon her to take charge of his family once again. With Aunt Mary installed in the guest room, all household procedures during the absence of Annie were again rehearsed, every eventuality foreseen, everyone's post of duty defined.

It was, Julia thought whimsically, as if the Spanish Armada were about to be launched against the fortress home. Though her father bore no resemblance to schoolbook pictures of Sir Francis Drake, he sounded like Drake as he laid down link by link the chain of command — from himself when at sea, through Aunt Mary and thence to Julia who had access to the fo'c'sle of Johnny's thought. To his wife the Captain had given a curious document the week before her sailing, addressed to no one, which he asked her to keep in her purse at all times. "You'd think," Annie said in private to her daughters, "we might be picked up as hobos in Hawaii and would have to show credentials. Credentials in Papa's homeland! Your father is a strange one." But she dutifully stowed away in her purse the paper that read:

> *San Francisco,*
> *March 30th 1884*
>
> I promise to come to Honolulu after Mrs. J. M. Cavarly and daughter and son on or about Aug. 15th if I do not sail for Panama on the "Colima" or any other of the P.M.S.S. Co.'s steamers on their regular sailing day for Panama on August 1st 1884.
>
> J. M. CAVARLY

Had he sensed, Julia wondered later, the blow that was to be dealt their mother upon arrival in Honolulu, a shock that would rob her of all coherent thought? The letters from Grandfather Bolles had been noncommittal about health after his first message following the San Francisco visit, which confessed that he had not been well a day since leaving them. By May, however, he had resumed his usual selfless tone:

MY DEAR ANNIE:

I have but a few moments to write today. Mother had been ailing but is now better. A sad accident happened last Sunday. Mrs. Bush, wife of the Minister of the Interior, was thrown from a horse and lived only a few hours. A little squabble in the King's Cabinet & the Crown Attorney has resigned. When the King returns, who is now on Hawaii, there will be without doubt a breakup of the whole Cabinet. We hope for the best and don't see how things can be much worse in Gov't affairs. With my best love to all, I am, Truly yours,

B. F. BOLLES

In November, Annie's mother had written that Father had a bad cough for the past three weeks and didn't seem to improve much, but all else in Kapena Place was rolling along as usual.

The corsets came all right. They fit nicely. Thank you, Annie, for your trouble; will do as much for you the first opportunity. . . . One piece of music you sent, Mary has in two different books, so if you have none like it, I will send it back. She is much pleased with the other songs and is singing them now. I hope you are all well and would like to see you all very soon. Hope you will come some day, *soon.* . . .

The underscoring of *soon* from her undemonstrative mother had worried Annie. It seemed like a signal of some sort. When he returned in late November, the Captain noticed at once her preoccupation and suggested advancing the Hawaiian trip to Christmas.

"You at sea, me in the Islands . . . and Julia, Jane and Johnny all alone like orphans in this big house over the holidays?" Annie cried, and that was that.

Before he had sailed on his next trip which would keep him at sea over Christmas and the New Year, he took Lizzie and Julia aside, told them he didn't like their mother's peaked looks, and gave them the longest list of instructions for her care they had ever received. Breakfasts on trays whenever they could prevail upon her to stay late abed, no shopping tours downtown when it rained, fires *every* day in *all* grates and a tumbler of hot spiced wine each night after she was in bed, using the case of vintage Madeira they would find stored in the basement.

Julia's Christmas letter from him was like a continuation of his worried farewell. It frightened her a little. For the first time he suggested that there might come a day when she would no longer have her mother, or himself either. Sailing down the wintry coast wrapped in thoughts of home, gloomy, tender and anxious, he had decorated his letter with rubber stamps and had addressed her with a new formality, as if to conceal beneath such epistolary trappings his gnawing concern:

COLIMA	COLIMA	COLIMA
J. M. Cavarly	*J. M. Cavarly*	*J. M. Cavarly*

San José de Guatemala
December 14, 1883

Miss Julia Frances Cavarly,
San Francisco, Calif.

MY DEAR DAUGHTER:

I am seated at my desk to answer the very nice letter you wrote me when I was down the coast on my last voyage. I have nothing of importance to communicate to you, but would impress upon you the importance of close application to your books and school, for I want you to graduate at the High School and then be in readiness for whatever befalls your lot in life, for you can't have your mother and father always to look out for you. Be a good girl and receive any and all instruction from your Mother in kindness, and help her all you can. Though you can never begin to repay her very great kindness to you. I hope that you are all very well, and that you may have a Merry Christmas and a Happy New Year. It is now 2:00 P.M. and we are in hopes to finish discharging our cargo and get away on our voyage about midnight. Julia Frances, this leaves me in most excellent health and good spirits. Hoping that it may find you all at home as well as it leaves me, I am — Your affectionate Father who loves his family which he left at home.

JOHN MANSFIELD CAVARLY

COLIMA	COLIMA	COLIMA
J. M. Cavarly	*J. M. Cavarly*	*J. M. Cavarly*

Julia had one glimpse of her mother's happiness when Diamond Head was sighted on May 15th, 1884. "She's up on deck with Frank," Lizzie wrote, "already straining her eyes to find Grandpa on the pier which is still so far away all the people on it are mere blobs. I'm putting this letter in the ship's mailbox for the return passage, so you can know we all arrived safely. Mama says to tell Papa in your next to him that she wasn't seasick a single minute coming down. I've never seen her so excited as now. We're past Diamond Head and coming in slowly to the dock. She dressed for Grandpa as if meeting an Old Beau! The hat she bought from Mrs. Coughlin's with the ostrich plume curling down from the brim — Oh! I've got to run now. I wouldn't miss The Great Reunion for anything. Not even to go on gabbling with you my dear sister, who made all this possible for Mama by staying home and running the roost . . ."

Lizzie was never able to write about the next half hour. The moment the Honolulu packet dropped anchor and put down her gangplank, a bearded man in black frock coat ran up it and went straight to the purser's office. A steward then appeared on deck and asked Mrs. Cavarly to accompany him to the office to receive some special news. The news was that Grandfather Bolles had died suddenly, just five days before.

No cable then, no ship's radio, the death notice came slowly to the mainland on the ambling packet's next trip up. Julia lived meanwhile in a glow of happiness which she transmitted to Jane and Johnny each night when they sat before the fire, guessing what their mother was doing at that exact moment. Johnny figured the difference in time between mainland and Islands, set the moon higher in the west than it was over Sutter

Street and gave Julia the proud material for her next letter to their father. It would more than make up for Johnny's thoughtless absence from the house when the Captain had sailed away — an absence hurtfully noted by him in his letter from Acapulco, which she had diplomatically deleted from her reading aloud:

> S.S. *Colima*
> At Acapulco,
> June 9, 1884

MY DEAR DAUGHTER JULIA:

I write you this letter back from Acapulco. I am well and trust and hope that this will find you all well at home and good children. I have written to your mother and Lizzie, and put under cover to you. I do this for I don't know when they are coming home and when you get this, you will have received letters from your mother telling when she is coming back . . .

She paused to exclaim to her brother and sister, "My goodness, he's homesick for Mama already! He *knows* she's not coming back till August. He's going down to fetch her himself if the *Colima* schedule works out that way!" Then she resumed:

> If she is to be back by the 15th to 20th of July on the "City of Sydney" on her next voyage, you will of course not send it, but if she is to remain and come on the "City of Sydney" on her next voyage, you of course will send it. I hope that you have all been very well since I left you and I hope that you will continue well. You are all to be obedient to Aunt Mary. If Johnny is not good I of course shall attend to him when I come back. Remember that he is *not to leave the block* without permission of Aunt Mary. Such was the order I left. I did not see him to say goodbye. I think he might have stopped at home long enough for that. I expect to have a good report from Aunt Mary about you all. Now, don't disappoint me, be good children. I send my best wishes to Aunt Mary and my best love to all of you children. From your father who is far away from you all,

> J. M. CAVARLY

The first letter from Honolulu in her mother's handwriting came a day after the Captain's from Acapulco. It seemed a thin letter for a first report. Julia said philosophically as she slit it open, "Mama's probably having such a good time, she has no time to write!" Then she pulled out a black-bordered editorial from the *Honolulu Daily Bulletin. Jule dearest, Send this to your father by fastest connection; tell him I'll write soon and am bearing up,* Annie had written across the top of the clipping, with the *p* on her "up" straggling down in fainting line into the opening words of the news story:

> The death of Mr. Benjamin F. Bolles has taken from our midst one of Honolulu's respected citizens . . .

Julia's throat closed, Jane began to cry and Johnny stood at bay with clenched fists, glaring at the clipping in her trembling hands. "Let me read it to thee," said Aunt Mary. Her uninflected Quaker voice continued the sorrowful tidings:

> For nearly 40 years he has been a prominent merchant in these Islands. He was born at New London, Connecticut, March 27, 1814 and at the time of his death was in his 71st year. On his arrival here in 1846 he went to Lahaina, Maui, where he carried on his mercantile business for 16 years. From Lahaina he moved to Honolulu in 1862 and established the well-known house of Bolles & Company. Until the last year he has been a most active merchant, attending with promptness and diligence to the demands of business. His habits of early and regular attendance at his counting room were an example to others. Perhaps no one quality will be longer remembered by his business associates than his genial temperament and good nature. It has only been within the past year that impaired health gave evidence of his age, for with his buoyant spirits, active habits and comely person, he appeared much younger than he really was. . . .

Julia sobbed aloud, remembering the wild windy rides out to Waikiki and the way he had talked to Zu-Zu, and Aunt Mary said, "Thee must attend, my child. Thy mother would wish thee to know."

He had died on May 10th and the funeral had taken place the following Sunday (two days before their mother had landed, Julia checked back heartbroken). Reverend A. Cruzan had conducted the services. The wreaths and emblems in flowers were extremely beautiful, prominent among them being a large cross of white ginger flowers.

"*Who sent those?*" Julia's strangled voice sounded like a sea gull's. Johnny came over from his fighter's corner and put an arm about her shoulder, glaring now at Aunt Mary saying, "Hush, child, thee must not interrupt." She hadn't smelled Grandfather's ginger flowers in that room, their spicy sweetness slightly rotten at the end of his visit.

"*I did, Dudy,*" Johnny said, looking Aunt Mary straight in the eye, defying her to "thee" and "thou" him at that moment and deliver an uplifting lecture on lying. "*I* sent them . . . for Mama, *see?*" he said and stalked out of the room, a ten-year-old man who preferred to have his grief alone, in the sandlots.

Julia kept letters moving from Panama to the Islands and from the Islands down the coast to the Mexican and Central American ports her father listed, with arrival day, date and hour, each time he sailed. She never missed a connection, but gave all credit for this to Johnny's help with the intricate mail schedules. *He's a whiz at calculating!* she wrote to her father, hoping that her small seed of comfort would momentarily take his mind off their mother's mourning in Honolulu.

When home, the Captain wandered about the house touching Annie's things — her shawls, sewing basket and the book of Emerson's *Essays* always kept on her bedside table. These objects had not changed, but had she? Anxiety devoured him for what her great loss might have done to her. On his July leave, Julia and Jane made the mistake of playing one of her favorite pieces for him, in a duet for which they had practiced assiduously.

When they finished and looked around for his praise, they saw great round tears rolling down his weathered cheeks.

Julia could not say "But it's not *Mama* who died, Papa!" because she *had* died for him at that moment. His grieving face rehearsed her death. The tears rolling into his beard were his silent mourning for his favorite pianist whom not even two daughters, graced with her sweetness and many of her same expressions, could ever replace.

"Goodness!" she said afterward to Jane. "If anything ever happened to Mama, I just don't know *what* we'd do with him!" The two sisters gazed stricken at one another, gray eyes into brown eyes, trying to shape up between them the vague form of love which was a word seldom spoken by their New England parents, yet a state of being they lived in constantly — a reaching out of thought one to the other when apart, an unabashed hand-holding when together, as natural as their breathing.

To pad out letters to their distraught father, they read every paper, eagle-eyed for the kind of news their mother always clipped and sent. They studied the old scrapbooks for clues. The preponderance of shipwreck news and deaths of sea captains startled them. There was a series the *Chronicle* carried, entitled "Beneath the Billows" which their father apparently cherished — a gruesome catalogue of ship losses on the Pacific Coast from the year 1864. All the recent hue and cry about the Pacific Mail being a monster monopoly, that had betrayed its stockholders through criminal mismanagement, was pasted side by side with the fluctuating quotations of the Pacific Mail stock on Wall Street. Poems by Longfellow and Whittier — always about children; poems about mothers —

> *Mother, I see you with your nursery light,*
> *Leading your babies all in white,*
> *To their sweet rest . . .*

— by Mrs. Helen Hunt; love poems, almost too sweet to be real, until you envisioned the Captain carefully clipping them for Annie from the English-language papers of Hong Kong (his sentimental side seemed to grow in proportion to his distance from home), and health articles of every description from "The Virtues of Celery as a Cure for Rheumatism" to the "Dental Dangers of Acids and Sour Fruits."

"We could send him almost *anything*," said Jane, visibly awestruck by the catholicity of their father's reading taste.

They had a windfall on August 28th, 1884. The *Chronicle* brought forth its Centenary Issue on Fra Junipero Serra — three full pages of California's early history liberally illustrated with sketches of the Franciscans and their missions. It was the Captain's final month of waiting for their mother's return, an especially bitter one for him since duty prevented him going to Honolulu to fetch her. The huge historical diversion Julia and Jane stuffed into their last letter to Panama was a godsend.

They had their reward when the Captain returned. He handed to Julia for safekeeping another full-up Compass Book in which he had copied extensive extracts from the Centenary Issue, with many blue underscorings to attest his interest in the Spanish padres who had been the first Europeans to settle around the Bay.

"Your own mother couldn't have taken better care of me in this trying time," he said, and they all stood a little taller under his smile of approval as he handed them "the Captain's cake" which, he said magnanimously, they might sample at once if anyone was subject to hunger cramps before dinner. But, when they opened the box in the nursery and looked at the cake, they decided to wait until dinner before cutting into it.

"With Papa there to see," Johnny said in a burst of generosity that admitted his father, for the first time that Julia could remember, into his private world of special experiences.

The cake was iced with a wonderful replica of the S.S. *City of Sydney,* on which their mother, with Lizzie and Frank, would be embarking just about the same time the Captain would sail again for Panama. Three pink dots under white-iced hats indicated their faces at the ship's rail. Everybody knew the Captain's wife was coming home, everybody in the whole Pacific Mail family, including the *Colima's* chef who, during her half-year absence, had had *his* share of anxiety trying to tempt his skipper toward appetite with everything from *huachenango à la Vera-cruzana* to Floating Island.

In the wild joy of reunion with Annie, Julia never dreamed that all she and Jane had borne to keep the family together and satisfied was but a rehearsal for a greater separation to come. How, when the central sun returned to its orbit, could anyone imagine being without it ever again? The way Annie clasped them to her, crying "Never again, my darlings — oh, *never* again" seemed to certify that separation as an accidental, unscheduled event having nothing to do with the essential unity of their tight little family.

They never did eat their mother's face on the cake frosting. The sugary decoration was carefully cut out and saved until she arrived, to show her how they and their father had celebrated her home-coming in advance, two weeks before. It helped them to have something foolish to talk about while they embraced her and covertly examined her to see if Grandfather's death had taken something from her, some indefinable quality of spirit none of them could put a name to but which would be known by its absence if taken away. But she appeared to be unchanged, even to Johnny's jealous red-rimmed eyes. The girls wept with relief; he took his out on Frank. "You got the wrong ribbon on your sailor hat," he said truculently. "S.S. *City of Panama*, my gosh. Where you been all this time? Don't you know Papa's on the *Colima* now?"

Their mother had worn for her return the exact costume and hat that had been her going-away outfit. Her unchanged exterior gave to her anxious children the quick appeasement she had hoped it would; and the familiar frame of the home did the same for the Captain two weeks later. "Papa still on the *Colima*,

Mama at home, God in His heaven and all's right with the world!" Julia wrote in her diary, then added in parentheses: "(Except maybe for the Old Salt. He's mad as hops about the P.M.S.S. training school)."

All through the remainder of '84 and well into '85, the Captain railed at home about the "Pacific Mail Cadets." The shortage of seasoned commanders, plus the popularity of the transpacific service in the eyes of embryonic navigators, had prompted the company to set up a cadet-training school of its own, organized along lines similar to those in vogue at Annapolis. Young lads were selected and put aboard Pacific Mail ships to learn the ropes under the eyes of their stern and grizzled commanders.

"And mind you," the Captain cried, "we can't put 'em in the fo'c'sle, oh no! That's too rough for these young gentlemen. We have to put 'em in the First Officer's department and permit them to mess with the officers!" He snorted sarcastically. "As if anyone could learn to be a sailor starting halfway up the ladder like that — even Johnny would know better, wouldn't you, son?"

Johnny diplomatically held his tongue during the outbursts. He thought it the proper way to go to sea, nicely berthed with officers. That's the way he would go, *if* ever he went. No stinking old fo'c'sle for him, no sirr-ee!

The Captain had had a pair of cadets aboard the *Colima* for one voyage, then they had been transferred back to the S.S. *Colon* on the Aspinwall-New York run, on their own request because they got homesick when too long away from their home port.

"Homesick!" the captain hooted. "At fourteen *I* went off on a whaler for three years — and came back a *man*, by God! What in thunder is sailoring coming to? Homesick, my eye!"

Once he returned from Panama with a clipping from the *New York Tribune* which he gave to Julia for his scrapbook, with an elaborate apology for not having had a pair of tongs to handle it so that neither he nor she would soil their hands. The article reported the grievances several of the cadets had told to the

Tribune reporter. Two of the company's top commanders — Captain Tanner of the *Colon* and Captain Maury of the *City of Tokio* — were described by the cadets as tyrants who had commanded them to polish the brasswork and holystone the decks, and even once to clean out the pigpens aboard.

"The whippersnappers expected to learn seamanship from the bridge — help Maury bring the *Tokio* back from the Orient, no doubt!" The Captain's eyes glinted with scorn and he laughed harshly. "Maury told me how he fixed them! When they brought their grievances to him, he told them they were not cadets, but *ship's boys* and would be treated as such. He forbade them to mess with the officers, made them set up their own mess and refused them a waiter. That was one of their main complaints, fancy! No waiter!"

In the end, the training school idea was abandoned. The seasoned skippers had made it so rough for the cadets that most of them deserted. Of the few who stuck it out, only one eventually became a commander, and his career wound up as the Captain had prophesied, though he was not to be there to see it. Captain Ward was to be the commander who gave the champagne party aboard the ill-fated *Rio de Janeiro* in 1901 when she was waiting inside the Golden Gate for the fog to lift, and was never seen alive again.

The family was relieved when the hallelujah about the Pacific Mail cadets died down, Julia perhaps most of all. It had not been good for Johnny to hear his father telling what *he'd* do if he ever had the luck again to get two of those pampered nurslings aboard his command. Julia believed it was pride in his calling that had stung their father to such spleen, and loyalty to his good friends and fellow commanders, Maury and Tanner, which had made him smack his lips over thoughts of revenging their honors maligned in the *Tribune* article.

"In a way," she told Johnny philosophically, "those Old Salts have a right to be touchy. Where would the Pacific Mail be without them? They're the only continuous thing in the whole company. Goodness — there have been seven different presidents since you were born, Johnny . . . new Boards of Directors every year — new ships, too, to replace the lost ones. I was counting them all up the other day when I put Papa's scrapbooks in order. Only the captains' names stay the same. They *are* the company, when you come to think of it."

Gently she drew her brother back to a reluctant admiration for his father. But it was an admiration tempered with the instinct for self-preservation.

"Sure, I guess so," Johnny conceded. "But *I'd* never want to sail with him, gosh no! Frankie's his sailor boy, not me!"

"Not I," Julia corrected. Then she laughed and ruffled his hair. "But that time's so far off, we don't even have to begin to think of it now," she said comfortably.

She was to eat her last words before the next year ended.

During the school vacation of '86, the Captain decided Johnny was big enough to have his first taste of the sea. Going on thirteen, tall and well built, his son reminded him of himself at about the same age, as capable of sailing before the mast as he had been. The perfect opportunity presented itself in the form of a barkentine moored in the Bay, skippered by an old friend, who agreed to take Johnny for one trip up to Astoria, Oregon, and back.

The Captain made all arrangements in secret and sprung his plans on the family one night, his eyes shining with joy for the beautiful present he was giving to Johnny. He was so carried away by his own inner delight, he failed to notice Annie's hand reaching out quickly for Johnny's, nor the face of his son blanching at the thought of four weeks in the fo'c'sle of a lumber carrier skippered by one of the "old school" men who had come up from before the mast.

"I couldn't put my boy in more capable hands — and aboard a sailing ship, to boot!" The Captain tugged his beard and nodded happily at the girls clustered around Johnny so as to obliterate him from his father's direct gaze until he could catch his breath.

"When does he go, Jack?" Annie asked in a voice so small she had to repeat her question.

"Tomorrow. They'll sail day after, but I'll want him aboard a day and a night before, so he can see the finish of loading and get himself nicely bunked in."

"But his clothes, Papa!" Julia cried, catching at the only straw that might promise delay.

"Clothes? Just his old dungarees and a few sweaters — d'ye think he's going on a summer cruise?" he laughed at her fanciful notions, then added for Annie's comfort, "They'll fit him out with boots and slickers from the slopchest, *if* he needs them, which I doubt. Summer is generally pleasant up the coast."

He fetched his old ditty box and held it on his lap. It was all scratched and weather-beaten but still sound with brass-bound corners, hinges and padlock. Something about the way he stroked it, then peered under its lid at the spools of coarse linen thread, the big-eyed needles and cards of buttons of every size, took the sting out of his autocratic disposal of Johnny's summer vacation. When he looked up and said huskily, "Come here, son," Johnny stepped forward at once, visibly overcome by what was about to happen.

"This is yours now, son! Everything's in it you'll need for repairs on your voyage — threads, needles, thimble, scissors . . ." he named the objects in a litany of love as he touched them, "a leather finger-guard for sailmaking . . . a little awl to punch new holes in belt or shoes . . . fishhooks, even, if you can escape your Mate's eye and hang a line overboard when off watch." He looked up. Pride flashed in his dark eyes. "You can tell your bunkmates that this ditty box went with your father more times around the Horn than probably the whole crew can count together . . . to the Arctic, the Antarctic, the Indian Ocean, Malaya . . ." He handed to Johnny the sacred box that contained his youth as a sailor boy before the mast, wordless now, overcome by the moment he had dreamed of ever since Maggie McLatchie had laid his first son in his arms, so long ago.

Your bunkmates, your Mate . . . Annie heard the possessives that passed on to his son everything her husband had ever felt about every ship he pridefully joined. She knew then that she could make Johnny understand, later when she would go to his darkened room to say good night, what his father was trying to give him — a bit blundery and very sudden, perhaps, but straight from his sailor's heart.

The sisters packed his duffel bag that night, putting little notes of comfort into the pockets of his dungarees. Annie went through the ditty box, under the Captain's approving gaze. She tucked in a package of laxative tablets while he reminisced about the dosages of castor oil *his* Mates had always administered at the end of the first week out to sea, whether you needed them or not, and straight from a tin cup, by God!

Next morning he walked out of the house side by side with Johnny who, despite the ditty box under one arm and the duffel bag under the other, kept right in step with his rolling-gaited sire and never once looked back. The sisters peering from parted curtains at the only part of the going-away the womenfolk were allowed to witness, had never seen their father so proud. He began talking to the cable-car conductor even before he had comfortably settled himself on the open dummy. He was telling the poor little street-bound man that his son was going to sea.

Annie dabbed at her eyes with a lace handkerchief though she did not know then that she was having her last glimpse of father and son walking in perfect step. Johnny could not tell coherently, for a long time after, just exactly what had happened before he deserted . . .

He had been scared, even a little embarrassed, riding down Sutter on the open dummy with his father. The Captain told everyone that his son was going to sea — the conductor, the grip-man, even passengers waiting at curbs to get on, all the people he knew all along the line down to the pier. The dingiest old ship you ever saw was tied up at Meiggs Wharf. Aboard it they went, his father before him, dodging expertly the cargo whizzing about them on the loading cranes.

An old man with a beard and a limp and a beat-up visored cap pulled down over gimlet eyes had been introduced as Captain Slocum and Slocum had given Johnny the kind of a look you'd give to a louse. Immediately he had called his Mate who had belly-dancers tattooed on his biceps which danced when he flexed them. The Mate had led him to the dark pointed peak of the fo'c'sle and shown a berth topmost under the deck where he was told to toss in his things.

Then he was taken below to help stow away the cargo that was swinging aboard. The Mate gave him an iron hook, told him to pick his teeth with it while waiting for crates to come down, and had left him there at the bottom of the Number Two hold with a half-dozen seamen, all but one of whom looked him over with sneers.

The one who didn't sneer said, "My name's Ben, what's yours, son?" and showed him how to use the hook as the crates swung down. All afternoon he had worked, scrambling up the curve of the hull as crates and bales diminished the working space of the dark hold that smelled of piss and sweat. He got to be a sort of hero with Ben who egged him up the staircase of crates where no one else could climb. He was doing all right, at least in *one* seaman's eyes, but he kept looking up to the open hatch, to see if his father, pacing the deck with old Slocum, would glance down and give him a glimmer of recognition. But the Captain acted as if none of the scum in the hold belonged to him; once Johnny had caught his eye, pleading for a nod of approval, and the Captain had stared back at him as if he'd never seen him before. If just once his father had tipped him a wink . . . but he hadn't. After a while the gimpy skipper and his father appeared no longer in the sky-frame of the open hatch, and he guessed the Captain had gone on to the *Colima* where coolies were doing what he had been left to do aboard a creaking old brig with a bunch of hairy apes for companions.

Ben saw him rubbing his arm muscles and said, "Just a few more, son, then we're out of this hell-hole!" and those were Ben's last words on earth. A crate poised high above the open hatch suddenly let go. Ben was in the way of it. It crashed down to the keel plates and flattened him from sight and a red jelly splattered out from the crate's edges, all over him, all over the men around him yelling, "*Christ A'Mighty* . . ."

Top-deck seamen repaired the broken tackle, lowered the boom and picked up the crate to see if anything was left of Ben that could be scraped together for burial. Then Johnny fled the dark hold full of screaming men. Soundless as a mouse he ran up its steep-pitched sides toward light and air and a sunset over San Francisco red as the blood spattered over his dungarees. He stumbled to the fo'c'sle for his father's ditty box, but left his seaman's clothes behind. Those he would never need again . . .

Annie was having tea with the girls before the fire when Johnny stood suddenly before them, panting from his run all the way home, deathly pale, speechless in his blood-stained clothes. Julia ran to him, saw the blood was from the outside and cried, "He's all right, Mama — it's not his!" Then Annie could move. They led him in shock upstairs to his room. He let himself be undressed like a wooden doll. Lizzie and Jane got him into bed while Julia rolled up the bloody pants on which his horrified eyes were fixed.

"My God, oh my God — *what* have they done to you!" Annie wept, dropping to her knees beside the bed, cupping his stiff white face in her hands and rocking it gently back and forth as if to loosen the mouth muscles drawn in tight with terror. "Tell me, darling . . . tell me," she begged. "Whatever it is, it's *all right* . . . do you hear me?" He seemed to, from far away. Some of the horror faded from his eyes but he was unable to reply. Presently he began to retch and they all became busy with him, helping him through his waves of nausea until they heard the Captain's footsteps in the entrance hall below.

Annie said, "You girls stay with Johnny . . . *I'll* go." Braced for the storm, with her little chin thrust forward and eyes like flaring phosphorus, she sailed out of the room and down the stairs to confront the cause of her son's collapse.

The Captain's voice roared up the stairwell, every threatening word distinct. "White-livered coward . . . a *deserter,* by God! A runaway from the mere sight of blood. Imagine me hearing *that* from Slocum when I went back to see how the boy was making out. My son, a white-livered deserter! *He's going back to that ship tonight!* If I have to take him by the scruff of his neck!"

"*Wait,* Jack!" Was that their mother's voice lifted in command? "You listen to *me* this time . . ." They heard the sliding doors of the parlor pulled shut. Muffled now, the Captain's outcries rose and fell in angry waves, with a light sound continuously above them like a wind — their mother talking him down, steadily, determinedly, and quite outraged for his unjust accusations.

The girls had heard her stand up to the Captain before, but never like this. Julia shot a glance of apprehension at Lizzie over Johnny's recumbent form. Would this develop into a real break between those two below who had never been known to lift their voices one to the other? "She'll win him around," Lizzie whispered. "It's only his pride that's bleeding . . ."

Tears smarted in their eyes as they remembered the beautiful morning, with the Captain striding forth beside his son, so proud you couldn't touch him with a ten-foot pole . . . and the evening before when he handed over his weathered old ditty box, like a king passing on his crown to his princeling heir. In a way, they could understand the awful jolt of disappointment that had momentarily transformed their father into a raging bull.

After a while, the voices behind the closed doors calmed down, almost to inaudibility. Annie's occasional rising inflections blew scattered words up to them. "All right, Jack, *if* you must . . .

To *that,* I'll agree . . . No, absolutely not . . . Only for *half* the voyage."

Then the sliding doors rumbled open on their tracks. Lizzie gave Julia and Jane a sign, and they all went down to greet their strangely subdued father. Annie passed them on the stairs, hurrying back to Johnny with the news of the Captain's compromise punishment.

He was to go to sea on his seachest. Every afternoon after school, he was to repair to the basement and sit on his chest for two hours to meditate on cowardice. Two hours by the clock for the space of half the Captain's next voyage which, God be thanked, was only the run to Panama on the speedy *Colima.*

"It's the best I could do under the circumstances," Annie murmured as she hugged Johnny to her. "There had to be *some* punishment . . . you know your father. But this is a whole lot better than having to go back on that old ship, isn't it, darling?"

Johnny felt her arms about his neck like little bird-bones and her heart beating fast as after a long flight. Tears flooded his eyes which she took to be thankfulness for his escape.

"Everything's going to be all right," she whispered. "Everything!"

Loyally and punctually for his mother's sake, Johnny went to sea on his seachest. But his meditations were a far cry from what the Captain had prescribed. He substituted hatred for cowardice and sat counting up all the things about his father you could really hate . . . his drunk-looking walk, his arrogance, his penny pinching, his one-track mind soaked in sea water, the way he was always absent when their mother needed him the most . . . You could go on with the list till the cows came home.

His handsome face showed nothing of his secret thoughts. He put on a mask of indifference that seemed to suggest how idiotic was this old-fashioned punishment which only an eccentric like his father could have dreamed up.

But sometimes, when Julia visited him as he sat brooding on his chest beneath the barred window of the basement, she thought the stripes of sunlight across his back looked like whip-lash marks. Then her gay announcement — "Only five days, twenty hours and seventeen minutes more, Johnny!" came out quite choked, not at all as she had planned.

Chapter 17

IN THE YEAR FOLLOWING his premature baptism in the sea, Johnny developed two different personalities which he would put on or take off as easily as he changed caps. When his father was at sea, he was demonstrative, talkative and sunny-natured, but the moment the Captain came home, his other self took over. He spoke only when addressed directly and refused to sing in his father's presence, begging off with feigned colds from the evening hymns about the piano with his sisters. In after-school hours he vanished completely and arrived home only just in time for dinner. Then he appeared polite, respectful, but as impersonal as if he had dropped into this family by mistake, and was only waiting for their meal-time hospitality to him to end so that he could move on to the more important affairs in his private life. These matters, his attitude made clear, had nothing to do with the sea talk that went on around the table out of deference, no doubt, to the bearded old fellow who sat at the head of it, at whom he sometimes gazed as upon a specimen under glass.

The Captain pretended to disregard the boy's studied withdrawal from everything that concerned his seafaring life. He concentrated his attention on Frank who, at ten, could never hear enough of his yarning about the rough-and-tumble days before the mast, the bloodier and stormier the better. But sometimes, when he had related a particularly exciting yarn, one that even Annie had not heard before, it smote the girls' hearts to see his dark eyes turn first to Johnny's face for the look of admiration that was never there.

Equally disturbing was the implication of their father's frequent entertaining. For a while it looked as if he were summoning cohorts to sustain him in the glorification of the sea as a career, to impress Johnny. But one day, gazing at Lizzie and Julia in their long skirts and combed-up chignons, he remarked that one of these fine days he supposed they would be thinking about marriage. Then his entertaining changed imperceptibly into what seemed to be a showing off of the fine seamanly fellows *he* would consider acceptable as sons-in-law. "It's *your* turn now, Liz and Dudy," Johnny said with a grimace when another dinner party was announced.

The Captain's friends were all shellbacks, all bearded and usually over-age (or appeared so with premature wrinkles about their eyes from squinting at sun and stars), and they became beet-necked and inarticulate when he presented them to his daughters who had not the remotest idea of marrying sailors, not even admirals or commodores. Annie kept up the small talk until after the dessert was served and consumed. Then the Captain's guests sat back and began to spur each other with reminiscences. The tales went on and on, always about the sea, its ships, its wrecks and the latest deaths of its famous skippers, while the girls politely concealed their yawns and thought mournfully of the pyramids of unwashed Canton ware that would await them next morning.

Their father's hint of matchmaking would have sent them into nervous breakdowns had he persisted in his curious idea; but the moment he was back at sea, he abandoned it completely. Then he wrote to his daughters, each in her turn, as if they could not possibly have any other life interest than his current voyages, Annie's health and the weather down Panama way. Even when one of his last dinner guests was an officer aboard his command, his name was never mentioned nor even the ghost of a suggestion that anything could ever occur to change his ideal home front:

Per S.S. *San Blas*
S.S. *Colima*
La Libertad, March 11, 1887

MY DEAR JULIA:

I write in reply to yours of January 13th. As I have had the pleasure of seeing you since that letter was written, it's not necessary for me to refer to it at all as we have discussed the purport of it while I was home. We are two weeks out from San Francisco today and all is working well on board. I did have the rheumatism quite badly when I first left San Francisco (do *not* mention this to your Mother) but at present I am all right. It's getting to be hot down here. The winter is over and the sun will soon be vertical in this latitude. In May at La Libertad it's piping hot but on the next voyage down, with coolies, we don't stop here, only at Acapulco. You will get your letter only a few days after Lizzie gets hers and Lizzie's letter was written eight days before yours. Could not help it as we are changing from the old schedule to the new and we are irregular about meeting steamers. I will endeavor to answer Jane's letter from Panama, via New York, and then I am square yards again with you girls. I have nothing much to write you for I don't get anything new now on the ships. We have but few passengers and I don't have much to say to them. Give my love to your Mother, sisters and brothers and much love to you. As ever your affectionate father,

J. M. CAVARLY

His service on the Panama line looked likely to continue indefinitely. He had been on the *Colima* now for more than four years. Once, in the summer of '85, after the shocking loss of the S.S. *City of Tokio* on Honshu in Japan, he had talked himself out of a transfer to the China line because of Annie's slow recovery from her father's death. The next spring, the company's S.S. *Honduras* had foundered off the coast of Salvador, which again put a premium on seasoned skippers for the Panama run. "Or," Lizzie had said, "one like Papa who sails under a fixed lucky star!"

Julia always protested the idea of luck. In her eyes the Captain's perfect safety record stemmed from his own self. In his last full Compass Book, brought home to take its place on the nautical bookshelf, she had counted twenty-two new observations of the coastline that he had already sailed past for more than 130 round trips to Panama. Many observations had red-inked corrections written over them at right angles to the original entries — *I would steer S E ¼ E in future as S E is not enough off shore;* or, *This is a good course for daylight only,* and so on in ceaseless amendment to his careful charting.

Even Johnny showed a fleeting interest in the Captain's preoccupation with that single coastline after Julia pointed out that it alone (not counting the China coast) had claimed more than a dozen Pacific Mail ships, side-wheeler and screw, since the company had begun the service.

"And not one of them Papa's, of course," she added, clapping shut the Compass Book which explained why.

"Sure, when you've got a one-track mind like his," Johnny said. "Anybody gets good, sticking to one thing."

Julia hoped that one day Johnny would of his own free will look into the diary-books which the Captain left out on the open shelves with that unexpressed desire. Then he would discover how far his father's interests really ranged. Events of importance that had happened around the world were noted in them, with source from which he had copied, and dates. His admiration for men who had done exceptional things or had made records hitherto unscored, showed up in red-starred transcripts such as:

> Lieutenant Lockwood of the Greely Expedition reached the highest Northern Latitude ever reached by a human being— i.e. 83.24 North Lat and 40.46 West Long.
>
> Mr. George Paynter, the "bar keeper" on the Cunard steamer "Gallia" has crossed the Atlantic 500 times. He made his first

trip in 1851. Since then he has been on 27 different ships, all Cunarders, and has sailed a total of 1,500,000 miles. Mr. Paynter is only a little over 50 years old.

His love for facts and figures reflected in statistics culled from his omnivorous reading, oddly jumbled together on the pages but not in his mind, as they all well knew. When their father talked on any subject, he talked with precision, plucking from the pigeonholes of his memory the exact fact to embellish his point, already fixed in permanence by the mere act of once having written it down:

Napoleon I was born 1769, was made Emperor in 1804, died 1821 at 52 years of age.

Mr. Collis P. Huntington states that 10,000 tons of railroad iron will lay 252 miles of railroad track.

224 gallons of water make one ton.

The gross earnings of the Suez Canal in 1883 were thirteen millions of dollars and stockholders' dividends were 16%.

$25,000 in gold weighs 100 pounds.

Work was begun on the Panama Canal in 1880.

The birthdays of his fellow captains were also listed in the diary pages. Here and there under the inked dates were pencil marks from faint erasures — 1832, the Captain's own year of birth, and you could imagine him meditating with pleasure on the fact that he was five years younger than Captain David Austin, or, more thoughtfully, eight years older than Captain F. P. White. The captains watched each others' birthdays like jealous women and celebrated them when they came together in some port, always with accent on the accumulated years as if it were a miracle they had survived thus long in their continuing struggle with the sea that always won, in the end:

Panama Bay, Feb. 24th, 1883

I went over to Aspinwall Feb. 24th and 25th for Captain

Rathbone's birthday. He is 56 years old. Captain Dow is three months older, Rathbone says.

Their deaths appeared only in the scrapbooks, in obituaries usually captioned "Life's Voyage Over" or "With the Outgoing Tide." Their funerals were events in which Annie and the girls participated, especially when the Captain was a pallbearer. The burial ceremonies were as strange and clannish in character as had been the lives of the deceased themselves, lived in dedication and anonymity in the city of youth and brightness whose every love affair, new strike of fortune or total ruin through speculation were intimately recorded in the prismatic press.

Their fellow commanders gathered in Trinity Church like bearded monks to mourn their passing. The seniors among them were named as pallbearers. The nave of the old church echoed to their coughs and nose trumpeting as yet another was read off on his voyage to the "Ocean Beyond" and, when the Captain was a pallbearer, his daughters watched his slow pacing and downcast face and did not quite know why they had such awful lumps in their throats. Later they would realize that with each sea captain's funeral they had been witnessing the slow attrition of an era their own father had helped to create, the era of San Francisco's greatness among maritime ports of the world. At the time, it sort of embarrassed them to see so many elderly men weeping as a colleague's coffin was carried down the church aisle. After the interment, always strictly private, Annie went with Mrs. Farnsworth to pay a condolence call on the deceased's widow.

Their father's post-funeral activity was a mooning over the death notices in his scrapbooks. He would take any three or four of his dead comrades' obituaries, make little studies of their service years with the Pacific Mail and their ages at death. Almost always their average years at death came to around fifty-two. He would, for instance, take at random Captain Comstock dead on the high seas at forty-one, then Sutton who commanded the *Montana,* dead at forty-four; add Jefferson Maury of the

City of Tokio, dead at sixty-six, to Captain Watkins of the great old side-wheeler *Colorado,* dead at fifty-nine, and divide his total of 210 years of seafaring life by four, staring somberly at the average fifty-two years each one had lived. Most of their ships were gone too, their wreckages strewn all the way from the rocky shoals off Mexico and Central America to the Japan Sea and the China coast.

No daughter could comfort him as he chewed his pencil and studied his computations. But, from his mournful revery, one good thing usually emerged. Eventually he would put away his sepulchral scrapbooks, relight his pipe and look with live eyes at the daughters he had made fatherless with his thoughts. Then he would say, "I reckon I'll have to begin thinking about retiring one of these fine days . . . your mother wouldn't want to go around the world with a rheumatic old dodderer!"

Then the pearl of his promise to their mother and to himself gleamed again in their thoughts and restored their belief that all his self-denials (and their mother's, in consequence) would add up in the end to something more than the financial security for his children, toward which he also labored. When you could look ahead to that trip around the world and see him, for once, taking irresponsible pleasure from the sea, and Annie taking pleasure from the mere fact of having him continuously at her side, then both their sacrificing lives made sense.

In the next two years, the Captain was to shorten his promising forecast about "one of these fine days." First it was to become "When I retire," and then, "Mebbe just a few more voyages."

The summer and fall of '87 was a gala time for Annie, her richest in opera and theater as it was one of San Francisco's richest. Adelina Patti was back for a return engagement at the Grand Opera House, Lily Langtry had returned to the Baldwin Theater with a new young leading man, Maurice Barrymore, and at the Bush Street Theater where the Captain always took his family between bouts with opera and serious drama his favorite minstrels were alternating with a youthful new comic from Boston named Nat Goodwin.

Annie hummed Patti's arias from *Lucia* and *Traviata* and seemed to have taken wings again. While her daughters became deeply engaged in the religious and social affairs of Plymouth Church, and her sons lived their secret lives in the shanty club-houses of the sandlots, Annie went forth with Mrs. Farnsworth to look at the *tableaux vivants* of the current Authors' Carnival, to hear Julia Ward Howe preach a sermon in the Unitarian Church (with a rousing windup of "Battle Hymn of the Republic" sung by the entire audience) or to attend the Music Festival in the Mechanics' Pavilion.

Then the winter of '87-'88 set in, the coldest in San Francisco history. It rained constantly. After the rains, a glaze of ice appeared on the streets. Once in January there was a fall of snow. Though the bitter cold kept the girls indoors, huddled around the fireplaces, it never restrained Annie from walking over to the hilltop on Pacific Avenue to catch a glimpse of the Captain's ship coming in the Gate. Since he no longer permitted her to make the long cable-car ride down to the docks, this windy watch from a neighborhood hilltop had become her practice. Rain or shine, ice or fog, she always went and she always seemed to know, as if by telepathy, the exact hour when the *Colima's* prow would be driving through the stormy strait.

Colds were the inevitable result of her exposures, but she always managed to control these for the five or six days the Captain was home. Immediately after he sailed, she took to her bed to wrestle through attacks of grippe or bronchitis that left her looking as bloodless as the ivory figurines on the mantelpiece.

When Julia looked back over her 1888 diary, she was dismayed to find how many days' entries had begun — *Mama caught a bad cold and is in bed today,* or *Mama suffered terribly with bronchitis last night and Lizzie and I are keeping her in bed today.* In November she had written *Mama is not very well now and the Honolulu folk are begging her to come for a visit but she thinks, foolishly!, that she can't leave us.*

In the spring of '89, the Captain was appointed for the second time to the command of the S.S. *City of Peking* on the China run, with calls at Honolulu on the westbound trip. It was then that he began to say, "Just a few more voyages . . ."

After his months-long absences, the change that had come over Annie was noticeable. In the midst of her grown children she seemed to have dwindled in size. But it was something more than this natural shift in relative size that made her seem smaller. Squinting at her worriedly, as he had often squinted at familiar headlands imperceptibly wearing under the erosion of the sea, the Captain tried in vain to put his finger on the exact spot where the subtle change had taken place. Lizzie and Julia observed only that when she dressed for their father's returns she spent much more time before the mirror pinching at her ear lobes to bring a little blood into them, to make them look less like dead-white shells.

"Keep a weather eye on your mother," the Captain said to his girls each time he sailed. "I thank God I have such good daughters!" From out at sea he stressed the good daughter theme in letters:

> *City of Peking*
> *S.F. toward Yokohama*
> *June 18, 1889*

MY DEAR DAUGHTER JULIA:

I see that in two months from today you will be 21 years old. And, Julia, thus far you have been a good child. I have great confidence in my daughters and never dream of any trouble from them. Continue to be what you have been and it's all I can ask — a Good Daughter! At four this A.M. we crossed the meridian of 180.00 from West to East longitude and we drop a day. When we cross the meridian coming back from East to West we will have two days of the same date, or two Mondays,

or two Tuesdays etc in the same week. . . . Our first night
out from home, we got a howling gale of wind from N W which
gave us an awful shaking up. Since then, smooth seas and fine
weather. We arrived at Honolulu on the morning of the 8th
day from S.F. and left the same afternoon at 5:04 o'clock. We
were 7 days, 19 hours and 13 minutes from San Francisco to
Honolulu, this allowing for the difference in time between the
two ports. I had a splendid day at Honolulu, saw all the family.
I've told your Mother all about that. This leaves me all right
and I hope it may find you all right at home, especially your
Mother.

Two days later he wrote a round-robin to all the girls, with
one sentence underscored heavily in red as if to tell them how
long time seemed when he was outbound from his ailing wife:

> *City of Peking*
> *At Sea, Toward Yokohama,*
> *June 20, '89*

MY DEAR DAUGHTERS:

Yesterday June 19th at 9:00 in the evening, we were 1,722
miles from Honolulu and just over half way from that port to
Yokohama. We are getting along on our voyage thus far very
well and all are well on board. I hope to arrive in Yokohama
in six days from this morning. *It's a long long way over this big
ocean from S.F. to Yokohama.* I think I did the rounds in Honolulu pretty well and slighted no one. Honolulu is nice to visit
but I should not like to live there nor any place in the tropics.
I presume I shall get letters by the "S.S. Arabic" as I wrote
back by her pilot asking all of you to write to me. It's quite a
bit of trouble for me to sit down and write to you a long letter
as I am doing. I have many details to attend to on shipboard.
I send my love to your Mother and to you all. Ever your affectionate father,

> J. M. CAVARLY

Before they received that letter, another of his former commands, the lovely yacht-like S.S. *Granada,* ran ashore and eventually pounded to pieces on a sandy beach at Point Tejupan,

sixty miles north of Manzanillo, Mexico. The *Arabic* had already sailed for the Orient with their letters and there was now no way to tell the Captain of the loss they knew would break his heart, despite the fact that all passengers, skipper and crew had been taken off safely.

Once again the girls started collecting shipwreck clippings for their father, this time for a ship they knew, indeed had actually sailed upon when the Captain had picked them up in Honolulu on his way home from the Antipodes. It made a difference, knowing the ship. They experienced something of the same personal loss their father had always felt when one of his ships went down.

Listening to her sisters recalling their experiences on that one voyage they had made with him, Julia remembered it was in the Captain's quarters of the S.S. *Granada* that he had first revealed his round-the-world plans for Annie and himself. Did it *mean something*, she wondered, that now the setting of his promise lay smashed to pieces on a Mexican beach? A tremor shook her as she imagined the cabin's mahogany-paneled walls, which had enclosed his glowing words like a splendid frame, now split wide open and adrift with sand on an alien beach. The sea always gave signs of impending events . . .

She caught her mother's eyes reflectively upon her as she felt the nameless fear. As usual, in the evenings now, Annie lay on the sofa to ease her bothersome back. Johnny and Frank sat cross-legged on the floor beside her like two contrasting buddhas, one blond, the other dark.

"Don't fret, Julia dear," Annie said softly. "You'll manage beautifully."

For once, her mother had not read her thoughts. Annie was thinking no farther ahead than October when the family would be separated once again — she with Lizzie and Frank in Hawaii and Julia taking her place as head of the house throughout the coming winter. Doctor Mack had laid down the law — no more San Francisco winters for Mrs. Cavarly.

"I was only thinking how glad I am that *you'll* still be here when Papa comes home to learn about the *Granada.*" Julia smiled at her mother. "He carries on so! I could *never* pull him out of shipwreck doldrums as you do. But I can manage everything else . . ."

In the end, Julia had to pull the Captain out of spiritual doldrums more prolonged than any caused by a shipwreck. Shortly after Annie sailed for the Islands, the schedule of the S.S. *City of Peking* dropped the Honolulu call on its westbound journey and he had to face the prospect of six months without a glimpse of his wife. His letters to her poured in from the ports of the Orient, with cover notes to Julia saying, for example, "This letter to your Mother, which you will put on the *next sailing* of the Honolulu packets, leaves Yokohama at 11:00 A.M. on February 6th, 1890. Will you please make a note of the hour and day of the month you receive it." And that would always be the first question he would ask upon his return, though Annie's replies would be awaiting him, stacked in chronological order upon his desk. Before opening them, he must first know when she had received each of his.

Jane kept the mail record — so many letters from Yokohama, so many from Hong Kong, received in San Francisco on such and such a date and dispatched to Honolulu so many days, hours and minutes later on such and such a sailing of the Honolulu packets. When he found that the S.S. *China* had been two days late arriving in San Francisco, he cursed his fellow skipper for dawdling on the way when a letter to Annie rode in the vessel's hold.

In his letters to the girls during this trying period, he seemed to forget that Julia was twenty-one, Jane almost twenty and Johnny already entered in Heald's Business College, a sixteen-year-old student with a flair for figures that earned him stars in every mathematics and accounting course. The Captain always addressed them as children:

> *City of Peking*
> *At Yokohama, Japan*
> *Friday Feb. 14th, 1890*

MY DEAR CHILDREN — JULIA, JENNIE AND JOHN:

We arrived here last night at 11:15 P.M. after a safe and comfortable enough voyage for a winter passage. We were 21 days, 14 hours and 35 minutes from San Francisco to Yokohama and if no one else was satisfied with it, I was. We steamed 5,179 miles which is a long tedious way with head gales and rough seas to encounter. We came in in good shape for which I was truly grateful. On my arrival here I was surprised to receive a letter from your Mother and one from Lizzie. They were dated at Honolulu January 12th and 13th, two days after the ones received at San Francisco per "Mariposa." Lizzie writes that your Mother is improving for which I am truly grateful. I hope and trust you are all well at home. I am all right. Cold about all gone and will be as soon as we reach Hong Kong. It's cold here in Yokohama and about everyone has had a bad cold, so we have to look out and not get any additions. We leave for Hong Kong tomorrow morning, Feb. 15th, at daylight. You will not hear from me again until I get home. With much love to you all, hoping you are all well,

J. M. CAVARLY

He was home for a fortnight in March of that year, his last shore leave before Annie would return and restore to San Francisco the kind of bedrock mooring to which he could tie up in peace. He was almost flighty with anticipation. He asked the girls again and again if they believed all the good news that Lizzie had written of their mother's health and queried Johnny about any private opinions he might have had from Frank, weighing their optimistic replies against some kind of dark dread that one of Annie's letters had planted in him, though he refused to reveal what it was.

The last night before sailing he spent aboard the *City of Peking* but, although absent from the house, he had not yet relinquished its command.

A special note with last-minute instructions was delivered by his cabin boy:

P.M.S.S. Docks,
San Francisco, April 4th

DEAR JULIA:

The "S.S. Oceanic" leaves San Francisco on April 15th for Yokohama. I would thank you to write to me and post a letter to me on April 14th. Put a five-cent stamp for a single letter, address to the care of Alex Center, Agent of P.M.S.S. Co., Yokohama. And on the 15th, you are to write to me again and send a bundle of papers and any letters you may have for me from your Mother. Take this bundle to the "S.S. Oceanic" and ask the Quartermaster at the gangway to please give the packages to Captain Smith. The "S.S. Rio" sails on April 26th and arrives Yokohama May 16th. I don't leave there until May 21st and there will be an opportunity to get letters and papers by her. You can write to me again through the mail and post your letter April 25th. And on the 26th, write to me again and send any letters you may have for me from your Mother. Take the letter to the mail wharf and give it to Mr. Trempen. Hoping that all will go well with you at home I am ever your affectionate father,

J. M. CAVARLY

Julia and Jane walked over to the Pacific Avenue hill to watch the *City of Peking* sail out the Golden Gate. Smoke from her twin stacks plumed out heavily behind, as if their father had called for maximum steam pressure to get his last voyage before Annie's return over as quickly as possible. Actually, he was to break a record on that trip.

"But in the wrong direction, poor Papa!" Jane said when they received his news in mid-May. Their mother was due back the next day.

"It will make Mama happy anyhow," Julia said, "even if *he* can't be here for her homecoming. It's odd how she shares his joy in things like record runs." She smoothed out the letter sheet and pinned to it the envelope the Captain enclosed for his wife, containing the same news he had written to them:

> *City of Peking*
> *Harbor of Yokohama*
> *April 23rd, 1890*

MY DEAR CHILDREN — JULIA, JENNIE AND JOHN:

We arrived at Yokohama yesterday afternoon making a splendid voyage from San Francisco to this port, of 16 days, 6 hours and 59 minutes. The "City of Peking" is on her 62nd voyage and this is the best Western Passage she has ever made, beating her former best passage over twelve hours. We are to leave tomorrow at daylight for Hong Kong. I am well and have been since I left home, only a cold that will leave as soon as I commence going South. I had a letter from Captain William Ward saying that he had much rainy foggy weather from this port to Hong Kong and back from there to Yokohama. I hate foggy weather at sea, will endeavor to take all care that I can, but to sail a ship one has to take chances all of the time and can't help it. I have written a long letter to your Mother which you can give to her when she comes home. We had on arrival some very bad news for two of our passengers — a Mr. Baker and daughter. They are residents of Kobi, Japan. Mr. Baker left Kobi last February to go East and bring out their daughter, a girl perhaps fifteen years of age who had been in New York to be educated, leaving Mrs. Baker at the Grand Hotel in Yokohama. We arrived here all right and Mr. Baker and daughter were in a hurry to get off, he to meet his wife and the girl to see the mother she had not seen in two years. The salutation that met them was that Mrs. Baker was buried three days before our arrival. They had to bear their grief.

> J. M. CAVARLY

His abrupt ending told the girls how deeply he had been affected. To come to a mooring after weeks of messageless voyaging and find that death had got there first was a possibility he had thought about every time he sailed out the Golden Gate. They imagined him putting himself into the shoes of his passenger whose beloved wife lay beneath a mound of Japanese earth.

"Poor Papa," Jane said. "I suppose he buried each one of us as he announced the news to that Mr. Baker."

"No . . . only Mama," Julia said. "I guess he's been burying her in his mind ever since he first fell in love with her. Loving and leaving her, burying and digging her up — after every birth, every earthquake, fire, riot and flood . . ." Her compassionate eyes widened to laughter. "Like an old dog," she added, "with his favorite bone!"

The sisters danced over to the floor register of the new furnace the Captain had had installed as a surprise for Annie. Johnny was the stoker for this exceptional device, then a rarity in the private homes of the city. Over the draught of hot air flowing up they twirled gaily, watching their long full skirts billow out.

"Like the whirling dervishes Mama's going to see when they get to India!" Jane cried.

"Or maybe the Granada gypsies if they stop in Spain!" Julia laughed breathlessly, twirling, feeling the heat bloom beneath her skirts and thinking of her mother coming home next day, brown as a Kanaka, not a frog in her throat nor even the shadow of one (Lizzie had written that in at least a dozen letters over the past half year), her singing voice restored and her singing spirit pervading the Captain's house and turning it again into a home.

They burst into tears as they watched their mother come down the gangway of the S.S. *Alameda* supported by Lizzie and Frank. Propped between them, she looked like an elegant small doll with a bisque-white face and enormous blue eyes that would snap shut if they tipped her back. Johnny reached the foot of the gangway first and took her in his arms as his father would have done.

"You never told us . . ." Julia gasped to Lizzie.

"Told you what? She's simply been seasick all the way up."

Lizzie had not seen the change. She had been too close. Jane hushed Julia with a warning glance as Johnny released their mother to give them their turn to embrace her.

"My faithful stay-at-homes," Annie murmured. "Oh, how proud I am for the way you managed. Your father wrote in every letter how pleased . . . how *very* pleased . . ."

In the carriage they could look at her without wanting to scream. The fog had stung a little color into her cheeks. She had come home just in time, she told them. A secret danced in her eyes.

Their father, in his last letter to her from Hong Kong, had told her that the Pacific Mail Board of Directors had requested him to produce a personal record of his years of service with the company, the names of every ship he had commanded, as well as any data he recalled of his previous experience under sail. They planned apparently to present him with some sort of testimonial for never having lost one of their ships.

"We're to begin the recapitulation just as soon as he comes home from this trip in June," Annie said with a glimmer of pride. "The Board wants it for their September meeting in New York." She paid no attention to the new sights they drove past. She didn't even glance at the billboards outside the Opera House.

"I'm so fortunate I've got all of you to help me remember," she said. Her blue eyes swept their faces one by one, beginning with Lizzie's. "My *Sacramento* child . . . Jule, my *Montana*, Jennie my *Constitution!* And my boys . . . Johnny the *Acapulco* and Frank the *Peking* baby!"

Even in the carriage she was beginning to do what she had come home to do — to remember back, to live again for the Captain the lives of his ships, the twenty-two Pacific Mailers he had commanded and the eight whalers and clippers that had preceded his transition from sail to steam. She had already embarked upon the only trip around the world she was ever to have.

Chapter 18

ORDERING ANNIE TO BED, Dr. McDougall used the only threat he knew would put her there and keep her there. If she did not regain a few pounds, he would not permit her up for the Captain's return. At first she was indignant; then she bargained with him. Exactly how many pounds did Shylock require? Doctor Mack said at least five and there was to be no trickery in the weighing.

Like an obedient child Annie drank milk, which she disliked, and ate Maggie's custards rich with cream, sugar and eggs, setting her fierce will against the problem of her emaciation so she could be on her feet when the *City of Peking* steamed through the Golden Gate. "Five pounds in three weeks? I can do it!"

She did and completed as well the roster of the Captain's commands so no time would be wasted during his week ashore. "Forty-two years of seafaring to mull over and set in order, ten of them before we were married!" She peered at herself in the mirror as Julia brushed her long ash-blond hair that had not a single gray strand. "Not that he needs *me* to help his remembering!" She laughed softly. "Can you imagine your father forgetting a single date, ship or port?"

Julia shook her head. In the mirrored reflection, her mother appeared so restored that it was with difficulty she remembered

just what she and Jane had wept about when she had come off
that Honolulu ship a few weeks before. Would her father's
piercing eyes see, as in palimpsest, the shadowed trace of what
had looked like a mortal illness?

"Of course," Annie smiled back at her thoughtful look, "I *will*
be useful to prod him on things I'm sure he'd omit from that
testimonial report if I weren't here to insist. He simply cannot
be trusted to blow his own horn."

"You're not so trustworthy yourself," Julia said under her
breath. No one had ever heard Annie complain of a physical
ache or pain. It was as if the mere mention of bodily ills were
somehow indecent. This made her such a difficult patient that
the doctor had more than once threatened to cut her from his
calling list. Even now Julia suspected she was pretending a well-
being that she did not feel. But her father would know. Nothing could be hidden from his eyes.

At first, the Captain appeared to see nothing beyond the
trembling living image of a picture he had carried for six months
in his heart. Annie's diamond earrings winked like small harbor lights as he stood her off from him, beneath the gasolier of
the entrance hall on his arrival evening. Only his overwhelming joy that she was home again showed in his face as he raptly
inspected her.

"Well, Annie . . . well!" he said thickly. He flashed a look of
relief at Julia and Jane standing on the stairs above. "We missed
you, Annie dearest . . . something terrible." Even when he
lifted her and felt her feather lightness, the girls' watchful eyes
detected no change in his expression.

"We've lost our bet with Lizzie," Jane whispered. "It's exactly
as she said it would be — the Big Barometer registers no
change."

And so it seemed for the week the Captain was in port. He
listened to Lizzie recount the highlights of the Hawaiian sojourn, expressed amazement that Annie had stood up to such
rounds of continual visiting (which always took the starch out

of him) and teased his wife for having left nothing to do on her next trip. He listened to the doctor explain his regime to restore to his patient some of the pounds she had trotted off in the Islands and snatched at his opinion that her loss of weight was probably the main cause of her occasional backaches. He listened to Annie's own voice each evening, leading her quintet of sons and daughters through the songs he loved best. Then he really settled back. From his armchair near the fire, with his reading-light extinguished so he could see them all more clearly beneath the piano lamp, he was the shadowed shape of contentment. There was about him the kind of quiet Julia remembered from her only sea voyage years ago aboard the S.S. *Granada* — the sudden repose of a ship when its anchors are cast.

Later, from their parents' bedroom came sounds of merriment that went on far into the night. They always retired with the scrapbooks which were their arbiters when they started to squabble over conflicting memories of the seafaring years. They did not get very far with their recapitulation during the Captain's June days ashore. Associations led them astray again and again. The *Anglo-Saxon's* tonnage reminded Annie of how high above the sea that small fo'c'sle deck had seemed, the first time he led her up to it. "In the Gulf Stream and there was a moon," she said. "No, no, Annie — in the Antibes Current, above Cancer . . . around Latitude 30 North." The Captain chuckled. "You never got your sea legs till after Hatteras!"

"Well . . . it *was* in '59. Just think, Jack. Thirty-one years ago . . . !" and there would be a silence then as they met each other's eyes astonished at the flight of time.

Passing through the upstairs hall, the girls sometimes paused outside their parents' half-open door and smiled at the kind of love-making going on in the big room — a sparking of memories from hundreds of associations shared, laughter leaping from small inconsequential words that had special meanings unknown to anyone outside the context of their long love. "The old darlings!" Julia would whisper and look at Lizzie with shining eyes. They thought of their own beaux, still in the tongue-tied stage, but shyly serious. Would *their* married lives (after their suitors screwed up courage to speak to the Captain) sum up finally to this kind of richness?

"Thirty-one years . . . *Holy* mackerel!" came the muted voice of their father, then, inevitably, "Eleven thousand three hundred and fifteen days, Annie — fancy that!"

At the farewell dinner before weighing anchor again for China, the Captain announced that he and Annie had progressed to his fifth Pacific Mail command — the S.S. *Sonora* of wooden side-wheeler vintage. That left just seventeen more vessels to dredge up, then his sailing record would be complete.

"We'd have finished in this stint," he added with a twinkle, "if your mother were not such an addict of embroidery. What she can think of to add to a simple roster of ships' names, dates of command and courses run! She's trying to make a sampler of it with fancy lettering, bits of verse and texts from Scripture . . . even a few albatross and whales if she can cram them in."

He gazed at his wife playing deaf across the table. The amusement in his eyes seemed to vanish for a moment. Then, offhandedly, he sprung a surprise.

"Your mother's so eager to see that tomfool testimonial, which of course won't be presented till I retire, that I've decided to do just that, after the August sailing of the *Peking*. This voyage and one more . . . then she'll have her sailorman's sampler!"

"Jack . . . you're joking!" Annie stared thunderstruck at him, then around the table at her thunderstruck children. Julia's foot pressed Jane's beneath the table.

Their father *had* seen something after all. In those seven days ashore after the separation of six months, he had finally got his sights adjusted to penetrate their mother's small bright clouds of make-believe, and whatever he had seen behind them he obviously did not like.

The Captain stuck to his jocose role. "Don't you *want* me home, Annie dearest?" He looked around the table with an injured air. "Or any of you? To look at your faces, you'd think I'd announced the end of the world." He rolled his napkin and pulled it through an ivory ring. "Aye, aye . . . the end of the world," he said mournfully.

Then of course they all protested — Annie with tears of joy, the girls with glad cries concealing their confirmed anxieties and Johnny tossing his head like a startled stallion with runaway glints in its rolling eyes.

"Papa a landlubber!" Frank whispered to Jane. If his father had announced that all the oceans had spilled off the edge of the world leaving therefore nothing to sail upon, he could perhaps have understood the resignation news.

After the August sailing . . . words of magic and of promise, words to rally around, words with which to start weighing anchors. . . . Every weekend for the remainder of June and all through July, the girls took Annie visiting, via the Sunday *Chronicle,* some one of the countries she was sure to see on her trip around the world. Two travel articles profusely illustrated with line-drawings always covered the front page of the Sunday editions. They read them aloud to Annie and the assembled family, with the Atlas open to the world map which Johnny and Frank studied under Jane's tutelage.

The Sunday of June 8th was a day of Spanish travels — "Tetuan in Morocco" and "Spanish Jottings from San Sebastián." Then they had a Japanese day — "Street Scenes from Yokohama" with The Radish Hawker, The Paper Lantern Maker, The Human Water Cart and The Keysmith pictured entrancingly throughout the text. On the Sunday of June 22nd, the first installment of a new novel by Bret Harte also appeared — *Through the Santa Clara Wheat — A Romance of California* — a promiseful continuity that would carry through until the Captain's return from his next-to-last voyage. Annie adored to be read to and would relax for hours while her daughters' voices transported her to Arab souks, Chinese bazaars, English monasteries and Roman catacombs.

On Sunday July 6th, Jane was the "reading cicerone" for a visit to the "Ragpickers of Paris"; the next week Julia read her family off to "The City of Seville." On the 20th, they roamed the Tivoli Gardens and also took a look at "The Students of Paris — Their Habits and Mode of Living" and, on the last Sunday of July, they visited, through Lizzie's reading, the Abbey of Glastonbury in West England — "Joseph of Arimathea's Holy Thorn — How St. Dunstan Fought the Devil — The Famous Abbey and the Life of the Monks." In July, the maritime news section began publishing the date of the Captain's last trip — "August 23rd — S.S. *City of Peking* for Yokohama and Hong Kong."

They had time for a visit to "Cadiz and Malaga" before the Captain sailed home in mid-August. Annie said laughingly, "I could begin to write my travel diary right now!" Then she caught Johnny's approving grin and added soberly, "Except that it would be cheating!"

The Captain's port leave in August was like a prelude that hinted reassuringly of what life would be when he would come home for good. He appeared to have cast overboard, somewhere in the Pacific as he had sailed toward them, the last vestiges of his tempestuous nature along with his quarterdeck voice.

"Just one more," he said relieved. "My last voyage . . ." and you could feel Gibraltar moving into the house in October, a huge comforting presence as steady as the rock of ages. He made his retirement at the age of fifty-eight sound like a victory. Fifty-two years, he reminded his family, was the average life span of the Pacific Mail skipper, according to his reckoning. Thus, he had had luck. He had managed to snatch from the consuming sea an additional six years, practically without impairment to his health.

"Practically?" Annie cried.

"Just that old devilment of rheumatism, Annie dear. Nothing that a winter in Hawaii with you won't cure." He tugged his beard and nodded. "The *City of New York* is scheduled to stop there on her way to Australia in November. That's when I figgered we'd go!"

During his week ashore not a sign of worry about his wife showed anywhere. He poked around the house looking at things to be mended, painted or renewed. He was by nature a jack-of-all-trades like all sailors, he said, smacking his lips at the prospect of such a deal of tinkering to do. He suggested to each daughter that she make up a list of any additional Chinese objects desired, to fill vacant corners in their rooms. "It's your last chance at goods direct from the Hong Kong shops," he said with a grin.

In the evenings he and Annie completed the report of services. Then Annie wrote the whole thing out clean in duplicate, as the company had requested — five sheets of legal foolscap for each copy, every page a meticulous creation of penmanship like Tiffany engraving. They dated the report August 22nd, 1890, his last night at home before sailing, and addressed it to the Acting General Agent of the Pacific Mail at San Francisco.

Annie decided that the whole family should hear it read aloud before the copies passed from their possession on the morrow, and chose Jane as the reader since she had been a history major. "There's history in those pages," she said proudly, "no matter how your father belittles them." She pulled Johnny and Frank close to her on the sofa as Jane began to read:

"W.R.A. Johnston, Esquire. Sir: In obedience to the order received calling for a record in duplicate of my services in the P.M.S.S. Company, I beg to report as follows . . ."

Julia watched her father's face as Jane read the roll call of his ships. He stood with his back to the fire puffing serenely at his pipe, his black eyes glinting amusedly as if saying "All this tomfoolery over an ordinary seafaring career." Once he caught her glance and winked, nodding toward Annie sitting now with her eyes closed, lips pursed, as if judging a literary work being given to the world for the first time. He really meant what he said earlier, Julia thought with a rush of thanksgiving.

She had helped him to pack for his last trip to China starting the next day at noon. Twice she had asked, "Are you sure about Mama, as sure as you act?" The first time he pretended an absorption in the socks he was counting. He went on inspecting the darns in them his daughters had made at the prevailing rate of 25 cents the half-dozen darns regardless of size. "This one looks like Jane's mending," he had said, "drawn in tight around the hole to make it smaller." The second time she asked, he dropped what he was doing and took her by the shoulders, squaring her off from him.

"If I weren't sure your mother is all right," he said, "you *know* I'd not be sailing tomorrow. You think I'd put myself out of communication a whole month going, a whole month returning, if I thought for a minute . . . ?" He shook her a little angrily, then suddenly pulled her to him. "Don't think I haven't fretted, Jule dear," he said huskily. "Like you when she was first back from the Islands looking as if any breeze would blow her away. I went right to Mack's office then, had him on the carpet for an hour. He finds nothing to cause alarm. She had an early change of life, but you girls knew that. She's coming out of it now, Mack says."

He tilted up her chin. "She's a Mother Carey's chicken, Annie is," he said gently. "She follows all my ships. When I see those little petrels out in the middle of the ocean, I always think of her. They never seem to rest. When not flying, they're walking on the water, patting their web feet on the surface . . . never still a minute. Mebbe she's just plain tired, Jule dear. Mebbe when I leave the sea, she will too."

And now he was leaving the sea in the laconic paragraphs of the last page of the service record: "My total voyages to Panama was 140" (Jane paused over that as if questioning his singular verb) "and 129 were made as Captain, and 13 voyages to China and Japan as Captain, which is my record of most 27 years in the

Company's service." It wound up with a few statements of his years under sail which brought the circle full around to connect the bearded man warming his coattails at the fire with the beardless youth emerging from the simple words: "My first voyage to sea was on board the ship 'Devonshire,' a Black X London Packet; we sailed from New York for London August 24th, 1848. I was a sailor boy. My next voyage I went around the world in the bark 'Venice,' also a sailor boy . . ."

He was listening now to Jane's reading, his head cocked to one side for the names of his clippers, his eyes on Annie with her arms about the two boys, signaling them with a slight pressure as if to say *This is where I came in!*

"1853, 2nd officer of the clipper ship 'Montauk' around Cape Horn. . . . 1854, 1st officer of the clipper ship 'Shooting Star' in the China trade. . . . 1856 to 1858, 1st officer of the 'Golden Eagle' in the Cape Horn trade." And then there it was, Annie's ship, the *Anglo-Saxon* — his first command. Her eyes glowed as Jane sailed her for four years and then sank her, all in one short sentence. "This ended my career in sailing ships, having doubled Cape Horn fifteen times and the Cape of Good Hope three times and many voyages across the Atlantic Ocean. . . . It is 42 years this month since I commenced to go to sea and almost 32 years since I first took command of a ship. Very respectfully. . . ."

In the momentary silence that followed the reading, Johnny gave a low whistle. "Gee whiz," he said under his breath, "Forty-two years!" and looked up at his father with unconcealed amazement as if Noah had suddenly materialized in the room.

"Aye, aye, son," the Captain chuckled. "Two score years, plus . . . and your Old Man's still able to hobble about. Still got one last trip left in his feeble old bones!" He shook with suppressed laughter. From the fob chain spanning his chest, the gold locket with a curl of Annie's hair in it danced up and down. No comments needed now to be made on the sailing record. Johnny unwittingly had spoken for all of them with his awestruck *Forty-two years!*

Their father's laughter was contagious. A gale of mirth swept around the circle. Was it relief because those long sea-tossed years were ending for Annie as well as for him? Or because of Johnny's astonished look which had obviously meant more to his father than any testimonial embellished in gold, actually *was* the testimonial as far as he was concerned? It made no difference. The mood, gay and lighthearted, was the perfect send-off for the last voyage. The Captain mopped his eyes and said over and over, "Aye aye . . . one last trip for these feeble old bones, aye aye."

Annie leaped to her feet and went to the piano. A ripple of grace notes picked up their laughter, then some bass chords said *Aye, aye* — fortissimo at first then in diminuendo dropping to something mournful and low that sounded suspiciously like a musical steal from "Old Black Joe." *Aye, aye . . . feeble old bones . . .*

Thus, their last night. Julia confided to her diary that it had been "a real hallelujah" — an emotional milestone of sorts looming bright with promise. The end of the road lay just ahead. "Papa said he'd take her to Hawaii first — to rest up, I expect, for their round-the-world trip. Now our little Mother Carey's chicken is following her last ship, thank goodness. The next time, she'll be a passenger!"

Their last night was to be truly their last night together with everybody on deck hale and hearty and the Captain in his most winning mood as though deliberately putting his best foot forward to show them what they had been missing all these years and would soon have continuously when he came home for good. Afterwards, long afterwards, when constructive thought again became possible for Julia, she would stare at that word "hallelujah" in her diary and make herself see it not as evidence of some dreadful blindness that had fallen over all of them at the time, but as the Old Testament word that it really was — an ejaculation of thanksgiving to God for His gifts, in their case the gift of that last happy night.

Three weeks after the Captain sailed, Annie called Lizzie and Julia to her bedroom and told them she had bled slightly in the night, probably from unsuspected hemorrhoids. "Only very slightly, mind you, and there was absolutely no pain," she said calmly. "It's probably not worth troubling the doctor with, what do you think?" Her little face reflected a childlike dread for a medical poking about and begged them to brush it off as she had done. She bent to pull the coverlets back over the sheet.

Lizzie's startled eyes met Julia's and clung, for an instant, like the clasped hands of conspirators. When her mother looked up, Lizzie had her voice back and her face wore a mask of reassurance. "Papa would come at me like a typhoon if I didn't call in old Sawbones just once, for a look at you," she said. "Now back into bed and let Jule fix you up."

Julia was thankful for the excuse to rummage through Annie's bureau drawers in search of an appropriate hair ribbon for a bedside reception. She was not quick like Lizzie. The stain on the bedsheet lingered in after-image in her horrified eyes as she picked up lengths of ribbon of various colors.

"September 10th," she said aloud. "I'll record this in my diary — day, date, hour and minute. Papa's such a stickler for exact time." Her voice as she rambled on became natural and easy like Lizzie's. "When you told me about all the housewifely duties before you went away, you really should have stressed that peculiarity a little more! He caught me up several times." She turned about smiling. "I'm going to do you up in blue to match your eyes."

Words, words. Words for housewifely duties and hair ribbons, words to describe a mother's eyes and a father's passion for exact time, all spoken easily with no censor in the throat to impede them, no stricture there or in the heart . . . only one word was never spoken. Even Doctor Mack could not bring himself to say it, as if silence would make it go away, cease to exist, become something no one had ever heard of except as a zodiacal constellation shaped like a crab or as the northern boundary of the summer solstice. Cancer . . . the Tropic of Cancer.

The doctor stared at them a long time before he could speak. Then he said abruptly, "It's *not* hemorrhoids as your mother so fondly believes. It's a bleeding from high up in the caecum. There's a . . . a growth, I think. What's more, she's had it longer than she let on. I think she delayed telling until the last mail ship for China sailed. There's almost nothing we can do. Once those things start bleeding . . . Fetch me a brandy, Jule!"

A growth . . . those things . . . They sat frozen waiting for him to go on. He looked above their heads at an ivory figurine on the mantelpiece as if addressing it instead of them. "She's not to know, of course. Let her go on thinking what she thinks. Keep her off her feet if you can. I'd put the nurse on the case right now, only I don't want to frighten the little lassie . . . until I have to." He looked at them then and let them have it directly. "Send one of the boys on the run for me the moment she starts hemorrhaging . . . it's apt to happen soon, very soon." He shot a question at Julia as he picked up his satchel. "When's the Captain due in?"

"Sometime the last week of October — we'll know exactly as soon as the *China* comes in with his Yokohama letters." She clung to his coat sleeve wanting to ask if October would be too late, but the words refused to come. He read the query in her frightened eyes and gave her a twisted smile that could mean anything. This too was part of the conspiracy. Never say when . . .

They had perhaps six weeks before the Captain would arrive and no way to get in touch with him. The Pacific was not like the Atlantic which had had a cable laid across it in 1866. The Pacific was seventy million square miles of silence broken only when ships met on its surface and talked to each other with megaphones, mirrors or signal flags. And no ships the sisters could discover would pass the *City of Peking* on her way home. Their terror for the way Annie was slipping was incommunicable to the person most intimately concerned.

By October 2nd, when his safe-arrival letters reached them from Yokohama, Annie was a bled-white figure that might have been carved out of ivory were it not for her blue eyes huge with life and hope. A glint of defiance shone in them whenever she caught a sign of anxiety on any of the faces hovering over her. She had no intention of letting this thing get the best of her just as she stood, so to speak, on the threshold of liberation from her strange hermit-like life. Her glance, slightly mocking, made this quite clear.

The Captain's voice speaking to them from a month back was as pacific as the ocean over which his written words had come to them:

City of Peking
At sea — S.F. to Yokohama
Sept. 5th, 1890

MY DEAR DAUGHTERS:

I was given to understand while in San Francisco last time that I was owing you all a letter. I presume that I was and I will now endeavor to write to you as I go along on my last voyage to Yokohama. We are today twelve days out from San Francisco and hope to reach Yokohama in about five days more. We have been as far North as 45 deg. 30 min. to adhere to the Great Circle route as near as practical and the weather is quite cool. Tomorrow we'll be in about 41 deg. 00 min. and that will be just about right. We have had thus far a very nice voyage. All are well on board and we have had only one death which was a Chinese passenger with consumption. The body was embalmed and will be taken to China. We have quite a number of maiden lady missionaries ranging in age from 31 to 40, I should judge. I hope they do lots of good where they are going but one of them looks too sickly for such duty. She is bound to Rangoon, a terrible hot place and I don't think the poor thing can stand it long there. Several are bound for Japan which is a better climate. I am expecting to reach Yokohama in time to send mail on the S.S. *China* which sails from there on Sept. 13th. The boy has brought my chow, or lunch, so adieu for the present . . .

They read their letters in privacy first, then aloud to Annie after making certain they contained no undertone of anxiety. Julia received the arrival letter when he reached Yokohama. It bore the date September 10th, the day her mother had first revealed her "hemorrhoids." Julia had to read it over twice, alone, before she could trust her voice to carry on clearly in the sickroom:

> *City of Peking*
> *At Yokohama*
> *Sept. 10th, 1890*

MY DEAR DAUGHTER JULIA:

We arrived safely here in port this morning, all right and safe once more for which I am truly thankful for it's always a great relief to me to arrive safely in port. Then I feel I can lay off the care and responsibility of my command, for a short time anyway.

We are to leave for Hong Kong on the morning of the 12th and I will get my letters ready and mail them tomorrow. I did *not* tell your mother that I had a most fearful attack of neuralgia last night. I was most crazy with it. I went to the doctor and he threw a spray of cocaine on it and in a short time I got relief. I was up the night before and stood on the bridge in the night air with my cap off and it was this that gave me the trouble. I have not been on shore yet but will go after breakfast. My doctor was on shore yesterday and visited the United States Naval Hospital, the doctor of which was an old friend. The report is that the cholera in Japan is on the decrease and that it has been almost entirely confined to the Japanese and those foreign residents who have lived with the Japanese and have eaten their food. So by all accounts the cholera is now not much feared in Yokohama. I told this all in detail to your mother, knowing how she was worrying about it. Well Julia, I am rather lost for a subject to write on. Well, here is one. There was an American lady here in Yokohama, married to a Britisher, a Mrs. St. John, a very bright and pretty little body perhaps 25 years old. The husband was a drunken wretch and finally this Mrs. St. John has turned a drunkard and has been sent off to Hong Kong to go into a convent. A sister of Mrs. St. John came out with us this trip to look out for her sister. They are both very pretty women. Ever your affectionate Pap.

"And now . . . no more letters." Julia forced a smile for her mother. "Next time, it will be the sailor himself. Three weeks, more or less . . ."

"I always said it in days," Annie whispered, unaware she talked in the past tense. "That always made it sound shorter."

She knew now that she was very ill, but if she guessed the cause of her rapid wasting, she refused to admit it, even to big familiar Maggie McLatchie who had moved in to take charge. But there were signs that she knew she was engaged in a contest with time. She kept a little calendar on her bed-table and crossed off the days as they passed. She had the aneroid barometer brought up from the Captain's study so she could watch the weather from her bed, concentrating on the indicator like a mesmerist, commanding it to stay up to 30 so no storms would hold up the *City of Peking,* even for one precious hour.

The girls drifted like ghosts through the downstairs rooms, in speechless grief as their mother dwindled to a little thing all eyes and whispers. They took turns playing the piano for her, keeping continual music flowing up the stairwell while tears flooded their faces. Every time they thought of their father sailing serenely toward them, toward this house over which pain poised like a dark sea bird with grappling claws, their hearts stopped in panic. The doctor had said, "Pain may never come, there are so few nerves in that tract. But we must watch for its signs anyhow. She'll never admit it. She knows once I start morphine . . ."

Their fright seemed to turn them into children. They conceived the queer notion that their father would punish them horribly if they let Annie die before his return. He had left her in their hands to be guarded, cherished and preserved, ever since any of them could remember, and now it seemed they had failed him. Flogging was the punishment for falling asleep on watch. They drew straws to see who would go down to the docks to break the dreadful news, which could be even more dreadful by the time the *Peking* cast anchor. Julia drew the losing straw and asked Johnny to escort her. "Maybe with two of us on the docks . . ." she moaned, and then her voice broke. "Oh God, let her still be alive by then . . ."

Annie clung to life like a shipwrecked soul on a slender spar adrift in an ocean of pain. She denied the pains but the doctor guessed them when she began refusing all medicines for fear he would slip in the morphine he had promised not to give until she herself asked. Her fortitude surpassed anything he had ever encountered and it turned him into a cursing madman every time he came downstairs. "She'd go through hell to keep her wits clear until *he* comes," he groaned. "God damn that bloody old scow!"

The last waiting week began. The Marine Intelligence column posted the *Peking's* expected arrival for Saturday October 25th. Annie shook her head as Julia read it to her. She reached for her calendar on which she had circled Friday the 24th. *That's* when he'll dock," she murmured. "You mark my words."

Each day was a miracle of survival nobody could believe, but had to because there Annie lay with her huge eyes fastened on the barometer and a little smile playing about her colorless lips. *Fair,* it read, which in their latitude meant with light to fresh variable winds from the west. Her triumph over pain was achieved as quietly as her seeming domination over weather. Her eyes had a spooky brightness like the bits of blue glass in old cathedral windows which the Captain had once told his children was made of ground sapphires after a formula long since lost to man's knowledge.

Each afternoon the boys went over to the Pacific Avenue hilltop to watch for the *Peking*, and stayed until the fogs started rolling in through the Gate. On Friday noon they burst breathless into the house with the news that the *City of Peking* was off Land's End, with the pilot probably already aboard because she was coming straight in. Julia put on her hat, seized her gloves and bag and went directly out the door with Johnny. The *Peking* had already rounded North Point when they arrived on the docks.

She came down the Bay with pennants flying, went past them to the vacant waters that gave space for her waltzy swingabout and then Julia heard the steam whistle signal an exceptional voyage, two short, one long. "Johnny! that's his private word for Mama," she said in a choked voice. They had forgotten about that, forgotten in the midst of all their other anguish that of course he would be expecting Annie on the pier to welcome him home from his last voyage.

For his wife the vessel shone with spit and polish, for her she was dressed with flags and for her he gave the extra spurt of steam that made the *Peking* rush in scaringly to the dockside and stop in rending reverse within a hair's-breadth of the slimy green piles.

He had ordered the ship's band to play the music of *Pinafore*, Annie's favorite Gilbert and Sullivan, for the lowering of the gangplank and his was the first foot upon it after the dock workers had made it fast. *I polished the handles so care-ful-lee, That now I'm the ruler of the Queen's nav-ee* . . . Julia thought she was going to faint as he came toward them, thinking Annie behind them out of the wind. Then he saw their faces, read them from a distance, kept coming on, seeming now to be falling forward through the crowd as if struck from the rear.

He did all his crying in the carriage driving home. It was like rain dripping over a stone face as he made them give him every detail. When Julia's voice failed, Johnny's picked up. Day, date, time — exact hour they first knew, then each day that had followed, what then? When did Mack first tell them? When had Mc-

Latchie come on? Then what . . . *then what?* His "My God . . . *my God!*" punctuated their faltering words, sometimes like curses, sometimes like prayer.

In the house he took time to embrace Lizzie and Jane, to send Frank on the run to tell Doctor Mack he was home. Then he mounted the stairs with a slow heavy tread, drying his eyes as he went. Outside Annie's door he stood for a moment with his hand on the knob. His stricken face changed as he looked down from the landing. He seemed to be practicing a smile on them before he opened the door slowly and called ahead of him into the quiet room, "Ahoy there . . . anybody on board?"

He hardly left the room until Annie died six days later. He allowed himself just one day of clear continuous communication with her, then gave the nod to the doctor to start the morphine. "You keep me awake, Annie dear, like a little owl crying out in the night," he told her smiling. "We're going to help you get a little catnap."

His own pain started then as he watched her drift off, leaving him alone for the long vigil until the effects of the drug wore off. But, when at last her eyes fluttered open, all she ever saw was his gentle bearded face hovering patiently, waiting for her to wake up to his reassuring smile.

He exacted from his children the same will he displayed in suppressing all signs of grief while Annie was awake. No one who could not meet his challenge was allowed in the room. When she slept, they could all come in, regardless of their emotional states or appearances, and he would talk to them in a strange hollow voice, telling them not to cry. They must support him, follow his lead, never let their mother know she was near her end. Annie had always been fearful of death. No, they didn't know that, but he was telling them now. They must not let that fear come near her, *understand?* He sat with his watch in his hand, timing the duration of the last dose of morphine, an eminence of gray granite in the twilit room, seemingly as soulless and unshatterable.

He went totally to pieces the morning she died. His suppressed grief erupted with sudden tearing sobs as he fell to his knees and threw his long arms across the bed. The sight of him, gaunt and unshaven, burying his wild face in the coverlets, was as terrifying to his children as the sounds that came in shuddering paroxysms from his broken heart. Only the presence of Mrs. Farnsworth and the doctor gave them courage to remain in the room.

While the storm of grief howled about their ears, the barometer beside Annie's bed went right on registering the weather for that Saturday morning, November 1st, 1890. The indicator stood at 30 — FAIR — just as their mother had commanded it to be a week before, to bring her husband home safely from his last voyage.

Epilogue

THREE ITEMS IN MY MEMORABILIA wind up the Captain's story — his first letter to his children when he returned to the sea, his testimonial from the Pacific Mail, and a letter to his son John from the great old clipper skipper, Samuel A. Fabens, written after my grandfather's death in October of '95.

The Captain went back to sea barely three weeks after Annie died, finding life on land without her intolerable. The Pacific Mail mercifully tore up his resignation and gave him a command on the Panama Line. From the S.S. *San Blas* in the port of Ocos, Guatemala, he wrote to his children on December 2nd 1890, to tell them about the "nice spring bed" the company had given him and how he was sleeping much better at sea. "I am doing the best I can to bear up under this, the great affliction of my life," he wrote. "Be good to each other and don't ever forget the good examples of loving kindness you have been taught by your sainted Mother. Oh children, when your Mother was taken from you, you lost your dearest and best friend . . ."

He came to port at intervals and sailed away again, looking a little grayer each time, all snap and shine gone from his eyes. My mother Julia never liked to talk about those last years, but once she told me that the Old Salt was like one of the wrecks pictured so frequently in his scrapbooks — a great hull, tough-timbered, hung up on a reef and taking its pounding so stoutly you could hardly believe at times that there was a mortal gash somewhere in the planking below the water line.

After three years of seagoing command, the Captain willingly accepted transfer to the post of Port Captain of the Pacific Mail fleet serving Panama and the Orient out of San Francisco. He was beached at last, slowed up by the rheumatism that was his heritage from thirty years of Pacific fogs faced into and fought through from the bridges of Pacific Mail ships. Shortly after he became Port Captain, the S.S. *City of New York,* outbound for the Orient with a cargo of bullion and 125 Chinese in her steerage, weighed anchor from the Pacific Mail docks on October 26th, 1893, against the Captain's counsel, in a dense fog and a strong ebb tide; fifty minutes later she was spiked on the rocks off Point Bonita on the north side of the Golden Gate. It took her five days to break up, five days which San Franciscans turned into a sort of Roman holiday sight-seeing the wreck.

I can imagine, reading the San Francisco papers of that time, how the close-circling sight-seeing steamers with blaring brass bands, and the carriage parties driving out to the Cliff House by the hundreds to view the wreck from a distance of one and three-quarters miles, must have disgusted and horrified the Captain. Only one good thing came out of it for him. His son John, aged nineteen then, moved back into step with his Old Man, outraged by the spectacle of the big show the city made of the passing of one of his father's commands. He and Frank rode the sight-seeing steamers each day and reported to the Captain at night. Two hundred wreckers were aboard the battered hull, taking everything of value off it — the masts, the rigging and the deck-house, most of the bullion from the flooded holds — taking everything, the Captain doubtless thought, but the echoes of Annie's last concert aboard her which his memory salvaged as Johnny talked.

The Captain handed in his final resignation a year later. Lizzie was married and in her own home then, Jane had gone back

East to enter Cornell College and Julia was teaching in the Silver Street Kindergarten the methods of Froebel she had learned in Kate Douglas Wiggin's training school, worshipfully at the feet of that great lady author whose *Story of Patsy* and *The Bird's Christmas Carol* Annie used to read to her daughters. Johnny, having discovered that he had only to say along the waterfront whose son he was to have all doors open wide to him, was completing his training for the job of Junior Storekeeper aboard one of the ships of the O & O Steamship Company, and Frank was finishing high school.

As a Christmas present for 1894, the Captain received his testimonial from the Pacific Mail's Board of Directors in New York. I have it framed on my wall now, an illuminated document artfully penned and hand-colored, with the names of the Captain's twenty-two ships wreathed in scrolls about the eulogy that sums up in gothic lettering his long term of service with no loss. It must have triggered a lifetime of memories in my grandfather, all set off sharply against his never-ending awareness that Annie was not there to share. Nearly half the ships listed were then no longer afloat, casualties of fire or foundering or of prudent retirement because of over-age. Did he ask himself why *he* was still afloat? My mother said he read it once, seemingly to check if the roster of his commands was complete; then he handed it over to Johnny with a wry look, telling him only to observe the number of *Whereases* and *Resolveds* a big corporation required to say what any seaman worth his salt could express with two short words: Well done.

The Sutter Street house became a man's world in '95 when the Captain installed one of the Pacific Mail's "blue-gowned boys" in the kitchen as cook and another in his upstairs room as male nurse to help him with his bathing and dressing. Both pigtailed boys had sailed with him on many a voyage to China and knew exactly how he liked things. He chattered pidgin with them and sometimes seemed to imagine himself back at sea. Neither Lizzie, who came visiting often, nor Julia, the nominal mistress of the household, could give an order. Sing Low and Gaw Sung took in-structions only from the Captain, and ran his home like a slick section of cabin-class on an Oriental liner.

May 25th, 1895, a Wednesday morning Julia and Lizzie re-membered for the rest of their lives, the Captain came down-stairs for the last time to his customary seaman's breakfast of steamed oatmeal, pork chops and fried potatoes. Lizzie had read the morning *Chronicle* earlier and had hurried over to help Julia help their father. Julia would have hidden the newspaper had she dared, but the Captain was accustomed to finding it at his place at the table. The flaring headlines *COLIMA FOUNDERS AT SEA* struck him full in the face. Johnny tried to tell him as he fell into his chair that the details were meager, only a dis-patch or two from the Manzanillo agent, but the Captain's voice crying "My God . . . Oh, my God!" drowned him out. His tears fell over the huge center-page drawing of the S.S. *Colima* as he had known her, smartly under way with pennants flying, smoke plum-ing and a bone in her teeth. *Passengers one hundred twenty-one, all lost mebbe . . . No, no . . . here's one boat with fourteen reaching Mazatlan!* He was not reading aloud to them, he was talking to himself. *One* boat, he muttered thickly. *One?* And what did you do with the other seven, Captain Taylor? She carried *eight* lifeboats and four hundred sixty-eight life preservers . . . *look in my Bible if you doubt my word!* Johnny helped Gaw Sung get him back upstairs to bed.

They had to read him the news every day, word for word with no cheating, until June 2nd when the last party of five survivors was picked off a Mexican beach. One hundred and eighty-eight lives were lost including that of Captain Taylor, killed by a fall-ing mast. The vessel had sunk within ten minutes after she struck, driven on a reef by a powerful wind. Tejupan in Michoa-can Province was where she struck. There were biographies and pictures drawn from photos of all the ship's crew lost, boys who had sailed with him, whose biographies he could have written himself. Louis Brewster the millionaire coffee planter with plantations in Mexico was aboard her with his wife and three children; she was lost. Four waiters from the Palace Hotel on a pleasure cruise were saved. Professor Harold Whiting, head of Physics in Berkeley State Union, and all his family were aboard; two of his children discovered on a raft thus far. . . . On and on, day after day, Lizzie, Julia and Johnny took turns reading to a motionless, bearded mask staring at them with lampblack eyes from a linen-cased pillow trimmed with Annie's Irish lace.

The Captain lingered mutely on until October and died like Annie with his eyes on the aneroid barometer beside his bed. It recorded fair weather the day he died, October 29th, 1895, at the age of sixty-three years and twenty-seven days. The ship's doctor who attended him wrote "complication of ailments" on his death certificate, which was his fancy way of describing simple heartbreak.

Afterwards, there were many letters from their father's friends but none more fitting than the note from Marblehead, Massachusetts, dated November 12th, 1895, addressed to Johnny. It was written in a strong square script with downstroke shadings and beautiful flourishes about the capital letters:

MY DEAR YOUNG FRIEND:

I have received your letter advising me of the death of your Father, and the loss was so unexpected I was completely unnerved. You know, I presume, he was with my wife and self in the ship *Golden Eagle* on about a year and a half voyage from New York to San Francisco, thence down to Peru, remaining there four months, & thence around Cape Horn to France, and, during this long voyage, he was more a companion to us than an officer of the ship, and I have no remembrance of a single disagreeable word or thought passing between us. The whole voyage was remarkably pleasant, for, beside these good qualities, he was the best officer I ever had aboard all the many ships I have had under my control, a splendid seaman and a perfect way of commanding men without noise or unnecessary harshness. My wife and I have often called John

Mansfield to mind (the name our young child then 4 years old used to call him) and she feels his loss as badly as I do myself, and wishes to be kindly remembered to all your family and wants every member to visit us whenever you may return East. Please remember

I am most sincerely your friend,

SAM'L A. FABENS